610

W/3
REF

Rolf Heister

Dictionary
of Abbreviations in
Medical Sciences

With a list of the most important medical and scientific
journals and their traditional abbreviations

Foreword by Professor W. Forth

Springer-Verlag Berlin Heidelberg New York
London Paris Tokyo

Rolf Heister, M.D.
Ginsterweg 11
5205 Sankt Augustin/Bonn

FRG

ISBN 3-540-50487-7 Springer-Verlag Berlin Heidelberg New York
ISBN 0-387-50487-7 Springer-Verlag New York Berlin Heidelberg

Library of Congress Cataloging in Publication Data
Heister, Rolf. Dictionary of abbreviations in medical sciences. 1. Medicine-Abbreviations.
2. Medical sciences-Abbreviations. 3. Medicine-Periodicals-Abbreviations of titles. I. Title.
[DNLM: 1. Medicine-abbreviations. W 13 H473d] R123.H35 1989 610.148 89–4380
ISBN 0-387-50487-7 (U.S.)

© Springer-Verlag Berlin Heidelberg 1989
Printed in Germany

The use of registered names, trademarks, etc. in this publication does not imply, even in the
absence of a specific statement, that such names are exempt from the relevant protective laws
and regulations and therefore free for general use.

Product Liability: The publisher can give no guarantee for information about drug dosage and
application thereof contained in this book. In every individual case the respective user must
check its accuracy by consulting other pharmaceutical literature.

Typesetting, Printing and Binding: Appl, Wemding
2127/3145-543210 – Printed on acid-free paper

Foreword

Not everyone is a friend of the manifold abbreviations that have by now become a part of the scientific language of medicine. In order to avoid misunderstanding these abbreviations, it is wise to refer to a reliable dictionary, such as this one prepared by Heister. The abbreviation ED means, for instance, effective dose to the pharmacologist. However, it might also stand for emetic dose. Radiologists use the same abbreviation for erythema dose, and ED could also mean ethyl dichlorarsine. A common meaning of ECU is European currency unit, a meaning that might not be very often in scientific medical publications. ECU, however, also means environmental control unit or European Chiropractic Union.

Hopefully, those making inventions and discoveries will make use of Heister's dictionary before creating new abbreviations when preparing manuscripts for scientific publications. It is a very worthwhile goal not to use the same abbreviation for several different terms, especially if it is already widely accepted to mean only one of them. It may be impossible, however, to achieve this goal in different scientific disciplines. Therefore, although it is wise for the abbreviations used in a publication to be defined, it is also very helpful for readers and writers to use a dictionary such as this one. The author deserves our warmest thanks since we know that compiling such a comprehensive dictionary is based upon incredibly hard effort.

Munich, January 1989   W. Forth

Preface

Both as a student and later as practising physician I kept on being tripped up by medical and scientific abbreviations; sometimes this annoyed me. I spent hours with books or in libraries trying to find out the meanings of some of these abbreviations. At times, even recognized authorities had to admit defeat on the meaning of an acronym that did not belong to their immediate specialist field.

The proneness of our overseas colleagues to the use of abbreviations that may confuse the novice, but in the end seem sensible, became clear to me while I was working in the United States of America. In the meantime, many of these expressions have become part of day to day scientific and/ or clinical terminology.

Almost twenty years ago I started noting down all the abbreviations I met in the medical-scientific sector. At first this was for my own use. Then, thanks to the encouragement of some clinicians and scientists, I published this private collection as a "Dictionary of Medical Abbreviations" in Germany a few years ago. It seemed to be highly welcomed by the medical and related professions. I now present it as a thoroughly updated English version, containing approximately 15000 items, for my English-speaking colleagues throughout the world.

It was not my intention to put together the greatest possible number of abbreviations. I limited them to those that are found most commonly in the international literature, or that could cause difficulties when reading scientific papers. Some important or internationally used acronyms from other languages, such as Latin (L), French (F), German (G), Italian (I), or Spanish (S), were also included. Little account was taken of common abbreviations known to every student or of physical and chemical symbols and formulae. Some units of measurement were included, especially where foreign or less well known terms were concerned. Usually, the American way of spelling of terms was used, except where typical British organizations and titles were mentioned.

Some abbreviations are written in capital letters and others not (e.g. DOPA, Dopa); in such cases the most commonly used form was given, or both. Where abbreviations can be joined together or separated by full stops (e.g. ECG, E.C.G.), the simple form was usually chosen. Acronyms for titles, degrees and diplomas were separated by full stops, since they are usually seen in this format (e.g. M.D., D.V.H., etc.).

To make certain abbreviations better understood, an indication of the specialist area concerned was sometimes given, although it is almost impossible to confine some terms to a single field, since disciplines like chemistry, biochemistry, pharmacology, laboratory medicine, etc. are so mixed up with one another. The indication given is only meant to indicate the specialist area where the term is mainly used:

anat	= anatomy	neur	= neurology
bact	= bacteriology	obst	= obstetrics
biochem	= biochemistry	ophth	= ophthalmology
card	= cardiology	orth	= orthopedics
chem	= chemistry	otol	= otorhinolaryngology,
chir	= surgery		ENT
clin	= clinical	pharm	= pharmacology,
dent	= dentistry		pharmacy
derm	= dermatology	phys	= physics
gen	= genetics	physiol	= physiology
gyn	= gynecology	psych	= psychiatry, psychology
hyg	= hygiene	rad	= radiology
imm	= immunology	stat	= statistics
lab	= laboratory medicine	urol	= urology
mil	= military medicine	vet	= veterinary medicine

By a number of colleagues, it was also suggested to add an appendix with a list of the most important medical and scientific journals and their traditional abbreviations, as there appears to be considerable confusion in this area. This appendix with some 460 journal titles will be found on p.275.

For all the reasons mentioned, the dictionary lays no claim to being complete; new abbreviations appear in the literature almost every day. These will be taken into account in later, updating editions. Both the author and the publisher would be grateful for advice and suggestions.

Bonn, January 1989   Rolf Heister, M. D.

A

A	absorbance (spectropho-tometry)
A	acceleration
A	acceptor
A	accommodation
A	acetum; vinegar
A	acid
A	adenine
A	adenosine
A	adrenaline
A	albumin
A	ampère
A	amphetamine
A	ampicillin
A	androsterone
A	anode
A	argon
A *(ophth)*	axis
A	total acidity
a	annum; year
a	ante (L); before, in front of
a	anterior
a	asymmetric
a	axial
A.	aqua; water (also: Aq.)
A.	arteria (L); artery
A⁻	anion
Å	Ångström unit
A1, A2	aortic first (second) sound
AA	achievement age
AA	Alcoholics Anonymous (=AAA)
AA	amino acid
AA	amino acid arylamidase
AA	anticipatory avoidance
AA	aortic area
AA	aplastic anemia
AA	application area
AA	Association of Anaesthe-tists (UK)
Aa.	arteriae (L); arteries
A.a.	alopecia areata
āā	ana partes aequales (L); equal parts of each

AAA	abdominal aortic aneu-rysm
AAA	acute anxiety attack
AAA	Alcoholics Anonymous Association ("Triple A")
AAA	American Academy of All-ergists
AAA	American Association of Anatomists
AAA	American Anthropological Association
AAADS	American Academy of Applied Dental Science
AAALAC	American Association for Accreditation of Labora-tory Animal Care
AAAN	American Academy of Applied Nutrition
AAAP	American Association of Applied Psychology
AAAS	American Association for the Advancement of Science
AAB	American Association of Bioanalysts
AAB, AAb	anti-antibodies
AABB	American Association of Blood Banks
AABF	afferent arteriole blood flow
AACC	American Association of Clinical Chemists
AACCN	American Association of Critical Care Nurses
AACHP	American Association for Comprehensive Health Planning
AACP	American Academy for Cerebral Palsy
AACP	American Association of Colleges of Pharmacy
AACPR	American Association of Cleft Palate Rehabilitation
AACR	American Association for Cancer Research
AACR	American Association of Clinical Research

1

AAD	alloxazine adenine dinucleotide (= FAD)
AAD	alpha-acetyldigoxin
AAD	American Academy of Dermatology
AADM	American Academy of Dental Medicine
AADN	American Association of Doctor's Nurses
AADP	American Academy of Denture Prosthetics
AADP	aminopyridine adenine dinucleotide phosphate
AADR	American Academy of Dental Radiology
AADS	American Academy of Dermatology and Syphilology
AADS	American Association of Dental Schools
AAE	active assistive exercise
AAE	acute allergic encephalitis
AAE	American Association of Endodontists
AAF	acetic-alcohol-formalin (fixing substance)
AAF	acetylaminofluorine
AAF	(adrenal) ascorbic acid (depletion) factor
AAF	anti-atelectasis factor (= LAS)
AAFMC	American Association of Foundations for Medical Care
AAFP	American Academy of Family Practice
AAG	aortoarteriography
AAGL	American Association of Gynecological Laparoscopists
AAGP	American Academy of General Practice (now AAFP)
AAGUS	American Association of Genito-Urinary Surgery
AAHD	American Academy of the History of Dentistry
AAHM	American Association of the History of Medicine
AAHP	American Association of Hospital Planning
AAHPER	American Academy for Health, Physical Education and Recreation
AAI	American Association of Immunologists
AAID	American Association of Implant Dentures
AAIIP	Alfred Adler Institute for Individual Psychology (USA)
AAIN	American Association of Industrial Nurses
AAIT	American Association of Inhalation Therapists
AAL	anterior axillary line
AALAS	American Association of Laboratory Animal Science
AAM	American Academy of Microbiology
AAMA	American Association of Medical Assistants
AAMC	American Association of Medical Clinics
AAMC	American Association of Medical Colleges
AAME	N-acetylarginine methylester
AAMI	Association for the Advancement of Medical Instrumentation (USA)
AAMIH	American Association for Maternal and Infant Health
AAMMC	American Association of Medical Milk Commissioners
AAMPR	American Association of Medico-Physical Research
AAMRL	American Association of Medical Record Librarians
AAN	American Academy of Neurology

AAN	aminoacetonitril bisulfate	AAPB	American Association of Pathologists and Bacteriologists
AANA	American Association of Nurse Anesthetists		
AAO	Academy of Applied Osteopathy (USA)	AAPCC	American Association of Psychiatric Clinics for Children
AAO	American Academy of Otolaryngology	AAPHD	American Association of Public Health Dentists
AAO	American Association of Orthodontists	AAPHP	American Association of Public Health Physicians
AAO	American Association of Osteopathy	AAPMR	American Association of Physical Medicine and Rehabilitation
AAO	amino acid oxidase (=DAAO)	AAPS	American Association of Physicians and Surgeons
AAOC	American Association of Osteopathic Colleges	AAPS	American Association of Plastic Surgeons
AAOG	American Association of Obstetricians and Gynecologists	AAPT	American Academy of Physical Therapy
		AAR	antigen-antibody reaction
AAOGAS	American Association of Obstetricians, Gynecologists and Abdominal Surgeons	AART	American Association for Rehabilitation Therapy
		AART	American Association for Respiratory Therapy
AAOM	American Academy of Occupational Medicine	AAS	alkyl aryl sulphonate
AAOMS	American Association of Oral and Maxillofacial Surgeons (Chicago)	AAS	anthrax antiserum
		AAS	aortic arch syndrome
		AAS	atomic absorption spectrometry
AAOO	American Academy of Ophthalmology and Otolaryngology	AAS	Australian Academy of Science (Canberra)
		AASLD	American Academy for the Study of Liver Diseases
AAOP	American Academy of Oral Pathology	AASP	American Association for Social Psychiatry
AAOS	American Association of Orthopedic Surgeons	AAST	American Association for the Surgery of Trauma
AAP	alanine aminopeptidase	AAT	alpha-1-antitrypsine
AAP	alcohol-induced acute pancreatitis	AAT	aspartate aminotransferase
AAP	American Academy of Pediatrics	AATCC	American Association of Textile Chemists and Colorists
AAP	American Academy of Pedodontics		
AAP	American Academy of Periodontology	AATM	American Academy of Tropical Medicine
AAP	American Academy of Psychotherapists	AATP	American Academy of Tuberculosis Physicians
AAPA	American Association of Physicians' Assistants		

AA-tRNA	aminoacyl transport ribo-nucleic acid	intervention	regarding airways, breathing and circulation (sometimes referred to as ABC of Resuscitation: airways, breathing, circulation, drugs, ECG, fluids, gauging, hypothermia, intensive care)
AATS	American Association for Thoracic Surgery		
AAUS	Associated Anesthetists of the United States of America		
AAV	adeno-associated viruses	ABCP	Association of Blind Chartered Physiotherapists
AAV	AIDS associated virus (=HIV)	ABC plaster	hyperemizing plaster (with extracts of arnica, belladonna and capsicum)
AAV	Allgemeen Apothekers Verbond; General Association of Pharmacists (The Netherlands)		
		ABC solution	boric acid and carbolic acid solution
AAVC	accessory atrioventricular connection (=AAVP)	ABC test (ophth)	area-brightness comparison test
AAVP	accessory atrioventricular pathway (=AAVC)	ABC ABC, abc (dent)	axiobuccocervical
AB	abortion	ABD	anastomose bilio-digestive (F); anastomosis between bile duct and intestine
AB	Aid to the Blind		
AB, Ab	antibody		
AB	apex beat	ABE	acute bacterial endocarditis
AB	asthma bronchiale (L), asthmatic bronchitis		
AB, ab (dent)	axiobuccal	ABERP	accessory bundle effective refractory period (=APERP, ERP-AB, ERP-AP)
A.B.	Artium Baccalaureus (L); Bachelor of Arts		
A›B	air greater than bone (conduction)	ABF	androgen-binding fraction
		ABG	arterial blood gases
ABA	American Burn Association	ABG, abg (dent)	axiobuccogingival
ABB	antibody-coated bacteria (test) (=ACB)	ABJ	anastomose bilio-jejunale (F); anastomosis between bile duct and jejunum
abbr.	abbreviation, abbreviated		
ABC	antigen-binding capacity	ABL, abl (dent)	axiobuccolingual
ABC	atomic, biological, chemical (warfare)	ABMP	2-amino-5-bromo-6-methyl-4(3H)-pyrimidinone
ABC (imm)	avidin biotin peroxidase complex		
ABCC	Atomic Bomb Casualty Commission	ABO	absent bed occupancy
		ABO	A-B-O system (of blood grouping)
ABC apparatus	orthodontic device developed by E.H. Angle, H.A. Baker and C.S. Case	ABOB	anhydrous bis-hydroxy-ethyl biguanide
ABC	reanimation procedures	ABP	acute biliary pancreatitis

4

ABP	androgen-binding protein
ABP	arterial blood pressure
ABPA	allergic bronchopulmonary aspergillosis
ABPI	Association of the British Pharmaceutical Industry
ABPP	2-amino-5-bromo-6-phenyl-4(3H)-pyrimidinone
abPV	aberrant pulmonary vein(s)
ABR	Abortus Bang Ringprobe (G) (test)
ABR	absolute bed rest
ABR	auditory (or acoustic) brainstem response
ABr test	agglutination test for brucellosis
ABS	acrylonitrile-butadiene-styrene copolymers
ABS	acute brain syndrome
ABS	adaptive biosignal
ABS	alkylbenzyl sulfonate
ABS	Australian Biochemical Society
abs.	absent
abs.	absolute
abs.feb.	absente febre (L); in the absence of fever
ABTS	2,2'-azino-di-(3-ethylbenzthiazoline sulfonate)
ABVD regimen	cytotoxic combination therapy with adriamycin, bleomycin, vinblastin and DTIC
ABY	acid bismuth yeast (agar)
AC	acetylcholine (=ACh, AcCh)
AC	adrenal cortex (or corticosteroid)
AC	air conditioning
AC	air conduction
AC *(phys)*	alternating current
AC *(obst)*	amniocentesis
AC	analogue computer
AC *(physiol)*	anodal closure
AC *(ophth)*	anterior chamber
AC	anticoagulant(s)

AC *(pharm)*	anti-inflammatory corticosteroid
AC *(card)*	arythmie complète (F); absolute arrhythmia
AC *(anat)*	atriocarotid (or auriculocarotid)
AC, ac *(dent)*	axiocervical
A.C.	Académie de Chirurgie; Academy of Surgery (France)
a.c. *(otorhin)*	ad concham (L); just audible
a.c. *(pharm)*	ante cenam, ante cibos (L); before meals (Rx)
ACA	American Chiropractic Association
ACA	American College of Allergists
ACA	American College of Anesthesiologists
ACA	American College of Angiology
ACA	American College of Apothecaries
ACA *(pharm)*	(epsilon)-aminocaproic acid (=EACA)
ACA *(anat)*	anterior cerebral artery
ACA	automatic clinical analyzer
ACA ratio	ratio of accommodative convergence and accommodation
ACAT	acyl-CoA-cholesterol acyltransferase
ACB	antibody-coated bacteria (=ABB)
ACB	aorto-coronary bypass
ACC	accelerin-convertin, factor VI and VII
ACC	acidocillin
ACC	adenoid cystic carcinoma
ACC	alveolar cell carcinoma
ACC	American College of Cardiology
ACC	anodal closure contraction
acc.	accommodation

5

A.c.c.	arteria carotis communis; common carotid artery	ACFS	American College of Foot Surgeons
ACCA	American Clinical and Climatological Association	ACG	acycloguanosine
		ACG	American College of Gastroenterology
ACCG	apex-carotid cardiogram		
AcCh	acetylcholine (= ACh)	ACG	angiocardiography
ACCl	anodal closure clonus	ACG	aortocoronarography
AcCoA	acetyl coenzyme A	ACG	apex cardiography
ACCP	American College of Chest Physicians	AcG	accelerator globulin (factor V)
ACD	absolute cardiac dullness	ACGME	Accreditation Council for Graduate Medical Education (USA)
ACD	acid citrate dextrose		
ACD	actinomycin D		
ACD	American College of Dentists	ACGP	American College of General Practitioners
ACD	anterior chest diameter	ACH	active chronic hepatitis
ACD, A.c.d.	arteria coronaria dextra (L); right coronary artery	ACH	adrenal cortical hormone
ACD stabilizer	citric acid, trisodium citrate, anhydrous dextrose (for preservation of donor blood)	ACH, ACh	acetylcholine
		ACHE, AChE	acetylcholinesterase
		ACH index	arm (girth), chest (depth), hip (width) index (of nutritional state)
ACE	acetylcholine esterase (= AChE)		
		AChRAB	acetylcholine receptor
ACE	adrenal cortical extract	AChR-Ab	acetylcholine receptor antibody
ACE	alcohol-chloroform-ether (anesthetic mixture)		
ACE	American Council of Education	A.Ch.S.	Associate of the Society of Chiropodists
ACE	angiotensin converting enzyme	a.c. + h.s.	ante cibos et hora somni (L); before meals and at bedtime (Rx)
A.c.e.	arteria carotis externa; external carotid artery		
		ACI	acute coronary insufficiency
ACED	anhidrotic congenital ectodermal dysplasia	ACI	allowable concentration index
A-cells	alpha cells, acidophilic cells of the anterior pituitary		
		ACI	anticlonus index
		ACI, a.c.i.	arteria carotis interna; internal carotid artery
A-cells	alpha cells of the pancreatic Langerhans islets		
		ACIF	anti-complement immunofluorescence
ACEP	American College of Emergency Physicians		
		ACINF	Advisory Committee on Irradiated and Novel Foods (UK)
ACF	accessory clinical findings		
ACF	anhydrous citrovorum factor		
		ACIP	Advisory Committee on Immunization Practices (USA)
ACFO	American College of Foot Orthopedists		

ACLS score	arrest witnessed; cardiac rhythm; lay bystander to administer resuscitation; speed of medical help (high ACLS score indicates good prognosis in myocardial infarction)	ACP	American College of Pathologists
		ACP	American College of Physicians
		ACP	amorphous calcium phosphate
Ac.M.	Académie de Médecine; Academy of Medicine (France)	ACP	Animal Care Panel
		ACP	anodal closing picture
		ACP	Association of Clinical Pathologists (USA)
ACMF regimen	cytotoxic combination therapy with: adriamycin, cyclophosphamide, methotrexate, and 5-fluorouracil	AcPh	acid phosphatase
		ACPM	American College of Preventive Medicine
		ACPP	adrenocorticopolypeptide
ACNT	American College of Medical Technologists	ACP virus	adenoidal-conjunctival-pharyngeal virus
ACN	acute conditioned necrosis	ACR	American College of Radiology
ACN	American College of Neuropsychiatrists	ACR	anti-constipation regimen
		A/C ratio	albumin-coagulin ratio
AcNeu	N-acetylneuraminic acid	ACS	American Cancer Society
ACNM	American College of Nurse-Midwives	ACS	American Chemical Society
ACO	anodal closure odor	ACS	American College of Surgeons
ACO regimen	cytotoxic combination therapy with: adriamycin, cyclophosphamide and Oncovin	ACS	anodal closing sound
		ACS	antireticular cytotoxic serum
ACOG	American College of Obstetricians and Gynecologists	ACS	Association of Clinical Scientists (USA)
		ACS (card)	automated catheterization system
ACOHA	American College of Osteopathic Hospital Administrators	ACSM	American College of Sports Medicine
ACOI	American College of Osteopathic Internists	ACSP	Advisory Council on Scientific Policy
ACOOG	American College of Osteopathic Obstetricians and Gynecologists	ACT	achievement through counselling and treatment
		ACT	activated coagulation time
ACOP	American College of Osteopathic Pediatricians	ACT	anticoagulant therapy
		ACTA	automatic computerized transverse axial tomography
ACOS	American College of Osteopathic Surgeons		
ACP	accessory conduction pathway (=AAVC, AAVP)	Act-D	actinomycin D
		ACTe	anodal closure tetanus
ACP	acid cell phosphatase	ACTH	adrenocorticotrophic hormone
ACP	acyl carrier protein		

ACTN	adrenocorticotrophin	ADAP	American Dental Assistants' Program
ACTP	adrenocorticotrophic polypeptide	ADAVRS	Assistant Director Army Veterinary and Remount Service (UK)
ACU	antibody concentration unit	ADC	accident de la circulation (F); traffic accident
ACV	acyclovir	ADC	acidocillin
ACVB	aorto-coronary venous bypass	ADC	Aid to Dependent Children
ACVP	American College of Veterinary Pathologists	ADC	AIDS dementia complex
AD	addict	ADC	albumin, dextrose, catalase (medium)
AD	adenoid degeneration (virus)	ADC	analogue-digital converter (or compiler)
AD	alcohol dehydrogenase	ADC	anodal duration contraction
AD	anodal duration		
AD	anterior descending (artery)	ADC, adc (dent)	axiodistocervical
AD	antidepressive (drugs)	AdC	adrenal cortex
AD	antigenic determinant	ADCC	antibody-dependent cellmediated cytotoxicity
AD	arteriosclerotic disease	ADE	acute disseminated encephalitis
AD	atopic dermatitis		
AD	auris dextra (L); right ear	ADE	adrenalectomized
AD (gen)	autosomal dominant	ADE	audible Doppler enhancer
AD (stat)	average deviation	ADEC	Australian Drug Evaluation Committee
AD (pharm)	average dose		
AD, ad (dent)	axiodistal	ADG, adg (dent)	axiodistogingival
A.d. (card)	atrium dextrum (L); right atrium	ADGP	albumin-dextrose-gelatin phosphate
a.d.	aqua destillata (L); distilled water	ADH	alcohol dehydrogenase
ADA	adenosine desamidase	ADH	antidiuretic hormone (vasopressin)
ADA	American Dental Association	ADHA	American Dental Hygienists' Association
ADA	American Dermatological Association	adhib.	adhibendus (L); to be administered (Rx)
ADA	American Diabetic Association	ADI	acceptable daily intake
ADA	American Dietetic Association	ADI	artificial donogenic insemination (= AID)
ADAA	American Dental Assistants Association	ADI, adi (dent)	axiodistoincisal
ADADS	Assistant Director Army Dental Service (UK)	ADL	activities of daily living
ADAMHA	Alcohol, Drug Abuse, and Mental Health Administration	ad lib.	ad libitum (L); as desired (Rx)

ADM	adriamycin	ADS	action dynamique spéci-fique (F); specific-dynamic action
AdM	adrenal medulla		
ADMA	aldehyde dimethyl ace-tate		
		ADS *(mil)*	Advanced Dressing Station
ADMA	American Drug Manufac-turers Association	ADS	anatomical dead space
		ADS	antidiuretic substance (=ADH, ADP)
ad man. med.	ad manum medici (L); to the hand of the physician (Rx)		
		ADS	anti-donor serum
		ADS	Army Dental Service
ADME *(pharm)*	absorption, distribution, metabolism, excretion (of a substance)	A.d.S.	Académie des Sciences (Paris)
		ADSA	action dynamique spéci-fique des aliments (F); spe-cific-dynamnic action of food-stuffs
ADMS	Assistant Director Medical Service (UK)		
ADN	acide desoxyribonucleique (F); deoxyribonucleic acid (=DNA)	ad sat.	ad saturatum (L); to satu-ration
		adst.feb.	adstante febre (L); when fever is present
ADN	autonomous diabetic nephropathy	ADT	Accepted Dental Thera-peutics
ADNase	anti-deoxyribonuclease	ADT	accident du travail (F); accident at work
ADO	apnoic diffusion oxygena-tion		
		ADT	adenosine triphosphate (usually: ATP)
ADO, ado *(dent)*	axiodisto-occlusal		
		ADT	agar-gel diffusion test
ADP	adenosine diphosphate	ADT	alternate-day treatment
ADP	albumin degradation prod-ucts	ADT	"any desired thing", placebo
ADP	antidiuretic principle (=ADH, ADS)	ADTA	American Dental Trade Association
ADP	automatic data processing	ad us.	ad usum (L); according to custom
ADPG	adenosine-5-diphosphate glucose		
		ad us.ext.	ad usum externum (L); for external use
ADPL	average daily patient load		
		ad us.prop.	ad usum proprium (L); for own use
ADPR	adenosine diphosphate ribose		
		ADV	adenoid degeneration viruses, adenoviruses
ADR	Accepted Dental Remedies		
ADR	adverse drug reaction		
Adr.	adrenaline	ADX	acetyldigoxin
ADRI	Animal Diseases Research Institute (Nepean/Can-ada)	ADX	adrenalectomized
		AE	above elbow
		AE	activation energy
ADRRS	Adverse Drug Reaction Reporting System (USA)	AE	agar-gel electrophoresis
		AE	Antitoxin-Einheit (G); antitoxic unit
ADRV *(card)*	arrhythmogenic dysplasia of the right ventricle (=ARVD)		
		AE	avian encephalomyelitis

A + E	Accident and Emergency (Department)	AER	Association Européenne de Radiologie; European Association of Radiology
AEA	Atomic Energy Authority		
AEACA	acetyl-epsilon-aminocaproic acid	AER	Association of Eye Research
AEAIC	Académie Européenne d'Allergologie et Immunologie Clinique; European Academy of Allergy and Clinical Immunology	AER	auditory evoked response
		AER	average evoked response
		AERE	Atomic Energy Research Establishment
AEA sol.	alcohol-ether-acetone solution	AERP	atrial effective refractory period
AEB	atrial ectopic beat (= AEC, AES, APB, APC)	AERP	atrial excitation repolarization phase
AEC	at earliest convenience	AES	American Encephalographic Society (= AEEGS)
AEC	Atomic Energy Commission (USA)		
		AES	American Epidemiological Society
AEC	atrial ectopic contraction	AES	American Epilepsy Society
AECD	allergic eczematous contact dermatitis	AES	aortic ejection sound
AECG	ambulatory electrocardiography (Holter monitoring) (= AEM)	AES	atrial extrasystole (= AEB, APC)
		AESAL	Académie Européenne des Sciences, des Arts et des Lettres; European Academy of Sciences, Arts, and Literature
AEE	acute allergic encephalitis		
AEE	Atomic Energy Establishment		
AEEGS	American Electroencephalographic Society (AES)	AESGP	Association Européenne des Spécialités Pharmaceutiques Grand Public (Paris)
AEF	allogenic effector factor		
AEG	air encephalogram		
AEI	atrial ejection index	AET	amino-ethyl-isothiouronium chloride
AEL	acute erythroblastic leukemia		
		AET	antimycotic elution test
AEM	ambulatory ECG monitoring (Holter)	AEV	avian erythroblastosis virus
		AF	acanthosis factor
AEM	analytical electron-microscopy	AF	acid-fast
		AF	albumin-free
AeMA	Aero-Medical Association (USA) (= AMA)	AF	aldehyde fuchsin
		AF	ammonium formiate
AEP	auditory (or acoustic) evoked potential	AF	amniotic fluid
		AF	angiogenesis factor
AEP	average evoked potential	AF	aortic flow
AEq	age equivalent	AF	Armed Forces
AER	acoustic evoked response	AF	Arthritis Foundation
AER	albumin excretion rate	AF	atrial fibrillation
AER	aldosterone excretion rate	AF	audio frequency

AFA	automatic frequency adaptation	AFIP	Armed Forces Institute of Pathology
AFB	acid-fast bacillus	AFL	anti-fatty liver (factor in pancreatic tissue)
AFBA	Asociación Farmaceutica y Biochimica Argentina; Argentinian Pharmaceutical and Biochemical Association	AFL	antifibrinolysin
		AFLNH	angiofollicular lymphnode hyperplasia
		AFML	Armed Forces Medical Library
AFC	antibody forming cells	AF murmur	Austin Flint murmur
AFC	automatic frequency control	AFORMED	alternating failure of response mechanical to electrical depolarization
AFCET	Association Française pour la Cybernétique Economique et Technique; French Association for Economical and Technical Cybernetics (Paris)	AFP	adiabatic fast passage
		AFP	alpha-fetoprotein
		AFP	American Family Physician (journal)
		AFP	amplitude frequency product
AFCMF	Association Française des Chirurgiens Maxillo-Faciaux; French Association of Maxillofacial Surgeons	AFP complex	aescinum-flavonole-phosphatide
		AFQT	Armed Forces Qualification Test
AFCM regimen	cytotoxic combination therapy with: adriamycin, 5-fluorouracil, cyclophosphamide, and methotrexate	AFR	antifibrinolysin reaction (=AFT)
		AFR	ascorbic free radical
		AFRD, AFRI	acute febrile respiratory disease, . . illness
AFCP	antibody forming cell precursors	AF regimen	cytotoxic combination therapy with adriamycin and 5-fluorouracil
AFCR	American Federation for Clinical Research	AFRP	atrial functional refractory period
AFC regimen	cytotoxic combination therapy with: adriamycin, 5-fluorouracil and cyclophosphamide	AFS	American Fertility Society
		AFS	atomic fluorescence spectroscopy
A.f.d.	arteria femoralis dextra (L); right femoral artery	A.f.s.	arteria femoralis sinistra (L); left femoral artery
AFDC	Aid to Families with Dependent Children	AFT	antifibrinolysin test (=AFR)
AFEC	Association Française pour l'Etude du Cancer; French Association for the Study of Cancer (Paris)	AFT	antigen fixation test
		AFT_4	absolute free thyroxine
		AFTC	apparent free testosterone concentration
AFH	American Foundation for Homeopathy	AFTM	American Foundation for Tropical Medicine
AFI	amaurotic familial idiocy		
AFI	atrial filling index		

AG	anesthésie générale (F); general anesthesia	AGI	Associazione Genetica Italiana; Italian Genetics Association
AG	anion gap		
AG, Ag	antigen, allergen	AGL	acide gras libre (F); free fatty acid
AG	antigravity		
AG	antiglobulin	AGM	African green monkey
AG	atrial gallop	AGMK	African green monkey kidney (= GMK)
AG, ag (dent)	axiogingival		
		AGN	acute glomerulonephritis
A/G	albumin-globulin ratio	AGNE	acides gras non esterifies (F); non-esterified fatty acids
AGA	accelerated growth area		
AGA	American Gastroenterological Association		
		AGP	alkaline granulocyte phosphatase
AGA	American Gastroscopic Association		
		AGPA	American Group Practice Association
AGA	American Genetics Association		
		AGR	Advanced Gas-cooled Reactor
AGA	American Geriatrics Association		
		A/G ratio	albumin-globulin ratio
AGA	American Goiter Association	AGS	adrenogenital syndrome
		AGS	American Geriatrics Society
AGA (obst)	average (or appropriate) for gestational age (see also LGA, SGA)		
		AGS	American Gynecological Society
AGARD	Advisory Group for Aeronautical Research and Development (institution of NATO)	AGT	antiglobulin test (Coombs)
		AGTH	adrenoglomerulotrophic hormone
		AGTT	abnormal glucose tolerance test
AGC	automatic gain control (in hearing aids)		
		AGU	aspartylglucosaminuria
AGCT	antiglobulin consumption test	AGV	aniline gentian violet (solution)
AGCT	Army General Classification Test, "Army Alpha Test" (intelligence test)	AH	abdominal hysterectomy
		AH	aqueous humor
		AH	arterial hypertension (= AHT)
AGD	agar-gel diffusion (= ADT)		
AGE	angle of greatest extension	Ah	hypermetropic astigmatism
AGF	adrenal growth factor	AHA	American Heart Association
AGF	angle of greatest flexion		
AGF	anti-gammaglobulin factor	AHA	American Hospital Association
ag.feb.	aggrediente febre (L); when the fever increases	AHA	American Hypnotherapy Association
AGG	agammaglobulinemia	AHA	Area Health Authority
AGG	anti-gammaglobulin	AHA	aspartyl-hydroxamic acid
AGGS	anti-gas gangrene serum		
AGI	Alan Guttmacher Institute	AHA	auto-hemolytic anemia

AH-AB	antihemagglutinin antibody	AHMC	Association of Hospital Management Committees
A-H block	atrium-His block	AHN	Assistant Head Nurse
AHC	acute hemorrhagic conjunctivitis	AHOP	adiposity-hyperthermia-oligomenorrhea-parotid (syndrome)
AHC	aminohexyl cellulose		
AHC	anterior horn cell (disease)	AHP	acute hemorrhagic pancreatitis
AHC	antihemophilic factor C, factor XI	AHQS	asymmetric hind-quarters syndrome
AHD	antihyaluronidase		
AHD	arteriosclerotic heart disease	AHR	antihyaluronidase reaction
AHD	autoimmune hemolytic disease	AHR	Association for Health Records
AHE	acute hemorrhagic encephalitis	AHS	American Hearing Society
		AHS	American Hospital Society
AHE	acute hypertensive encephalopathy	AHS	Assistant House Surgeon
		A-H series (lab)	Ammon-Hottinger series
AHF	American Health Foundation	AHT	antihyaluronidase test (or titer)
AHF	American Hospital Formulary	AHT	arterial hypertension (=AH)
AHF	antihemophilic factor, factor VIII	AHTCG, AHTG	antihuman thymocytic globulin
AHF	Argentinian hemorrhagic fever, Junin fever	AHTP	antihuman thymocytic plasma
AHG	antihemophilic globulin (AHG-A=factor VIII, AHG-B=factor IX)	AI	adhesion index
		AI	aortic insufficiency
		AI	artificial insemination
AHG	antihuman globulin	AI	atherogenic index
AHGC test	antihuman globulin consumption test	AI, ai (dent)	axioincisal
AHGS	acute herpetic gingival stomatitis	A/I (psych)	aptitude index
		AIA	allyl-2-isopropyl acetamide
AHGS	antihuman globulin serum	AIB, AIBA	amino-isobutyric acid
AHH	aryl hydrocarbon hydroxylase	AIBS	American Institute of Biological Sciences
AHIL	Association of Hospital and Institution Libraries (USA)	AIC	antigen-immunosuppressive conjugate
		AICA	anterior inferior cerebellar artery
AHIP	Assisted Health Insurance Plan	AICAR	amino-imidazole carboxamide ribonucleotide
AHLG	antihuman lymphocyte globulin (=ALG)	AICD	automatic implantable cardioverter/ defibrillator
AHLS	antihuman lymphocyte serum (=ALS)	AICF	auto-immune complement fixation

AID	acute infectious disease	AIM	Association Internationale de Mutualité; International Association of Mutuality
AID	Agency for International Development		
AID	artificial insemination by donor	AIMM	Association Internationale des Musées Médicaux (F); International Association of Medical Museums
AID	auto-immune disease		
AIDS	acquired immune deficiency syndrome		
AIEA	Agence Internationale de l'Energie Atomique (F); International Atomic Energy Agency (Vienna) (=IAEA)	AIMS	APSAC Intervention Mortality Study (UK)
		AIMS	Arthritis Impact Measurement Scales
		AIN	American Institute of Nutrition
AIEB	Association Internationale pour l'Etude des Bronches; International Association for Bronchial Study	AIP	acute intermittent porphyria
		AIP	acute interstitial pneumonia
AIFD	acute intrapartum fetal distress	AIP	Anatuberculin integrale Petragnani
AIG	anti-immunoglobulin	AIP	Association Internationale de Psychotechnique (F); International Association of Psychological Technique
AIGE	Asociación Interamericana de Gastroenterologia; Interamerican Association of Gastroenterology		
AIH	American Institute of Homeopathy	AIP	automated immune precipitation
AIH	artificial insemination by husband	AIPA	Association Internationale de Psychologie Appliquée (F); International Association of Applied Psychology
AIHA	American Industrial Hygiene Association		
AIHA	auto-immune hemolytic anemia		
AIHC	American Industrial Health Conference	AIPF	All-India Pharmacists Federation
AIHP	American Institute of the History of Pharmacy	AIPP	2-amino-5-iodo-6-phenyl-4(3H)-pyrimidinone
AIIMS	All-India Institute of Medical Sciences	AIPU	All-India Pharmacists Union
AIIS *(anat)*	anterior inferior iliac spine	AIR	agglutination inhibition reaction
AIL	angio-immunoblastic lymphadenopathy	AIR	amino-imidazole ribonucleotide
AILD	angioimmunoblastic lymphadenopathy with dysproteinemia	AIRC	Associazone Italiana per la Ricerca sul Cancro; Italian Association for Cancer Research

AIRMEC	Association Internationale pour la Recherche Médicale et les Echanges Culturels (F); International Association for Medical Research and Cultural Exchange	AJC	American Journal of Cardiology (official abbreviation: Amer. J. Cardiol.)
AIS	acoustic information-processing system	AJM	American Journal of Medicine (official abbreviation: Amer. J. Med.)
AIS	adrenergic inhibitory system	AJR *(card)*	accelerated junctional rhythm
AIS	aortic isthmic stenosis; coarctation of the aorta	AJR	American Journal of Radiology (official abbreviation: Amer. J. Radiol.)
AISM	Association Internationale des Sociétés de Microbiologie; International Association of Microbiological Societies	AK	above knee (e.g. amputation)
		AK	acetate kinase
		AK	artificial kidney (see also FAK, HAK, PAK)
AISS	Association Internationale de Sauretage et de Premiers Secours en cas d'Accidents; International Association for Rescue and First Aid in Accidents	A.K.C.	Associate King's College (London)
		AL	acute leukemia, leukosis
		AL	adaptation level
		AL *(pharm)*	adeps lanae (L); wool fat
		AL	anesthésie locale (F); local anesthesia
AIT *(clin)*	acute intensive treatment	AL	anterior left
AIT *(lab)*	agglutination immobilization test	AL	auris laeva (L); left ear (=AS)
AIT *(psych)*	analytic intelligence test	AL, al *(dent)*	axiolingual
AITHA	Association Internationale de Thalassothérapie (F); International Association of Thalassotherapy	ALA	American Laryngological Association
		ALA	American Lung Association
AITIA	Aspirin in Transient Ischemic Attacks Trial (USA, 1972–1977)	ALA	(delta)-aminolevulinic acid
		ALa, ala *(dent)*	axiolabial
AIU	absolute iodine uptake	Ala	alanine
AIUM	American Institute of Ultrasound in Medicine	ALAD	(delta)-aminolevulinic acid dehydrogenase
AIV	technique of protein and vitamin supplementation of milk (named after the discoverer Artturi Ilmari Virtanen)	ALADPA	anomalous origin of left anterior descending from pulmonary artery
		ALaG, alag *(dent)*	axiolabiogingival
		ALaL, alal *(dent)*	axiolabiolingual
AIVR *(card)*	accelerated idioventricular rhythm	AL anhydr.	adeps lanae anhydricus (L); anhydrous wool fat
AJ	ankle jerk		

ALAS	aminolevulinic acid synthetase	ALI *(card)*	anterolateral infarction
ALAS	Asociación Latino-Americana de Sociologia (S); Latinamerican Association of Sociology	ALL	acute lymphatic leukemia
		ALL	allorhythmia
		ALLO	atypical legionella-like organisms
ALAT	alanine aminotransferase (=ALT)	ALM	acrolentiginous melanoma
Alb.	albumin	ALMA	Adoptee's Liberty Movement Association
ALC	Alternative Lifestyle Checklist	ALME	acetyl-L-lysine methylester
		ALMI	anterior lateral myocardial infarction
ALC *(vet)*	avian leukosis complex	ALO, alo *(dent)*	axiolinguo-occlusal
ALC, alc *(dent)*	axiolinguocervical		
		ALP *(lab)*	alkaline leukocyte phosphatase
ALCALPA	anomalous origin of left coronary artery from left pulmonary artery	ALP *(pharm)*	allopurinol
		ALP	alveolar lung proteinosis
ALCAPA	anomalous origin of left coronary artery from pulmonary artery	ALP *(anat)*	anterior lobe pituitary (=ALH)
		ALR	agglutination lysis reaction
ALCARPA	anomalous origin of left coronary artery from right pulmonary artery	ALROS	American Laryngological, Rhinological, and Otological Society
AlCr *(dent)*	aluminum crown	ALS *(neur)*	amyotrophic lateral sclerosis (=MLS)
AlcR	alcohol rub		
ALD	aldolase (also: fructose l,6-diphosphate aldolase; ketose l-phosphate aldehyde lyase)	ALS *(imm)*	antilymphocytic serum (=AHLS)
		ALS syndrome	Abt-Letterer-Siwe disease; infectious reticulo-endotheliosis
ALDH	aldehyde dehydrogenase	ALT	alanine aminotransferase (=ALAT)
ALD-L	liver aldolase		
ALD-M	muscle aldolase	ALTB	acute laryngotracheobronchitis
ALFT	alum-precipitated formol toxoid		
		alt.dieb.	alternis diebus (L); every other day (Rx)
ALG *(imm)*	antilymphocyte globulin (=AHLG)	alt.hor.	alternis horis (L); every other hour (Rx)
ALG, alg *(dent)*	axiolinguogingival	alt.noc.	alternis nocte (L); every other night (Rx)
ALGB	acute leukemia group B		
ALGG	gammaglobulin fraction of ALG	ALV	anterior wall of left ventricle
ALGOL	algorithmic language (for scientific-technical tasks)	ALV	avian leukosis virus
		ALVAD *(card)*	abdominal left ventricular assisted device
ALH	anterior lobe hypophysis; anterior pituitary gland		
		ALX	alexidine
ALI	annual limit of intake (e.g. of radioactivity)	AM	actinomycosis

AM	actomyosin	AMD	alpha-methyldopa
AM	ampèremeter, ammeter	AMD, amd *(dent)*	axiomesiodistal
AM *(phys)*	amplitude modulation, A-mode (ultrasound)	AMDS	Association of Military Dental Surgeons
AM	anovulatory menstrual cycle	AME	amphotericin B methyl ester
AM	arousal mechanism	AMEL	Aero-Medical Equipment
AM	aviation medicine		Laboratory
AM, am *(dent)*	axiomesial	AmFAR	American Foundation for AIDS Research
AM	myopic astigmatism	AMG, amg *(dent)*	axiomesiogingival
Am	ametropia		
aM	atypical mycobacteriosis	AMH	anti-Müllerian hormones
A.M.	Artium Magister (L); Master of Arts (= M.A.)	AMH	automated medical history
		AMHA-TP	automated micro-hemagglutination test with treponema pallidum antigen
a.m.	ante menstruationem (L); premenstrual		
a.m., AM	ante meridiem (L); before noon	AMHT	automated multiphasic health testing
a.m.	ante mortem (L); prior to death	AMI	acute myocardial infarction
AMA, a.m.a.	against medical advice	AMI	anterior myocardial infarction
AMA	Aero-Medical Association (USA) (= AeMA)	AMI	Association Médicale d'Israel; Medical Association of Israel
AMA	American Medical Association		
AMA	antimitochondrial antibodies	AMI	Association of Medical Illustrators
AMA	Australian Medical Association	AMI, ami *(dent)*	axiomesio-incisal
AMAc	acute metabolic acidosis	AMIEV	Association Médicale International pour l'Etude de Vie (F); International Medical Association for the Study of Life (Sofia)
AMAL	Aero-Medical Acceleration Laboratory		
AmB	amphotericin B		
AMC	acetylmethyl carbinol		
AMC	amoxicillin (= AOC)	AMI/HMI	acute myocardial infarction superimposed on healed myocardial infarction
AMC	Army Medical Corps		
AMC	arthrogryposis multiplex congenita		
AMC, amc *(dent)*	axiomesiocervical	AMIS	Aspirin Myocardial Infarction Study (USA)
AMCA, AMCHA	p-aminomethyl-cyclohexane carboxylic acid; tranexamic acid (= EACA, PAMBA, TAMCHA)	AMJ	Australian Medical Journal (official abbreviation: Aust. med. J.)
AM + CT	antibiotic medicine and clinical therapy	AMJA	American Medical Joggers Association

AML	acanthiomeatal line	AMREF	African Medical Research Foundation (Kenya/Tanzania)
AML	acute myeloic leukemia		
AML	Aero-Medical Laboratory (USA)		
AML	anterior mitral leaflet (=AMVL)	AMRL	Aerospace Medical Research Laboratories (USA)
AMLF	Association des Microbiologistes de Langue Française; Association of French Speaking Microbiologists (Canada)	AMRS	automatic message registering system
		AMS	American Microscopical Society
		AMS	antimacrophage serum
AMLFC	Association des Médecins de Langue Française du Canada; Association of French Speaking Doctors of Canada	AMS	Army Medical Service
		AMS	arteria mesenterica superior (L)
		AMS, A.M.S.	Assemblé Mondiale de la Santé (F); World Health Assembly
AMLS	anti-mouse lymphocyte serum	AMS	Association of Military Surgeons
AMM	Asociación Médica Mexicana; Mexican Medical Association	AMS, A.M.S.	Australian Medical Service
AMM	Asociación Médica Mundial (S); Association Médicale Mondiale (F); World Health Organization (=WHO)	ams	amount of substance
		AMSC	Army Medical Specialist Corps
		AMT	alpha-methyltyrosine
		AMT	American Medical Technologists
AMML	acute myeloic-monocytic leukemia	AMT-B	amphotericin B
AMN	alloxazine mononucleotide	amu	atomic mass unit
AMO, amo (dent)	axiomesio-occlusal	AMV	avian myeloblastosis virus
		AMV	augmented mode of ventilation
AMOL	acute monocytic leukemia	AMVL	anterior mitral valve leaflet (=AML)
AMP	adenosine monophosphate		
AMP	amphetamine	AN	afferent neuron
AMP	ampicillin	AN	amyl nitrite
AMP	average mean pressure	6-AN	6-amino-nicotinamide
amp	ampère	ANA	alanine-ß-naphthylamide
amp.	amplifier	ANA	American Neurological Association
amp.	ampoule		
amp.	amputation	ANA	American Nurses' Association
AMPIM	Animal Models of Protecting Ischemic Myocardium (NIH study, USA)	ANA	antinuclear antibody
		ANADase	anti-nicotinamide adenine dinucleotidase
AMPT	alpha-methyl-p-tyrosine		
AMQ	American Medical Qualification	ANAE	acid alpha-naphthyl acetate esterase
AMR	alternating motion reflexes		

18

ANAP	agglutination negative, adsorption positive	ANP *(card)*	arrival of negative potential
ANAP	anionic neutrophil-activating peptide	ANP	atrial natriuretic peptide (=ANF)
ANB angle	auriculo-naso-labial angle	ANPO	alpha-naphthylphenyloxazole
ANBPS	Australian National Blood Pressure Study (1973–1979)	ANR	acute nonresponder
		AN region	atrio-nodal region
ANC	Army Nurses' Corps	ANRL	antihypertensive neutral renomedullary lipids
AnCC	anodal closure contraction (=ACC)	ANS	8-anilinonaphthalene sulfonate
ANCOVA	analysis of covariance		
AnDTe	anodal duration tetanus (=ADTe)	ANS	autonomic nervous system
		ANSI	American National Standards Institute
an.ex.	anode excitation		
ANF	American Nurses' Federation	ANT	2-amino-5-nitrothiazole
		ANTU	alpha-naphthylthio-urea
ANF	American Nurses' Foundation	ANUG	acute necrotizing ulcerative gingivitis
ANF	antinuclear factor	ANZAAS	Australian and New Zealand Association for the Advancement of Science
ANF	atrial natriuretic factor (=ANP)		
AN factor	1-biotin sulphoxide (in cultures of Aspergillus niger)	ANZCP	Australian and New Zealand College of Psychiatrists
ANHS	American Natural Hygiene Society	AO	acridine orange
		AO	anodal opening
ANIT	alpha-naphthyl isothiocyanate	AO *(chem)*	anti-oxidants
		AO, A.O.	Arbeitsgemeinschaft für Osteosynthese; Working Group for Osteosynthesis (Germany)
ANL	all-or-none law		
ANLL	acute non-lymphoblastic leukemia		
ANM	Academia Nacional de Medicina (Argentina, Brazil); Académie Nationale de Médecine (France); National Academy of Medicine	AO	atrioventricular opening
		AO, ao *(dent)*	axio-occlusal
		AOA	Alpha Omega Alpha (honorary medical fraternity, USA)
ANM	amylum non mucilaginosum	AOA	American Optometric Association
ANMM	Academia Nacional de Medicina de México; National Academy of Medicine of Mexico	AOA	American Orthopedic Association
		AOA	American Orthopsychiatric Association (=ORTHO)
AnOC	anodal opening contraction (=AOC)	AOA	American Osteopathic Association
ANOVA	analysis of variance		
ANP	A-norprogesterone	AOAA	amino-oxyacetic acid

AOAC	Association of Official Agricultural Chemists	AORN	Association of Operating Room Nurses (USA)
AOAS	American Osteopathic Academy of Sclerotherapy	AOS	American Ophthalmological Society
AOB	alcohol on breath	AOS	American Otological Society
AOC	amoxicillin (= AMX)		
AOC	anodal opening contraction (= AnOC)	AOS	anodal opening sound
AOCA	American Osteopathic College of Anesthesiologists	AOSPS	American Otorhinolaryngologic Society for Plastic Surgery
AOCD	American Osteopathic College of Dermatology	AOT	Association of Occupational Therapists (USA)
AOCH, Aoch	arachnitis optico-chiasmatica	AOTA	American Occupational Therapists Association
AOCl	anodal opening clonus	AOTe	anodal opening tetanus
AOCPA	American Osteopathic College of Pathologists	AOTF	American Occupational Therapy Foundation
AOCPR	American Osteopathic College of Proctology	AOV, AoV	aortic valve
		AP	Academy of Periodontology (USA)
AOCR	American Osteopathic College of Radiology	AP	accouchement prémature (F); premature birth
AOCRM	American Osteopathic College of Rehabilitation Medicine	AP	acetylpyridine
		AP	action potential
AOD	adult-onset diabetes mellitus	AP	alkaline phopshatase (= APh)
AOD	arterial occlusive disease	AP	anomalous pathway
AoEDP	aortic enddiastolic pressure	AP	anterior pituitary
		AP	aortic pressure
AOG, AoG	aortography	AP	appendectomy
AOL	acro-osteolysis	AP	arithmetic progression
AOM	Academy of Medicine	AP	arterial pressure
A.O.M.	Artis Obstetriciae Magister (L); Master of Obstetric Art	AP	arthritis psoriatica (L); psoriatic arthritis
		AP	artificial pneumothorax
AON	all-or-none (law)	AP, ap (dent)	axiopulpal
AOO	anodal opening odor		
AOP	anodal opening picture	Ap	arteria pulmonalis (L); pulmonary artery
AOP, AoP	aortic pressure	A.P.	Académie de Pharmacie; Academy of Pharmacy (France)
AOPA	American Orthotic and Prosthetics Association		
AOP syndrome	adiposity-oligomenorrhea-parotid swelling syndrome (see also: AHOP)	A.p.	angina pectoris
		a.p. (obst)	ante partum (L); before delivery
AOR	adequate ovarian reserve (cp. DOR)	a.p.	ante prandium (L); before lunch (Rx)

a-p	anterior-posterior, antero-posterior	APASL	Asian-Pacific Association for the Study of the Liver
A+P	auscultation and percussion	APB	alternating pressure breathing (=APN, APNPB, PNPB, PNPV)
A-5-P	adenosine-5-phosphate		
APA	acute parenteral alimentation	APB	atrial premature beat (=AEB, APC)
APA	aldosterone-producing adenoma	APC	acute pharyngoconjunctival fever
APA	American Patients Association	APC	ampicillin (=AMP)
APA	American Pediatric Association	APC	analgesic preparation made of: aspirin, phenacetin and caffeine
APA	American Pharmaceutical Association (=APhA)	APC	antiphlogistic corticosteroid
APA	American Physiotherapy Association	APC	aperture current
APA	American Psychiatric Association	APC	atrial premature contraction (=AEB, APB)
APA	American Psychoanalytic Association	APCV	adenoidal-pharyngeal-conjunctival viruses
APA	American Psychological Association	APD	action potential duration
APA	American Psychotherapy Association	APD	amino-propylidene biphosphonate
		APD	anteroposterior diameter
APA	anti-pernicious anemia factor, vitamin B_{12} (=APAF, APF)	APD	aorto-pulmonary defect (=APSD, APW)
APA	Australian Physiotherapy Association	APD	atrial premature depolarization
6-APA	6-aminopenicillanic acid	APDC	ammonium-pyrrolidone dithiocarbamate
A.P.A.	Arzneimittelprüfungsanstalt (G); Drug Evaluation Agency (Switzerland)	APE	acetone powder extract
		APE	anterior pituitary extract
		APE	arecaidine propargylester
APAAP	alkaline phosphatase – antialkaline phosphatase	APERP	accessory pathway effective refractory period (=ABERP, ERP-AB, ERP-AP)
APACHE	Acute Physiology and Chronic Health Evaluation (a physiologically based classification system)	APF	animal protein factor, anti-pernicious anemia factor, vitamin B_{12}, extrinsic factor (=APA, APAF)
APAD	3-acetylpyridine-adenine dinucleotide		
		APF	anti-perinuclear factor
APAF	anti-pernicious anemia factor, vitamin B_{12} (=APA, APF)	APF	aphthoid Pospischill-Feyrter
		APG	anterior pituitary gonadotrophin
APAP	acetyl-p-aminophenol (=NAPAP)	APH	anterior pituitary hormone

APh	alkaline phosphatase (=AP). Sometimes also used for: acid phosphatase	Apo-A, Apo-B Apo-Lp	apoprotein A, apoprotein B etc. apolipoproteins
APHA	American Protestant Hospital Association	APP	aneurin pyrophosphate, cocarboxylase
APHA	American Public Health Association	APP	arginine-enriched polypeptide
APhA	American Pharmaceutical Association (=APA)	APP	avian pancreatic polypeptide
3-APHD	3-acetylpyridine-hypoxanthine-dinucleotide	APP, ApP	pulmonary artery pressure
API	aerosol penetration index	APPA	American Psychopathological Association
API	Arzneiprüfungsinstitut (G); Drug Evaluation Institute (Germany)	APPA	4-amidinophenylpyruvic acid
APIM	Association Professionelle Internationale des Médecins; International Association of the Medical Profession	APPG	aqueous procaine penicillin G
		APPP	Association of Planned Parenthood Physicians
		APPS	Association for the Psychophysiological Study of Sleep
APKD	adult polycystic kidney disease	APR	anterior pituitary reaction, Aschheim-Zondek reaction (=AZR, AZT)
APL, APLH	anterior pituitary-like hormone, chorionic gonadotrophin (=CG)	APRL	Army Prosthetic Research Laboratory
APM	Academy of Physical Medicine	APRL	arterial pressure reducing lipid
APM	Academy of Psychosomatic Medicine (USA)	APRS	adult personality rating schedule
APM	Arzt-Presse-Medizin (G); Press Information Service of the Austrian Medical Association	APRT, APRTase	adenine-phosphoribosyl transferase
APm	mean arterial pressure	APS	acute physiology score (see also: SAPS)
APMI (card)	abrupt pacemaker inhibition	APS	adenosine-5'-phosphosulfate
APMR	Association for Physical and Mental Rehabilitation	APS	alkaline primary secretion
		APS	American Pediatric Society
APN	alternating positive-negative (ventilation) (=APB, APNPB, PNPR)	APS	American Physiological Society
		APS	American Proctologic Society
APNPB, APNPV	alternating positive-negative pressure breathing, ... ventilation (=APB, APN, PNPR)	APS	American Psychological Society
		APS	American Psychosomatic Society
APO	apomorphine	APS	aminopolystyrene

APSA	American Pediatric Surgical Association	Aq.niv.	aqua nivalis (L); snow water
APSAC	anisoylated plasminogen-streptokinase activator complex	Aq.pluv.	aqua pluvialis (L); rain water
		Aq.pur.	aqua pura (L); pure water
APSD	aorto-pulmonary septal defect (=APD, APW)	Aq.tep.	aqua tepida (L); tepid water
APST	atrial pacing stress test	AR *(phys)*	absorption rate
APT	alum-precipitated toxoid	AR	accelerated reaction
		AR	achievement ratio (=AQ)
APT	aminopropyl isothio-uronium	AR	active resistive (exercise)
		AR	airway resistance
APTA	American Physical Therapy Association	AR	alarm reaction
		AR	alkali reserve
APTD	Aid to Permanently and Totally Disabled	AR	analytic reagent
		AR	anterior right
APTT	activated partial thromboplastin time	AR	antirheumatic (drug)
		AR	aortic receptor
APUD	amine and precursor uptake and decarboxylation (by chromaffin cells of the GI tract)	AR *(card)*	aortic regurgitation (=AI)
		AR, A/R	apical-radial (pulse)
		AR	arsphenamine
		AR	atrophic rhinitis
APW	aorto-pulmonary window (=APD, APSD)	AR	augmentation reaction
		ar *(chem)*	aromatic
APWS	abortive pickwickian syndrome	A.R.	Abderhalden reaction
		ARA	American Rheumatism Association
AQ	achievement quotient		
Aq.	aqua (L); water	ARA	antiribosomal antibody
Aq.astr.	aqua astricta (L); frozen water	ARA-A	adenine arabinoside
		ARA-C	cytosine arabinoside
Aq.bidest.	aqua bidestillata (L); twice distilled water	ARA-Hx	arabinosyl hypoxanthine
Aq.bull.	aqua bulliens (L); boiling water	ARAS	ascending reticular activation system (=ARS, RAS)
Aq.cal.	aqua calida (L); hot water	ARBOR	arthropod-borne (viruses), Arbo viruses
Aq.com.	aqua communis (L); common (drinking) water	ARC	AIDS-related complex
		ARC	American Red Cross
Aq.dest.	aqua destillata (L); distilled water	ARC *(ophth)*	anomalous retinal correspondence
Aq.ferv.	aqua fervens (L); (boiling) hot water	ARC	Australian Red Cross Society
Aq.fluv.	aqua fluvialis (L); river water	ARCAPA	anomalous right coronary artery from pulmonary artery
Aq.font.	aqua fontana (L); spring water		
Aq.gel.	aqua gelida (L); cold water	A.R.C.S.	Associate of the Royal College of Science (UK)
Aq.mar.	aqua marina (L); sea water		

ARD	absolute reaction of degeneration
ARD	acute respiratory disease
ARD	aortic root diameter
ARDS	Air Research and Development Command
ARDS	acute respiratory distress syndrome (= RDS) (also for: adult respiratory distress syndrome)
ARE *(pharm)*	amount (of substance) to be excreted
ARES	antireticulo-endothelial serum (= ACS, RAS, SAC, SARC)
ARF	acute renal failure (= ARI)
ARF	acute respiratory failure
ARF	acute rheumatic fever
ARG	aortorenography
ARG	autoradiography
Arg	arginine
ArgP	arginine phosphate
ARG syndrome	aniridia, (mental) retardation and genitourinary abnormalities
ARI	acute renal insufficiency (= ARF)
ARI	acute respiratory insufficiency (= ARF)
ARI	atrial refractory interval
A.R.I.C.	Associate of the Royal Institute of Chemistry (UK)
ARID	AIDS-related immune dysfunction
ARLS	anti-rat lymphocyte serum
ARM *(obst)*	artificial rupture of the membranes
ARMA	American Registry of Medical Assistants
ARMB	Académie Royale de Médecine Belge (F); Belgian Royal Academy of Medicine
ARMH	Academy of Religion and Mental Health

ARN	acide ribonucléique (F); ribonucleic acid (RNS)
ARNMD	Association for Research in Nervous and Mental Diseases
ARO	Association for Research in Ophthalmology (USA)
AROM	active range of motion
ARP	absolute refractory period
ARP	activité de la rénine plasmatique (F); plasma renin activity
ARP	Advanced Research Projects
ARP	American Registry of Pathologists
ARP, ARPl	anti-reflux plasty
ARPT	American Registry of Physical Therapists
ARPV	absolute refractory period of ventricle
ARQ	aortic regurgitation quotient
ARQ	automatic error-correcting system
A.R.R.C.	Associate of the Royal Red Cross (UK)
ARRS	American Roentgen Ray Society
ARRT	American Registry of Radiologic Technologists
A.R.R.T.	American Registered Respiratory Therapist
ARS	activating reticular system (= ARAS, RAS)
ARS	American Radium Society
ARS	American Rhinologic Society
ARS	aryl sulfatase A (= ASA)
A.R.S.P.H.	Associate of the Royal Society for the Promotion of Health (UK)
ART	algebraic reconstruction technique
Art.	articulatio (L); joint
art *(gen)*	antirepression of transactivation

art.	arterial	ASAIO	American Society for Artificial Internal Organs
A.R.T.	Accredited Record Technician	ASAL	arginine succinate lyase
ARV	AIDS-associated retrovirus (=HIV, HTLV, LAV)	ASAP	"as soon as possible"
		ASAPS	American Society for Aesthetic Plastic Surgery
ARV *(card)*	anterior wall of the right ventricle (=ARVW)	ASAS	arginine succinate synthetase
ARV	aortic regurgitant volume		
ARVD	arrhythmogenic right ventricular dysplasia (=ADRV)	ASAT	aspartate aminotransferase (=ASPAT)
		ASB	American Society of Bacteriology
ARVW	anterior right ventricular wall (=ARV)	ASB	American Society of Biochemists
AS	ampère second	ASB	assisted spontaneous breathing (=ASV)
AS	anaphylactic shock		
AS	ankylosing spondylitis	ASBC	American Society of Biological Chemists
AS	antiserum		
AS	anxiety state	ASC	acetylsulphanilyl chloride
AS	aortic stenosis	ASC *(mil)*	Advanced Surgical Centre
AS	aqueous solution	ASC	automatic sensitivity control
AS	aqueous suspension		
AS	arterial system	asc.	ascending
AS	arteriosclerosis, atherosclerosis	A-scan	amplitude scan (of ultrasound)
AS	asystole	ASCC	American Society for the Control of Cancer
AS, A.s.	auris sinistra (L); left ear (=AL)		
		ASCE	American Society of Childbirth Educators
As	astigmatism		
A.s.	atrium sinistrum (L); left atrium	ASCH	American Society of Clinical Hypnosis
ASA	acetylsalicylic acid, aspirin	ASCII	American Standard Code for Information Interchange (computer version)
ASA	Adam-Stokes attack		
ASA	American Society of Andrology		
		ASCLT	American Society of Clinical Laboratory Technicians
ASA	American Society of Anesthesiologists		
		ASCO	American Society of Clinical Oncology
ASA	American Standards Association		
		ASCO	American Society of Clinical Pathologists
ASA	American Surgical Association		
		ASCP	American Society of Clinical Pathologists
ASA	anti-sperm antibodies		
ASA	arylsulphatase A (=ARS)		
ASAD	free combination of: acetylsalicylic acid and dipyridamole	ASCPT	American Society for Pharmacology and Therapeutics
		ASCRS	American Society of Colon and Rectal Surgeons
AS+AI	aortic stenosis + aortic insufficiency		

ASCVD	arteriosclerotic cardiovascular disease	ASHD	atrial septal heart defect (=ASD)
ASCVD	arteriosclerotic cerebrovascular disease	ASHG	American Society of Human Genetics
ASD	accouchement sans douleur (F); painless delivery	ASHI	Association for the Study of Human Infertility
ASD	atrial septal defect (=ASHD)	ASHNS	American Society of Head and Neck Surgery
ASDC	American Society of Dentistry for Children	ASHP	American Society of Hospital Pharmacists
ASDR	American Society of Dental Radiographers	ASI *(card)*	anteroseptal infarction (=ASMI)
ASE	Antistreptolysin-Einheit (G); antistreptolysin unit	ASI *(psych)*	Anxiety State Inventory
		ASII	American Science Information Institute
ASE	axilla-shoulder-elbow (bandage)	ASIM	American Society of Internal Medicine
ASECS	antigen-specific electrophoretic cell separation	ASIS	Association for the Study of Internal Secretion
ASEP	American Society for Experimental Pathology	ASK	antistreptokinase
		ASL	antistreptolysin
ASF	African swine fever	ASLIB	Association of Special Libraries and Information Bureaus
ASF	aniline-sulphur-formaldehyde (solution for microscopy)		
		ASLO	antistreptolysin-O (=ASO)
ASFV	African swine fever virus	ASM	American Society for Microbiology
ASGB	Anatomical Society of Great Britain and Ireland		
		ASM, A.S.M.	Association Sportive de Médecine; Association of Sports Medicine (France)
ASGE	American Society of Gastrointestinal Endoscopy		
ASH	aldosterone stimulating hormone	AsM	myopic astigmatism
		ASMA	Aero-Space Medical Association
ASH	American Society for Hematology	ASMA	anti-smooth muscle antibody
ASH *(card)*	asymmetric septal hypertrophy	ASME	Association for the Study of Medical Education
AsH *(ophth)*	hyperopic astigmatism	ASMI	anteroseptal myocardial infarction
ASHA	American School Health Association		
ASHA	American Speech and Hearing Association	ASMS	American Society of Maxillofacial Surgeons
ASHBM	Associate Scottish Hospital Bureau of Management	ASMT	American Society for Medical Technology
		ASN	American Society of Neuroradiology
ASHD	arteriosclerotic heart disease	Asn	asparagine

ASNEMGE	Association des Sociétés Nationales Européennes et Méditerranéennes de Gastroenterologie; Association of European and Mediterranian Societies of Gastroenterology	ASR	antistreptolysin reaction (=AST)
		ASRT	American Society of Radiologic Technologists
		ASS	Adam-Stokes syndrome
		ASS	American Sociological Society
ASO	American Society of Orthodontists	ASS	anterior superior spine
ASO	antistreptolysin-O (=ASLO)	ASS	Azetylsalizylsäure (G); acetylsalicylic acid
ASO	arteriosclerosis obliterans (L); obliterating arteriosclerosis	ASSA	American Society for the Study of Arteriosclerosis
ASOOA	American Society of Ophthalmologic and Otolaryngologic Allergy	ASSH	American Society for Surgery of the Hand
		ASSMB	Association des Sociétés Scientifiques Médicales Belges (F); Belgian Association of Scientific Medical Societies
ASOS	American Society of Oral Surgeons		
ASP	American Society of Parasitologists		
ASP	American Society of Periodontists	ASSS	American Society for the Study of Sterility
		AST	antistreptolysin test (=ASR)
ASP	American Society of Pharmacognosy	AST	aspartate aminotransferase (=ASAT, ASPAT)
ASP	asparaginase		
Asp	asparaginic (aspartic) acid	AST	atrial stimulation
		ASt	antistaphylolysin
ASPAT	aspartate aminotransferase (=ASAT)	Ast.	astigmatism
		ASTEC	Association of Science Technology Centers
ASPAT	A-streptococci polysaccharide antibody titer	ASTHO	Association of State and Territorial Health Officials
ASPECT	Approach to Systematic Planning and Evaluation of Clinical Trials		
		ASTI	antispasticity index
		AStL	antistaphylolysin
ASPET	American Society of Pharmacology and Experimental Therapeutics	ASTM	American Society for Testing and Materials
		ASTMH	American Society of Tropical Medicine and Hygiene
ASPH	Association of Schools of Public Health	ASTO	antistreptolysin O (titer)
ASPM	N-(N-acetyl-4-sulfamoyl-phenyl)-maleinimide	AStR	antistaphylolysin reaction
		AStT	antistaphylolysin test
ASPRS	American Society of Plastic and Reconstructive Surgeons	ASU	Arizona State University (Phoenix)
ASR	aldosterone secretion rate	ASV	assisted spontaneous ventilation (=ASB)

ASVIP *(card)*	atrial synchronous ventricular inhibited pacing	ATEB	Association Nationale des Techniques Biologistes; National Association of Biological Techniques (France)
asx	asymptomatic		
AT	abdominal toxoplasmosis		
AT	accident du travail (F); accident at work	ATEE	N-acetyl-L-tyrosine-ethyl-ester
AT	achievement test	ATERP	atrial effective refractory period (=AERP, ERPA)
AT *(otol)*	adenotomy		
AT	adjunctive therapy	ATEU	AIDS Treatment Evaluation Unit (USA)
AT	air temperature		
AT, A.T.	Alt-Tuberkulin (G); old tuberculin	at.fib.	atrial fibrillation
AT *(mil)*	ambulance train	ATFRP	atrial functional refractory period (=AFRP, FRPA)
AT	amitriptyline		
AT	anaphylatoxin	ATG	antithrombocyte globulin
AT	angiotensin	ATG	antithymocyte globulin
AT	antithrombin	ATH	abdominal total hysterectomy
AT	antitrypsin (=ATr)		
AT *(lab)*	appearance time	ATH	acetyltyrosine hydrazide
AT	Aschoff-Tawara (node)	ATh	azathioprine
AT	atomic time	ATHC	allotetrahydrocortisol
AT *(psych)*	autogenetic training	ATK	Alt-Tuberkulin Koch (G); old tuberculin Koch
AT	(combination of) cytarabine + 6-thioguanine		
At	acidité total (F); total acidity	ATL	Achilles tendon lengthening
at	airtight	ATL	adult T-cell leukemia
at	technical atmosphere	ATL	anterior tricuspid leaflet (=ATVL)
A-T	adenine-thymine		
A+T	adenotomy and tonsillectomy	ATLV	adult T-cell leukemia virus
		atm	physical atmosphere
AT 10	antitetanic substance, dihydrotachysterol	ATMA	antithyroid microsomal antibody
ATA	alimentary toxic aleukia	ATME	automatic transmission measuring equipment
ATA	alkali test area		
ATA	antithrombocyte antibody	ATMI	acute transmural myocardial infarction
ATB	atrial tachycardia with block (also used for: atrioventricular block = AV block)		
		ATN	acute tubular necrosis
		at.no.	atomic number
		ATNR	asymmetrical tonic neck reflex
ATCC *(lab)*	American Type Culture Collection		
		ATP	adenosine triphosphate (=ADT)
ATCSA	Association of Thoracic and Cardiovascular Surgeons of America		
		ATPase	adenosine triphosphatase
		ATPD	ambient temperature and pressure, dry
ATE	adenotonsillectomy (=A+T)		
		ATPR	average threshold of pain reaction

ATPS	ambient temperature and pressure, saturated	AV	aortic valve
ATR	Achilles tendon reflex	AV	atrioventricular
ATR	attenuated total reflection	AV	audiovisual
ATr	antitrypsin	AV	autophagic vacuoles
ATS	American Temperance Society	av, a.v.	arteriovenous
		av.	average
ATS	American Therapeutic Society	A.V. *(chem)*	acid value
ATS	American Thoracic Society	AVA	aortic valve area
ATS	American Trauma Society (Chicago)	AVA	arrhythmogenic ventricular activity
ATS	antitetanic serum	AVA, avA	arteriovenous anastomosis
ATS	antithymocyte serum (=ATG)	AVA, avA	arteriovenous angioma
		AVC	aberrant ventricular conduction
ATS	anxiety tension state	AVC	allantoid vaginal cream
ATS	atropine sulfate	AVC *(card)*	apparent valve change
ATSD	Alzheimer type senile dementia (=SDAT)	AVC	atrioventricular canal
		AVC	atrioventricular conduction
ATT	alkali test time	AVC	automatic volume control
ATT	ammonia tolerance test	AVCERP	atrioventricular conduction effective refractory period
ATT	antitoxin titer		
att *(gen)*	attachment site	AVCMF	cytotoxic therapy with a combination of: adriamycin, vincristin, cyclophosphamide, methotrexate, and 5-fluorouracil
ATVL	anterior tricuspid valve leaflet		
at.vol.	atomic volume		
at.wt.	atomic weight		
ATZ	anal transitional zone	AVCS	atrioventricular conduction system
AU	antitoxin unit		
AU	arbitrary unit (in cytophotometry and microspectrophotometry)	AVD	aortic valvular defect
		AVD	apparent volume of distribution
AU	auris uterque (L); each ear	AVD	atrioventricular dissociation
ÅU	Ångström unit		
AUA	American Urological Association	avD	arteriovenous difference
		AVDA	American Venereal Disease Association
AUC	area under curve		
AUDI	International Society of Audiology	AVDC	atrioventricular dissociation with capture
AUL	acute undifferentiated leukemia	avD-O_2	arteriovenous oxygen difference (=av-O_2)
aur.fib.	auricular fibrillation	avdp	avoirdupois
AUSH-AG	Australia serum hepatitis antigen	AVERP	atrioventricular (node) effective refractory period (=AVNERP)
AV	acuité visuelle (F); visual acuity		
AV	anteversion (of the uterus)	aVF	augmented volt foot (ECG)

AVFRP	atrioventricular (node) functional refractory period ($=$ AVNFRP)
AVG	aortovenography
AVHD	acquired valvular heart disease
AVI	air velocity index
AVI	atrioventricular interval
AVJA	atrioventricular junctional arrhythmia
AVJT	atrioventricular junctional tachycardia
AVK	anti-vitamin K
aVL	augmented volt left arm (ECG)
AVMA	American Veterinary Medical Association
AvMV	avian myeloblastosis virus
AVN	atrioventricular node
AVNAERP	atrioventricular node antegrade effective refractory period ($=$ AVERP, AVNERP)
AVNAFRP	atrioventricular node antegrade functional refractory period ($=$ AVFRP, AVNFRP)
AVNERP	atrioventricular node effective refractory period ($=$ AVERP, AVNAERP)
AVNFRP	atrioventricular node functional refractory period ($=$ AVFRP, AVNAFRP)
AVNR	atrioventricular nodal reentry
AVNRT	atrioventricular nodal reentrant tachycardia ($=$ AVRT)
AVNT	atrioventricular nodal tachycardia
AVO	aortic valve opening
av-O_2	arteriovenous oxygen difference ($=$ avD-O_2)
AVP	antiviral protein
AVP	aortic valve prolapse
AVP	aortoventriculoplasty
AVP	arginine-vasopressin

AVP	arterial volume pulse
AVPC	aortic valve partial closure
AVPSVT	atrioventricular interval of paroxysmal supraventricular tachycardia
AVR	accelerated ventricular rhythm
AVR	aortic valve replacement
aVR	augmented volt right arm (ECG)
AV regimen	cytotoxic therapy with a combination of adriamycin and vincristin
AVRT	atrioventricular reentrant tachycardia ($=$ AVNRT)
AVS	aortic valve stenosis
AVS	Association for Voluntary Sterilization
AvSV	avian sarcoma virus
AVT	arginine-vasotonin
AW	above waist
AW	atomic warfare
A+W	alive and well
AWAR	anterior wall of aortic root
AWF	adrenal weight factor
AWI *(card)*	anterior wall infarction
AWM *(card)*	abnormal wall motion
AWMF	Arbeitsgemeinschaft Wissenschaftlich-Medizinischer Fachgesellschaften (G); Study Group of Medical Scientific Societies (Germany)
AWMI	anterior wall myocardial infarction
AWO	airway obstruction
AWP *(pharm)*	average wholesale price
AXM	acetoxycyclohexamine
Ax-Ro joint	axial rotation joint
AYF	anti-yeast factor
AYF	ayfactine
AYV	aster yellow virus
Az.	azote (nitrogen)
AZG *(pharm)*	8-azaguanine
AZR, AZT	Aschheim-Zondek reaction, ... test ($=$ APR)
AZT	azidothymidine

B

B	Bacillus
B	Balantidium
B *(physiol)*	barometric pressure
B *(chem)*	base
B *(phys)*	base (of a prism)
B *(chem)*	Baumé scale
B	behavior
B *(phys)*	bel
B *(rad)*	Benoist scale
B	benzoate
B, b *(dent)*	buccal
b	bar
b *(phys)*	Barn
b	bel
B.	bacillus (= Bac.)
B I *(chir)*	Billroth's operation I (gastric resection)
B II *(chir)*	Billroth's operation II (gastric resection with gastroenterostomy)
BA	backache
BA	bacterial agglutination
BA	basal activity
BA	basilar artery
BA	benzylamine
BA	Biological Abstracts
BA	biological age
BA	blood agar
BA	blood alcohol (= BAC)
BA	boric acid
BA	brachial artery
BA	bronchial asthma (= AB)
BA, ba *(dent)*	buccoaxial
B.A.	Baccalaureus Artium (L); Bachelor of Arts
B›A	bone greater than air (conduction)
BAA	benzoyl arginine amide
BAC	bacitracin
BAC	bacterial antigen complex
BAC	blood alcohol concentration
BAC	British Association of Chemists
BAC, bac *(dent)*	buccoaxiocervical
Bac.	bacillus (= B.)
BACOP	cytotoxic therapy with a combination of: bleomycin, adriamycin, cyclophosphamide, oncovin, and prednisone
BACR	British Association for Cancer Research
Bact.	bacterium
bact.	bacterial
BAD	British Association of Dermatology
BADE	2,2'-bi-(di-(carboxymethyl)-amino)-diethylether
BADP	brachial artery diastolic pressure
BAE	British Academy of Experts
BaE	barium enema
BAEA	British Atomic Energy Authority
BAEE	benzoyl L-arginine ethyl ester
BAEP	brainstem auditory (or acoustic) evoked potential
BAERE	British Atomic Energy Research Establishment
BAEV, BaEV	baboon endogenous virus
BAF	bovine amniotic fluid
BAG, bag *(dent)*	buccoaxiogingival
BAGG	buffered azide glucose glycerol (broth)
BAH *(card)*	biatrial hypertrophy
BAI	basilar artery insufficiency
BAI	basophil age index
BAIBA	beta-aminoisobutyric acid
BÄK	Bundesärztekammer; Federal Medical Council (Germany)

BAL	British anti-lewisite, dimercaprol (antidote)
BAL	broncho-alveolar lavage
BALT	bronchial-associated lymphoid tissue
BaM	barium meal
BAME	benzoyl arginine methyl ester
BAMP	brachial artery mean pressure
BAN	British Approved Name
BAN	British Association of Neurologists
BAN	British Association of Neuropathologists
BANA	N-alpha-benzoyl-D,L-arginine-2-naphthylamide
BANI	N-alpha-benzoyl-D,L-arginine-4'-nitroanilide
BAO	basal acid output (of the stomach)
BAO	British Association of Otolaryngologists
B.A.O.	Bachelor of the Art of Obstetrics
BAP	blood agar plate
BAP	brachial artery pressure
BAPA	N-alpha-benzoyl-arginine-p-nitroanilide (= BAPNA)
BAPhysMed	British Association of Physical Medicine
BAPM	British Association of Physical Medicine
BAPN	beta-aminopropionitrile
BAPNA	N-alpha-benzoyl-arginine-p-nitroanilide (= BAPA)
BAPS	British Association of Paediatric Surgeons
BAPS	British Association of Plastic Surgeons
BAPT	British Association of Physical Training
BAR	bacterial agglutination reaction
BARP	British Association of Radiology and Physiotherapy

BAS	balloon atrioseptostomy
BAS (mil)	Battalion Aid Station
BAS	benzyl analogue of serotonin
BAS (pharm)	boric acid solution
BAS	British Anatomical Society
BASH (card)	body acceleration synchronous with heart beat
baso	basophilic leukocyte
BASP	brachial artery systolic pressure
BAU	British Association Unit (unit of electrical resistance; 1 BAU = 0.9886 ohm)
BAU	Bundesanstalt für Arbeitsschutz und Unfallforschung; Federal Institution for Occupational Protection and Accident Research (Germany)
BAUS	British Association of Urological Surgeons
BAV	balloon aortic valvuloplasty (= BDV)
BAV	bloc atrioventriculaire (F); atrioventricular block
BB	blood bank
BB	"blue bloater"
BB (gyn)	breakthrough bleeding
BB	breast biopsy
BB	buffer base
BBA (obst)	born before arrival
BBA	Biologische Bundesanstalt; Federal Institute of Biology (Germany)
BBB	blood-brain barrier
BBB	bundle-branch block
BBBB	bilateral bundle branch block
BBBD	blood-brain barrier disruption
BBC	bromobenzylcyanide
BBD	bloc de branche droit (F); right bundle branch block

BBG	bloc de branche gauche (F); left bundle branch block
BBM	benzbromarone (= BBR)
BBOT	2,5-bis-(5'-t-butylbenzoxazolyl-2')-thiophene
BBR	benzbromarone (= BBM)
BBR	Berlin blue reaction
BBS	Besnier-Boeck-Schaumann (disease)
BBT	basal body temperature
BC *(gen)*	back-cross (generation)
BC	beta-carboline
BC	birth control
BC	bone conduction
BC	breathing capacity
BC	bronchial carcinoma
BC	bronchite chronique (F); chronic bronchitis
BC, bc *(dent)*	buccocervical
Bc	convergent scan (in two-dimensional sonography) (cp. Bd, Bp)
B.C.	Baccalaureus Chirurgiae (L); Bachelor of Surgery (= B.Ch., B.Chir., C.B., Ch.B.)
BCA	bile canaliculi antibodies
BCA	Blue Cross Association (USA)
BCAPA *(card)*	both coronary arteries from pulmonary artery
BCB	brilliant cresyl blue
BC/BS	Blue Cross/Blue Shield (USA)
BCC	Birth Control Clinic
BCCG	British Cooperative Clinical Group
BCD	bicarbonate dialysis
BCDC	binary-coded decimal code
BCE	basal cell epithelioma
BCE	buturylcholinesterase (= BChE, BuChE)
B-cells	beta-cells of the pancreatic islets

B-cells	bone-marrow derived lymphocytes
B-cells	bursa-equivalent lymphocytes
BCF	blood coagulation factor
BCF	Burton-Cabrera-Frank theory (of crystal growth)
BCG	Bacillus Calmette-Guérin (vaccination)
BCG	ballistocardiogram
BCG *(lab)*	bromocresyl green
BCGF	B-cell growth factor
BCG test	bicolor guaiac test (= BG)
BCH	basal cell hyperplasia
B.Ch., B.Chir.	Baccalaureus Chirurgiae (L); Bachelor of Surgery (= B.C., C.B., Ch.B.)
B.Ch.D	Baccalaureus Chirurgiae Dentalis (L); Bachelor of Dental Surgery
BChE	butyrylcholinesterase (= BCE, BuChE)
BCIC	Birth Control Investigation Committee
BCL *(card)*	basic cycle length
BCLL	B-cell chronic lymphatic leukemia
BCM	birth controll medication
BCME	bis-chlormethyl ether
BCNU	l,3-bis-(2-chlorethyl)-l-nitroso-urea
BCO	bilateral carotid occlusion
BCP	birth control pill
BCP	bromocresyl purple
BCS	British Cardiac Society
BCS	Budd-Chiari syndrome (= HVT, VOD)
BCT	blood coagulation time
BCTF	Breast Cancer Task Force (NCI department)
BCW	biological and chemical warfare
BD	base deficit
BD	base deviation (= BE)
BD	base of prism down
BD	bile duct
BD *(clin)*	borderline dull

BD, bd *(dent)*	buccodistal	BDZ	Bund Deutscher Zahnärzte; German Dental Association
Bd	divergent scan (in two-dimensional sonography) (cp. Bc, Bp)	BE *(rad)*	barium enema
b.d.	bis in die (L); twice a day (Rx) (=b.i.d.)	BE	base excess (=BD)
		BE	bacillary emulsion (tuber-culin) (=TBE)
BDA	Basle Drug and Alcohol Test	BE	below elbow
BDA	beclomethasone dipropio-nate aerosol	BE	bile esculin
		BE *(physiol)*	Bohr effect
BDA	British Dental Association	°Bé *(chem)*	Baumé degree
BDA	British Diabetic Associa-tion	Be^a factor	Berrens factor, Antigen Be^a
BDA	Bundesvereinigung Deutscher Ärzteverbände (G); Federal Association of German Medical Socie-ties	BEAR	Biological Effects of Atomic Radiation (Com-mittee)
		BEH	benign essential hyperten-sion
BDAC	Bureau of Drug Abuse Control	BEI	butanol-extractable iodine
		BEIR	biological effects of ioniz-ing radiation
BDB	bis-diazotized benzidine	BEL *(obst)*	Beckenendlage (G); breech presentation
BDC	bruits du coeur (F); heart murmurs		
BDC	burn-dressing change	BEP	base-encephalitogenic pro-tein
BDE	bile duct examination	BER	basic electrical rhythm
B.Dent.Sci.	Bachelor of Dental Science (Dublin)	BER	bit error rate
		BERA	brainstem electric response audiometry
BDG	bilirubin diglucuronide		
BDG	buffered deoxycholate glu-cose	BES	balanced electrolyte solu-tion
BDH	British Drug Houses	BES	Biological Engineering Society (UK)
BDI *(psych)*	Beck Depression Inven-tory	BESRL	Behavioral Science Research Laboratory (USA)
BDP	beclomethasone dipropio-nate		
		Be-T-E	benzilic acid tropine ester (=BTE)
BDP *(pharm)*	brodimoprim	BE test *(psych)*	Benton test
BDPE *(pharm)*	bromodiphenyl-(p-ethyl-phenyl)-ethylene	BET infusion	anesthesiological infusion model consisting of: bolus, elimination rate, transfer rate
BDS	biological detection system		
B.D.S.	Bachelor of Dental Sur-gery		
B.D.Sc.	Bachelor of Dental Science	BET method	Burnauer-Emmet-Teller surface determination by measurement of the adsorption isotherm
BDU	bromo-deoxyuridine		
BDV	balloon dilatation valvulo-plasty		

BeV	billion electron volts (internationally: GeV)	BH	bill of health
		BH	borderline hypertension
BF	bentonite flocculation (=BFT)	BH	brain hormone
		BH_2	dihydrobiopterin
BF	blastogenic factor	BH_4	L-5,6,7,8-tetrahydrobiopterin
BF	blood flow		
BF	(tuberculin) bouillon filtrate	BHA	bilateral (or benign) hilar adenopathy (=BHL)
BF	butter fat; adeps butyri (L)	BHA	British Homoeopathic Association
B/F	bound/free (antigens)		
BFD	bioelectronic functional diagnosis	BHA	British Hospitals Association
BFU *(imm)*	burst forming unit	BHA	butyl hydroxyanisol
BFU-E *(imm)*	burst forming unit – erythrocyte	BHA	beta-hydroxybutyrate
		BHAT	Beta-Blocker Heart Attack Trial (by the NHLBI, 1978-1980)
B-form	bacterial form of cells in culture medium colonies		
BFP	biologically false positive (reaction)	BHC	benzene hexachloride (=HACC, HCC, HCCH, HCH)
BFR sol.	buffered Ringer's solution		
BFT	bentonite flocculation test (=BF)	BHF	British Health Foundation
		BHG	Bureau de l'Hygiène Générale; Office of General Hygiene (France)
BFVD	British Federation against Venereal Diseases		
BFX *(pharm)*	bufexamac	BHI	biosynthetic human insulin
BG	bicolor guaiac (test) (=BCG test)	BHI	Bureau of Health Insurance
		BHIB	beef heart infusion broth
BG	blood glucose (=BS)	BHIS	beef heart infusion supplemented (broth or agar)
Bg, bg *(dent)*	buccogingival		
B-G	Bordet-Gengou (bacillus)	BHK	baby hamster kidney
BGA	blood gas analysis	BHL	bilateral (or benign) hilar lymphoma (=BHA)
BGA	Bundesgesundheitsamt; Federal Health Office (Germany) (comparable to the American FDA)		
		BHL	biological half-life
		BHM	Bureau of Health Manpower
BGE	butyl glycidyl ether		
BGG	bovine gamma globulin	BHN	bephenium hydroxynaphthoate
BGGRA	British Gelatin and Glue Research Association		
		BHPRD	Bureau of Health Planning and Resources Development
BGLB	brilliant green lactose broth		
BGM	Buffalo green monkey (laboratory animal)	BHS	British Homoeopathic Society
		BHT	7-(beta-hydroxypropyl)-theophylline
BGO	bismuth germanium oxide (scintillation substance)		
BGS	British Geriatrics Society	BHT	butyl hydroxytoluene
BGT	bilirubin glucuronyl transferase	BHTD	Bureau of Hygiene and Tropical Diseases (UK)

35

B.Hyg.	Bachelor of Hygiene
BI	base of prism in (cp. BO)
BI	bone injury
BI	Broca index
Bi	biot (1 biot = 10 ampère)
BIA	bioimmunoassay
BIAC	Bioinstrumentation Advisory Council
BIB	Bundesinstitut für Bevölkerungsforschung (G); Federal Institute of Population Research (Wiesbaden/Germany)
BIBRA	British Industrial Biological Research Association
BID	beta-ionization detector
BID	brought in dead (= DOA)
b.i.d.	bis in die (L); twice a day (Rx) (= b.d.)
Bi factor	Biles factor, antigen Bi
BIH	benign intracranial hypertension
BII	butanol insoluble iodine
BIL, bil.	bilirubin
bilat.	bilateral
BIMS	Bisoprolol International Multicentre Study
BIO	Biomedical Information Processing Organization (USA)
biol.	biological, biology
BioLab	Biological Laboratories (USA)
biomet	biometrical mean value
biophys.	biophysical
BIOS	British Intelligence Objective Subcommittee
BIOSIS	Biosciences Information Service
BIP	bacterial intravenous protein
BIP	biparietal diameter (of skull) (= BPD)
BIP	bismuth-iodoform-paraffin (Rx, USA)
BIP	bradycardia-indicating pacemaker
BIP	bronchiolitic interstitial pneumonitis
BIPM	Bureau Internationale des Poids et Mesures (F); International Bureau for Weights and Measures
BIPP	bismuth iodoform petrolatum paste
BIR	basic incidence rate
BIR	British Institute of Radiology
BISP	between ischial spines
bit	binary digit (information unit in data processing)
BITCH	Black Intelligence Test of Cultural Homogeneity
BITU	benzylthiourea
BIV	bovine immunodeficiency virus (= BVLV)
BJ	Bence-Jones (protein) (= BJP)
BJ	biceps jerk
BJ	Bravais-Jacksonien (used in French literature for Jackson epilepsy)
B + J	bone and joint
BJM	bones, joints, muscles
BJP	Bence-Jones protein
BK	bacillus Koch (used in French and Russian literature for Mycobacterium tuberculosis)
BK	below knee
BK	bradykinin
BKA	basophil-derived kallikrein of anaphylaxis
BKA	below knee amputation
BKN	blastokinin
BKTT	below knee to toe
BKWP	below knee walking plaster
BL	basal labyrinth
BL, bl (dent)	buccolingual
BL	Burkitt's lymphoma
Bl area (derm)	black light area
BLB mask	Boothby-Lovelace-Bulbulian oxygen mask
BlC	blood culture

Bleo	bleomycin (= BLM)	BMI	body mass index
BLG	beta-lactoglobulin	BMJ	British Medical Journal
BLH	borderline hypertensive		(official abbreviation: Brit.
BLL	Burkitt-like lymphoma		med. J.)
BLM	bleomycin (= Bleo)	BMJFG	Bundesministerium für
BLOT	British Library of Tape		Jugend, Familie und
	Recordings		Gesundheit (G); Federal
BLROA	British Laryngological,		Ministry of Youth, Family
	Rhinological and Otologi-		and Health (Ger-
	cal Association		many)
BLS	basic life support	BMN	betamethasone
BlS	blood sugar	BMO *(mil)*	Battalion Medical Officer
BlT	blood type		(UK)
BLV	bovine leukosis virus	B-mode	brightness modulation
	(= BoLV)	BMPP	benign mucous membrane
B-lympho-	bursa-equivalent lympho-		pemphigus
cytes	cytes	BMR	basal metabolic rate
BM	basal membrane	BMS	British Medical Society
BM	basal metabolism	BMS	Bureau of Medical Statis-
BM	bowel movement		tics
BM, bm *(dent)*	buccomesial	B.M.S.	Bachelor of Medical
B.M.	Baccalaureus Medicinae;		Science
	Bachelor of Medicine	BMSA	British Medical Students
BMA	British Medical Associa-		Association
	tion	BMSH	beta-melanocyte stimulat-
BMB	British Medical Bulletin		ing hormone
BMB joint	Beat Müller balance joint	BMSJ	British Medical Students
BMC	Biomedical Center		Journal
	(Uppsala/Sweden)	BMT	Biomedical Technique
BMC	bone marrow cells	BMT	bone marrow transplanta-
BMC	bone mineral content		tion
BMD	Becker muscular dys-	BM test	Boehringer mucoviscidosis
	trophy		test
BMD	bone mass density	BMV	biofeedback motivated
BMDP	Biomedical Dixon Pro-		ventilation
	gram (statistical software)	BMZ *(derm)*	basal membrane zone
BME	basal medium of Eagle		(= DMJ)
B.Med.	Baccalaureus Medicinae	BMZ	bumadizone
	(L); Bachelor of Medicine	BNA	Basle Nomina Anatomica
BMFT	Bundesministerium für		(1895) (cp. JNA, PNA)
	Forschung und Technolo-	BNDD	Bureau of Narcotics and
	gie (G); Federal Ministry		Dangerous Drugs
	of Research and Technol-	BNF	British National Formu-
	ogy (Germany)		lary
BMG	bilirubin monoglucuronide	BNMS	British Nuclear Medicine
BMHP	bromomercurihydroxy-		Society
	propane	BNO	bowels not opened

BNOA	British Naturopathic and Osteopathic Association
BNR	beam non-uniformity ratio
BO	base of prism out
BO	body odor
BO	bowels open
BO, bo (dent)	bucco-occlusal
B+O (pharm)	belladonna and opium
BOA	born on arrival
BOA	British Orthopaedic Association
BOA	British Osteopathic Association
BOC	butyl oxycarbonyl
BOD	biochemical oxygen demand
Bod unit	Bodansky unit (= BU)
BOEA	ethyl biscoumacetate
BOHS	British Occupational Hygiene Society
BOL	begin of life (with reference to pacemakers)
bol. (Pharm)	bolus
BoLV	bovine leukosis virus (= BLV)
BOMA	bilateral otitis media acuta
BOP	Buffalo orphan prototype (viruses)
BOR	bowels open regularly
boral	boron/aluminum; aluminium borico-tartaricum (L)
BOS	Basic Operating System
BOSTID	Board of Science and Technology for International Development
BOT	Board of Trade
Bot.	botany, botanical
bot.	bottle
BOW (obst)	bag of waters (amniotic sac)
BP	barometric pressure
BP	basic (myelin) protein
BP	bathroom privileges
BP	bed pan
BP	biopotential

BP	birth place
BP	bisexual potency
BP	bladder puncture
BP	blood pressure
BP	British Pharmacopoeia (= B.Ph.)
BP, bp (dent)	buccopulpal
BP	bypass
3,4-BP	3,4-benzpyrene
Bp	parallel scan (in two-dimensional sonography) (cp. Bc, Bd)
B.P.	Baccalaureus Pharmaciae (L); Bachelor of Pharmacy (also: B.Pharm.)
B.P., bp	boiling point
BPA	British Paediatric Association
BPAS	N-benzoyl-p-aminosalicylic acid
BPB	bromophenol blue
BPC, B.P.C.	British Pharmaceutical Codex
BPCA	British Pharmacopoeia Commission Approved
BPC-CSNS	blood pressure controlled carotis sinus nerve stimulation (cp. HRC-CSNS)
BPD (obst)	biparietal diameter
BPD	blood pressure (diastolic)
BPD	bronchopulmonary dysplasia
BPF	bradykinin potentiating factor
BPG	benzathin penicillin G
BPG	big plasma glucagon
BPH	benign prostatic hypertrophy
BPH	benzpyrene hydroxylase
B.Ph.	British Pharmacopoeia (= BP)
B.P.H.	Bachelor of Public Health
B.Pharm.	Baccalaureus Pharmaciae (L); Bachelor of Pharmacy (also: B.P.)

BPI	Bundesverband der Pharmazeutischen Industrie (G); Federal Association of the Pharmaceutical Industry (Germany)		BR	Birmingham Revision (of the BNA anatomical nomenclature)
BPL *(imm)*	benzylpenicilloyl (see also: PPL test)		BR	breathing rate
			Br *(dent)*	bridge
			Br. *(bact)*	Brucella
BPL	beta-propiolactone		br	breath
BPM	blood pressure (mean)		BRA	British Rheumatism and Arthritis Association
bpm	beats per minute			
BPMF	British Postgraduate Medical Federation		BRB	beta-receptor blocker (or blockade)
BPO	basal pepsin output (of the stomach) (= BPS)		BRC	British Red Cross (also: RRC)
BPO	benzyl peroxide		BRCS	British Red Cross Society
BPP, BP + P	blood pressure and pulse		BRI	Biological Research Institute (USA)
BPP	bovine pancreatic polypeptide			
			BRI	Bio-Research Index
BPP	bradykinin potentiating peptide (= BPF)		BRIC	benign recurrent intrahepatic cholestasis
BPR	brachial periosteum reflex (= BRR, RPR)		BRL	Beecham Research Laboratories
BPRS	Brief Psychiatric Rating Scale		BRM	biological response modifier
BPS	basal pepsin secretion (of the stomach) (= BPO)		BROLAC	bromothymol-blue lactose agar
BPS	Biophysical Society (USA)		BRP	bathroom privileges
BPS	blood pressure (systolic)		BRR	baroreceptor reflex
BPS, BPsS	British Psychological Society		BRR	brachioradial reflex (= BPR, RPR)
BPTH	bovine parathyroid hormone		BRS *(psych)*	Behavior Rating Scale
			BRS	British Roentgen Society
BPTI	basic pancreatic trypsin inhibitor		BRS	bromosuccinimide
BPV	balloon pulmonary valvuloplasty		BRVDU	E-5-(2-bromovinyl)-2'-deoxyuridine (= BVDU)
BPV	benzathin penicillin V		BRVP *(card)*	burst of rapid ventricular pacing
BPV	bovine papilloma viruses			
BP (Vet)	British Pharmacopoeia (Veterinary)		BS	bacterial suspension
Bq *(phys)*	Becquerel (unit for the activity of ionizing radiation)		BS	beta-sympatholytic (substance)
			BS	Biochemical Society (UK)
			BS	Biometric Society (USA)
BQC	2,6-dibromoquinone-chlorimide		BS	blood sugar (= BG)
			BS	Blue Shield (USA) (see also: BC, BC/BS)
BR	bathroom		BS	Boeck's sarcoidosis
BR	bed rest		BS	bowel sounds

BS	breathing sounds	BSp	bronchospasm
BS	British Standard	BSPM *(card)*	body surface potential mapping
BS	bronchial secretion	BSR	blood sedimentation rate (=ESR)
BS	bronchitic syndrome		
BS	Bureau of Standards	BSR	British Society of Rheology
B.S.	Bachelor of Science (also: B.Sc.)	BSRS *(psych)*	Behavior and Symptom Rating Scale
B.S.	Bachelor of Surgery (also: B.Ch.)	BSS	buffered saline solution
BSA	benzene sulphonic acid	BSSO	British Society for the Study of Orthodontics
BSA	blood serum (rapid) agglutination	BST	blood serological test
BSA	body surface area	BST *(psych)*	brief stimulus therapy
BSA	bovine serum albumin	BS valves	Björk-Shiley valves
BSA	British Sociology Association	BT	basal temperature
B.Sc.	Baccalaureus Scientiae (L); Bachelor of Science	BT	bedtime
		BT	bitemporal (skull diameter)
B-scan	brightness scan (two-dimensional technique in ultrasonography)	BT *(urol)*	bladder tumor
		BT	bleeding time
		BT	blue tetrazolium
BSCC	British Society for Clinical Cytology	BT *(pharm)*	bonne tolérance (F); good tolerability
BSCP	Biological Sciences Communication Project (USA)	BT *(neur)*	brain tumor
		BT *(gyn)*	breast tumor
BSD	balanced synthetic diet	BT *(pharm)*	bretylium tosylate
BSE *(gyn)*	breast self-examination	BT	bromelin test
BSFP	beta-S-fetoprotein	bt	binary digit (=bit)
BSG	British Society of Gastroenterology	BTA	N-benzoyl-l-tyrosine amide
		BTA	Blood Transfusion Association
BSG	British Standard Gauge		
BSG	bromsulpho-glutathione	BTA	British Thoracic Association
B+S glands	Bartholin's and Skene's glands		
		BTB *(gyn)*	breakthrough bleeding (=BB)
BSH	Bureau of Social Hygiene (UK)		
		BTB *(lab)*	bromthymol blue
BSI	British Standards Institution	BTC	basal temperature curve
		BTC	benzethonium chloride
BSL	benign symmetrical lipomatosis	BTC	blue tetrazolium chloride
		BTD	breast thermodetector
BSL	Biochemical Society of London	BTDS	benzoylthiamine disulphide
BSL	blood sugar level		
BSN	bowel sounds normal	BTE	benzilic acid tropine ester (=Be-T-E)
B.S.N.	Bachelor of Science in Nursing		
		BTEE	benzoyl tyrosine ethyl ester
BSP	bromsulphalein	BTFS	breast tumor frozen section
		BTG	beta-thromboglobulin

BTGF	type beta transforming growth factor	b.v.	balneum vaporis (L); steam bath
B.Th.U.	British Thermal Unit (=BTU)	BVA	British Veterinary Association
BTI	bronchial tract infection	BVC	British Veterinary Codex
BTMP	benfotiaminum	BVC	B-vitamin complex
BTPS	body temperature, pressure, saturation (parameters in pulmonary physiology) (cp. STPD)	BVDU	E-5-(2-bromovinyl)-2'-deoxyuridine (=BRVDU)
		BVH *(card)*	biventricular hypertrophy
BTR	biceps tendon reflex	BVH	B-virus hepatitis
BTS	Blood Transfusion Service	BVL	bilateral vasoligation
		BVLV	bovine visna-like virus (=BIV)
BTS	Blood Transfusion Society (UK)	BVM	bronchovascular markings
BTS	bradycardia-tachycardia syndrome	B.V.Sc.	Bachelor of Veterinary Science
BTS	Brenztraubensäure (G); pyruvic acid	BW	below waist
		BW	biological warfare
BTU	British Thermal Unit (=B.Th.U.)	BW	birth weight
		BW	body weight
BTX	benzene-toluene-xylene	B.W.	réaction de Bordet-Wassermann (F) (=BWR)
BTZ	butazolidine		
BU	base of prism up	BWD *(vet)*	bacillary white diarrhea (in chicken)
BU	Bodansky unit (=Bod unit)	BWG	Bland-White-Garland (syndrome)
BU	bromo-uracil, 2,6-dihydroxy-5-brompyridine	BWR	Bordet(-Gengou)-Wassermann reaction
BU *(clin)*	Burn Unit	BYE	Barile-Yaguchi-Eveland (medium)
bu	bushel		
Bu^a factor	Boisvert factor, antigen Bu^a	BYE	buffered yeast extract (agar)
BuChE	butyrylcholinesterase (=BCE, BChE)	By factor	Batty factor, antigen By
BUdR, BUDU	5-bromodeoxy-uridine	BZ-CoA	benzoyl-coenzyme A
BUI	brain uptake index	BZD	benziodaronum
BUMED	Bureau of Medicine and Surgery (US Navy)	BZD	benzodiazepine
BUMS	Boston University Medical School		
BUN	blood urea nitrogen		
BUPA	British United Provident Association		

C

C	(large) calorie
C	capacitance, capacity

C	carrier	CA	corpora allata (endocrine glands in insects)
C	cathode	CA	cortisone acetate
C	celsius, centigrade	CA	croup-associated (virus)
C	cervical (segment)	CA	cyproterone acetate
C	clearance	CA	cytarabine, cytosine arabinoside
C	clonus		
C	closure	CA	cytotoxic combination therapy with cyclophosphamide and adriamycin
C	cocaine		
C	coefficient		
C	compliance		
C	concentration	C.a.	candida albicans
C	(symbol for any) constant	C.a.	conus arteriosus
C	contraction	CAA	coarctation of the abdominal aorta
C	cortex		
C	costa (L); rib	CAAS	Canadian Association of Applied Spectroscopy
C *(phys)*	coulomb		
C	crystalline enzyme	CAAT	computer-assisted axial tomography
C *(rad)*	curie (= Ci)		
C	current	CAB	carbromal
C	cytosine	CAB	coronary artery bypass
c	(small) calorie (= cal)	CAB	cellulose acetobutyrate
c	candle	CABG	coronary artery bypass graft
c	cubic		
c	cyclic	CaBP	calcium binding protein
C. *(bact)*	clostridium	CAC	cardiac accelerator center
C1, C2, C3	cervical vertebrae 1, 2, 3 etc.	CaC	hypocalcemic component
		c.a.c.	cuillère à café (F); teaspoon (Rx)
CI, CII, CIII	cranial nerves I, II, III etc.		
		CaCC	cathodal closure contraction (= CCC)
C_1, C_2, C_3	1st, 2nd, 3rd rib		
C5	pentamethonium	C_aCO_2	arterial carbon dioxide content
C6	hexamethonium		
C10	decamethonium	CACX	cancer of the cervix
CA	carbenicillin	CAD	computer-aided design (system)
CA, Ca	carbonic anhydrase (= CAH)		
		CAD	coronary artery disease
CA, Ca	carcinoma	c.a.d.	cuillère à dessert (F); teaspoon (Rx)
CA	cardiac arrest		
CA	catecholamine(s)	Ca-Di-Na-EDTA	calcium disodium ethylene diamine tetraacetate (= Ca-Na$_2$-EDTA)
CA	cellulose acetate		
CA *(dent)*	cervicoaxial		
CA	Chemical Abstracts	CaDTe	cathodal duration tetanus
CA	chronological age		
CA	cold agglutination	CAE *(biochem)*	chloro-acetate esterase
CA	colloid antigen		
CA	common antigen	CAE	chloro-carbonic acid ethyl ester
CA	coronary artery		

CaEDTA — calcium ethylene diamine tetraacetate

CAEV — caprine arthritis encephalitis virus

CAF, CAFE — cellulose acetate foils (electrophoresis)

CAF — coronary artery fistula

CAF — cytotoxic combination therapy with cyclophosphamide, adriamycin, and 5-fluoro-uracil

Ca factor — Cavaliere factor, antigen Ca

CAFMS — Central American Federation of Medical Students

CAFVP — cytotoxic combination therapy with cyclophosphamide, adriamcin, 5-fluoro-uracil, vincristine, and prednisone

CAG — carotid angiogram

CAG — chronic atrophic gastritis

CAG — coronary angiography

CAH — carbonic anhydrase ($=CA$)

CAH — chronically active (or aggressive) hepatitis

CAH — congenital adrenal hyperplasia

CAH — cyanacetic acid hydrazide

CAHD — coronary atherosclerotic heart disease

CAIT — cold air inhalation test

Cal — (large) calorie ($=$ kcal)

cal — (small) calorie

C_{alb} — albumin clearance

CALD — chronic active liver disease

cALL — common-type acute lymphatic leukemia

CAM — chlorambucil

CAM — chorio-allantoic membrane

CAM — computer-aided manufacture (system)

CAM — cytotoxic combination therapy with cyclophosphamide, cytarabine (Alexan), and methotrexate

cAMP — cyclic adenosine mono-phosphate

CAMP test — Christie-Atkins-Munch-Petersen test

CAMSI — Canadian Association of Medical Students and Interns

Ca-Na$_2$-EDTA — calcium disodium ethylene diamine tetra-acetic acid

CAO — chronic airway obstruction

CAO — coronary artery occlusion

CaO$_2$ — arterial oxygen content

CaOC — cathodal opening contraction

CAOG — Central Association of Obstetricians and Gynecologists (USA)

CAOS — cytotoxic combination therapy with Cosmogen (actinomycin D), adriamycin (doxorubicin), Oncovin (vincristin), and Sendoxan (endoxan, cyclophosphamide)

CAP — carbamyl phosphate

CAP — catabolic gene activator protein

CAP — cellulose acetopropionate

CAP — chloramphenicol

CAP — chloro-acetophenone

CAP — 6-chloro-6-dehydro--17-alpha-acetoxyprogesterone

CAP — College of American Pathologists

CAP — Community Action Program

CAP — compound action potential

CAP (neur) — cortical artery pressure

CAP — cystine aminopeptidase

cap, caps — capsule(s)

CAPD — continuous ambulatory peritoneal dialysis

CAPP — Committee on Accident and Poison Prevention (USA)

CAPPS	Current and Past Psychopathology Scales	CAT	classical anaphylatoxin
CAPS	Canadian Association of Pediatric Surgeons	CAT	coli antibody titer
		CAT	College Ability Test
CAR	Canadian Association of Radiologists	CAT	computer averaged transients
CAR	computer-assisted radiology	CAT	computer averaging technique
CAR	cytosine arabinoside	CAT	computerized axial tomography
CARA	chronic aspecific respiratory ailment	catc.	catalytic concentration
CARD	compact automatic retrieval device	CATT	computerized axial transmission tomography
CARF	Commission on Accreditation and Rehabilitation Facilities	caud.	caudal
		CAV	congenital absence of vagina
CARL	Chemical and Radiological Laboratory (Canada)	CAV	congentinal adrenal virilism
CARNA	computer-assisted radionuclide angiography	CAV	cusp of the aortic valve
CARP	computerized anatomical reconstruction package	CAV	cytotoxic combination therapy with cyclophosphamide, cytarabine (Alexan) and vincristine
CARS	Canadian Arthritis and Rheumatism Society	CAVB	complete atrioventricular block
CAS	Canadian Anesthetists Society	CAVB	coronary artery venous bypass
CAS	Chemical Abstracts Service	CAVC	complete atrioventricular canal
CAS	coronary artery stenosis		
CAS	Council of Academic Societies	CAVD *(psych)*	"completion, arithmetic problems, vocabulary, following directions" (intelligence test)
c.a.s.	cuillère à soupe (F); soupspoon (Rx)		
CASH	Cancer and Steroid Hormones (study of the Centers for Disease Control)	CAVH	continuous arteriovenous hemofiltration
		CA virus	croup-associated virus
CASHD	coronary atherosclerotic heart disease	C_{aw}	airway conductance
		CB	chest-back (ECG lead)
CASS	Coronary Artery Surgery Study (USA, Europe)	CB	contrast bath
		CB	Coomassie blue
CAST	Clearinghouse Announcements in Science and Technology	C.B.	Chirurgiae Baccalaureus (L); Bachelor of Surgery (=Ch.B.)
CAT	catecholamines	CBA	chronic bronchitis and asthma
CAT *(psych)*	Children's Apperception Test		
		CBC	carbenicillin
CAT	choline acetyltransferase (=ChAc, ChAT)	CBC	complete blood count
		CBC	cortisol binding capacity

CBD	cannabidiole	CC	cholecalciferol
CBD *(clin)*	closed bladder drainage	CC	citrate cycle
CBD *(anat)*	common bile duct	CC	classical conditioning
CBDC *(derm)*	chronic bullous disease of childhood (also called: IgA linear dermatosis)	CC	closing capacity (of the lungs)
		CC	cloxacillin
CBF	calcium binding fragment	CC	coefficient of correlation
CBF	cerebral blood flow		
CBF	coronary blood flow	CC	Commission Certified (stains)
CBFP	chronic biological false-positive (reaction)	CC	common cold
		CC	computer calculated
CBG	corticosteroid binding globulin, transcortin	CC	Coronary Club
		CC	corpora cardiaca (endocrine organs in insects)
CBHo	chlorobenzene homologues		
		CC	corpus callosum
CBI *(psych)*	Children's Behavior Inventory	CC	critical condition
		CC	current complaints
CBI *(psych)*	close-binding-intimate	Cc	concave
CBL	carbenoxolone	cc	Angloamerican expression for: ccm, cm³, ml
CBl	citrate blood		
CBN	Commission on Biological Nomenclature	C.C.	Code Civile (of French legislation)
CBo	carbobenzoxy...	c.c.	constant current
CBP	chronic bacterial pancreatitis	CCA	centro-central anastomosis
		CCA	chimpanzee coryza agent, CCA viruses
CBPS	Connecticut Blood Pressure Survey		
		CCA	chondrocalcinosis articularis
CBR	chemical, biological, and radiological (arms)	CCA	circumflex coronary artery
CBR	complete bed rest	CCA	clear-cell acanthoma
CBR	crude birth rate	CCA	colonic carcinoma antigen
CBS	Canadian Biochemical Society	CCA	Commission for Conventional Armaments (UN)
CBS	p-chlorobenzene sulfonamide	CCA	cephalin cholesterol antigen
CBS	chronic brain syndrome	CCA	chick cell agglutination (unit)
CBV	cerebral blood volume		
CBV	circulating blood volume	CCAT	conglutinating complement absorption test
CBW	chemical and biological warfare		
		CCAVC	common complete atrio-ventricular canal
CBW	critical band width (of noise)		
		CCB	cytochalasin B
CBZ	carbamazepine	CCBV	central circulating blood volume
CC	cardiac catheter		
CC	cervical carcinoma (=CCX)	CCC	calcium cyanamide citrated
CC	chief complaint		

CCC	cathodal closure contraction	CCI	chronic coronary insufficiency
CCC	ciclacillin	CCI	collateral circulation index
CCC	Columbia Clinical Classification (of breast cancer)	CCI	Commission on Chronic Illness
CCC	comprehensive cardiac care	CCICMS	Council for Coordination of International Congresses of Medical Sciences
CCC	Copyright Clearance Center		
CCC	cycocel (growth-inhibiting substance used in agriculture)	CCIM	coronary care intensive medicine
		CCK	cholecystokinin
CCCl	cathodal closure clonus	CCK-PZ	cholecystokinin-pancreozymin
CCCP	carbonylcyanide-m-chlorphenylhydrazone		
CCCR	closed chest cardiac resuscitation	CCK substances	secale alkaloids (ergocornin, ergocristin, ergokryptin)
CCD	calibration curve date	CCL	centrocystic lymphoma
CCD	charge-coupled device	CCL	convoluted cell-type leukemia
CCD	counter current distribution		
CCD	crossed cerebellar diaschisis	CCM	Commission Consultative Médicale (F); Commission for Consultant Medicine
CCDN	Central Council for District Nursing		
CCE	citrate cleavage enzyme; ATP citrate lyase	CCM	congestive cardiomyopathy
		CCME	Coordinating Council of Medical Education
CCE	ceratoconjunctivitis epidemica	CCMH	concentration corpusculaire moyenne en hémoglobine (F); mean cell hemoglobin ($=HB_E$, MCH)
C-cell	calcitonin cell		
CCF	cancer coagulative factor		
CCF	congestive cardiac failure ($=$CHF)		
		CCMS	clean catch midstream (urine)
CCF	cephalin cholesterol flocculation (reaction)	CCMT	catechol-o-methyl transferase
CCFA (bact)	cycloserine cefoxitin fructose agar	CCNU	1-(2-chloroethyl)-3-cyclohexyl-1-nitroso-urea
CCH	Congress Center Hamburg (Germany)	CCP	Cancer Control Program
CCh	carbamylcholine	CCP (mil)	Casualty Collecting Post
CCHB	congenital complete heart block	CCP	chronic calcified pancreatitis
CCHE	Central Council for Health Education (UK)	CCP	critical closing pressure
		CCPD	continuous cyclic peritoneal dialysis
CCHTI	Coordinating Committee for Human Tumor Investigation	CCPM	Critical Care and Pulmonary Medicine

CCR	carcinoma chrome reaction
C_{cr}	creatinine clearance
C.C.R.N.	Critical Care Registered Nurse
CCS	Canadian Cancer Society
CCS *(mil)*	Casualty Clearing Station (NATO)
CCSP	Cooperative Cholesterol Standardization Program
CCT	cathodal closure tetanus (= CCTe)
CCT	central conduction time
CCT *(pharm)*	chocolate-coated tablet
CCT *(pharm)*	coated compressed tablet
CCT *(rad)*	combined cortical thickness
CCT	congenitally corrected transposition (of the great arteries)
CCT *(obst)*	controlled cord traction
CCT	cranial computerized tomography
CCTe	cathodal closure tetanus (= CCCl)
CCU	Coronary Care Unit
CCV	catecholamine containing varicosity
CC virus	common cold virus
CCW	counter clockwise
C_{cw}	chest wall compliance
CD	cadaver donor
CD *(vet)*	canine distemper
CD	canine dose
CD	cardiac diameter
CD	cardiovascular disease
CD	Carrel-Dakin (solution)
CD	celiac disease
CD *(obst)*	cesarian delivered
CD	chronotropic dose
CD	Civil Defence
CD	coma diabétique (F); diabetic coma
CD, Cd	coli dyspespia, coli enteritis
CD	compact disc

CD	completely denatured
CD	computer diagnosis
CD *(obst)*	conjugata diagonalis (L); diameter of the pelvic inlet
CD	contact dermatitis
CD	contagious (or communicable) disease
CD	contrast density
CD *(neur)*	convulsive disorder
CD	convulsive dose
CD *(pharm)*	curative dose, therapeutic dose (= DC, D_{cur}, Dos.cur.)
CD	cystic duct
CD4, CD8	T-cell receptors
CD_{50}	medium curative dose
cd	candela (photometric unit for light intensity)
CDA	Canadian Dental Association
CDA	comparative determinant analysis
CDA	congenital dyserythropoietic anemia
CDAA	chloro-diallylacetamide (herbicide)
CDAI	Crohn's disease activity index
CDAS	Civil Defence Ambulance Service
CDC *(obst)*	calculated date of confinement
CDC	carindacillin
CDC	Centers for Disease Control (Atlanta/USA) (formerly called: Communicable Disease Center)
CDC, CDCA	chenodeoxycholic acid
CDC	Civil Defence Committee
CDD	chemically defined diet
CDE *(vet)*	canine distemper encephalitis
CDE system	blood grouping system of the rhesus antigen complex
CDF	cardiac depression factor

CDH	congenital dislocation of the hip	CE	converting enzyme
CDI *(psych)*	Children's Depression Inventory	CE	cytopathic effect
		CEA	carcino-embryonic antigen
CDL	Central Dental Laboratories (USA)	CEA	carotid endarterectomy
		CEA	chronic exogenous allergic alveolitis
CDLE *(derm)*	chronic discoidal lupus erythematosus	CEAN	computed EEG analysis (=CEEG)
cDNA	complementary DNA	CEC	circulation extracorporelle (F); extracorporeal circulation
CDNB	1-chloro-2,4-dinitro-benzene		
CDO	chlordiazepoxide (=CDZ)	CED	cephaloridin (=CER)
CDP	Coronary Drug Project	CEE	central European encephalitis
CDP	cytidine diphosphate		
CDPC	cytidine diphosphate choline	CEEG	computer-analyzed electro-encephalogram (=CEAN)
CDRI	Central Drug Research Institute (India)	CEEP	Confédération Européenne d'Etudes de Phytopharmacie; European Confederation of Phytopharmaceutical Research
CDS	Civil Defence Services		
CDSA	conventional digital subtraction angiography		
CDSC	Communicable Disease Surveillance Centre (London)		
		CEF	cycle efficiency (of cardiac work)
CDT	carbon dioxide therapy	C_{eff}	effective compliance
C.D.T.	Certified Dental Technician	CEFMG	Council on Education for Foreign Medical Graduates (=ECFMG) (USA)
CDTA	1,2-cyclohexane diamine tetraacetate	CEHM	Centre Européen d'Histoire de la Médecine (F); European Center for the History of Medicine (Strasbourg/France)
CDV	Civil Defence Volunteer		
CDVR	coronary diastolic vascular resistance		
CDWS	Civil Defence Warden's Service	CEI	cardiac effort index
		CEJ	cement-enamel junction
C_{dyn}	dynamic compliance	CELO	chicken embryo lethal orphan (virus)
CDZ	chlordiazepoxide (=CDO)		
CDZ	conduction delay zone	CEM	channel electron multiplier
CE	California encephalitis	CEM	conventional-transmission electron microscope
CE	cardiac enlargement		
CE	cerebral elastance	CEMAC	Centre d'Etude des Maladies des Artères Coronaires (F); Study Center for Coronary Artery Disease (France)
CE	chemical energy		
CE	chick embryo		
CE	cholesterol ester		
CE	condensing enzyme		
CE *(stat)*	constant error	CEMAP	cortically evoked motor action potential
CE	contractile element (of muscle)	CEP	cephradin

48

CEP	Conféderation Européenne d'Etudes Phytosanitaires (F); European Federation of Plant Protection	CF	cancer-free
		CF	carbolfuchsin
		CF	cardiac failure
		CF	cationized ferritin
CEP	congenital erythropoietic porphyria	CF	cefalotin (=CET)
		CF	chemotactic factor (=CHF)
CEP	countercurrent electrophoresis	CF *(card)*	chest-foot (ECG lead)
CEP	cyano-ethyl phosphate	CF	Christmas factor, factor IX (=PTC)
CEPA	chloro-ethane phosphoric acid	CF *(bact)*	citrovorum factor
CEQ	Council on Environmentral Quality	CF	colicin factor
		CF	colored female
CER *(dent)*	caries, extractio, restauratio (L); tooth decay, extraction, repair	CF	complement fixation
		CF	coronary flow
		CF	cystic fibrosis, mucoviscidosis
CER	cephaloridin (=CED)	CF	cytotoxic factor
CER	conditioned emotional response	c.f.	carrier-free
CERA	Central European Rehabilitation Association	CFA *(imm)*	complement fixing antibody titer
CERN	Centre Européen pour la Recherche Nucléaire (F); European Center of Nuclear Research	CFA *(lab)*	complete Freund adjuvant
		C-factor *(clin)*	certainty factor
		C-factor *(psych)*	cleverness factor
CES	central excitatory state	CFC	capillary filtration coefficient
CESD	cholesterol-ester storage disease	CFC	colony forming capacity
CESG	Cerebral Embolism Study Group	CFC	colony forming cells
		CFF, CFFF	critical flicker fusion frequency
CESS	Cooperative Ewing Sarcoma Study	CF-factor	cystic fibrosis factor
CESSD	Consilium Europaeum Strabismi Studio Deditum (L); European Council for the Study of Strabism	CFGA	carcinofetal glia antigen
		CFI	complement fixation inhibition
		CFICA	complement-fixing islet cell antibody
C-esterase	choline esterase	CFL	clearing factor lipase
CET	cefalotin (=CF)	CFM	cerebral function monitor
CETI	"Communication with Extraterrestrial Intelligence"	CFM	chlorofluoromethane
		cfm	cubic feet per minute
CET virus	central European tick virus	CFMG	Commission on Foreign Medical Graduates (USA)
CEV	California encephalitis virus	C-form	cocci form (of cells in media colonies)
CEW	contractile element work	CFPS	continuous flow plasmapheresis system
CEX	cephalexin		
CEZ	cephazolin		

CFR	Committee on Family Research (Leuven/Belgium)
CFR	complement fixation reaction (=CFT)
CFR	coronary flow reserve
CFS	Cystic Fibrosis Society (USA)
cfs	cubic feet per second
CFSE	crystal field stabilization energy
CFSTI	Clearinghouse for Federal and Technical Information (now: NTIS)
CFT	cardiolipin flocculation test (cp. CMFT, VDRL)
CFT	complement fixation test
CFT *(psych)*	Culture Free Test
CFU *(bact)*	colony forming unit
CFU-GEMM	colony forming unit – granulocte, erythrocyte, macrophage, megakaryocyte
CFU-GM *(imm)*	colony forming unit – granulocyte, macrophage
CFU-Mk *(imm)*	colony forming unit – megakaryocyte
CFX (=CGM)	cefoxitin
CG	choking gas
CG	chorionic gonadotrophin (=CGH, CGT)
CG	control group
cg	center of gravity
CGD	chronic granulomatous disease
CGH	chorionic gonadotrophic hormone (=CG)
CGI	clinical global impression
CGIS *(psych)*	clinical global impression scale
CGL	chronic granulocytic leukemia
CGL	corpus geniculatum laterale (L); lateral geniculate body
CGM	central grey matter

CGM	corpus geniculatum mediale (L); medial geniculate body
CGMH	concentration globulaire moyenne en hémoglobine (F); mean cell hemoglobin (=CCMH, Hb$_E$, MCH)
CGMP	Conférence Générale des Poids et Mesures (F); General Conference for Weights and Measures
cGMP	cyclic guanosine-3',5'-monophosphate
CGN	chronic glomerulonephritis
CGP	N-carbobenzoxy-glycyl-l-phenylalanine
CGP	chorionic growth hormone prolactin (=HPL)
CGP	circulating granulocyte pool
CGRP	calcitonin gene-related peptide
CGS	catgut suture
CGSB system	centimeter-gram-second-biot system
CGS system	centimeter-gram-second (cm, g, sec); absolute measure system (for distance, weight, time)
CGT	N-carbobenzoxy-alpha-glutamyl-l-tyrosine
CGT	chorionic gonadotrophin
CGTT	cortison glucose tolerance test
CGU	chronic gastric ulcer
CH	Chédiak-Higashi syndrome (=CHD)
CH	Christchurch chromosome
CH	complement hemolysis
CH	crown-heel (length of fetus)
Ch	choline
ch, CH	cheval vapeur (F); horse power (=HP, PS, CV)
CHA	Catholic Hospital Association
CHA	Chest and Heart Association (USA)

CHA	Children's Hospital Association (USA)	CHESS	chemical shift selection imaging
CHA (pharm)	chlorambucil	chest PT	chest physical therapy
CHA	congenital hypoplastic anemia	CHF	central Asian hemorrhagic fever
CHA	cyclohexylamine	CHF	chemotactic factor (=CF)
ChA	choline acetylase	CHF	chronic heart failure
ChAc	choline acetylase	CHF	congestive heart failure (=CCF)
CHA	candida hemagglutination (test)	CHFD	controlled high flux dialysis
CHAI	cytopathic human auto-interfering (virus)	CHF-DC	congestive heart failure due to dilated cardiomyopathy
ChAT	choline acetyltransferase	CHF-MI	congestive heart failure due to myocardial infarction
CHB	complete heart block		
CHB	congenital heart block		
Ch.B.	Chirurgiae Baccalaureus (L); Bachelor of Surgery (also: C.B.)	ChFR	Chédiak flocculation reaction
CHC	Canadian Hospital Council	ChG	chymotrypsinogen
CHC	Community Health Center	CHI	chemotherapeutic index (=CI)
CHC	Community Health Council	CHIP	Comprehensive Health Insurance Plan
CHD	Chédiak-Higashi disease	Chir.D.	Chirurgiae Doctor (L); Doctor of Surgery (also: Ch.D.)
CHD	childhood disease		
CHD	chronic heart disease		
CHD	congenital heart disease	CHL, Chlf.	chloroform
CHD	constitutional hepatic dysfunction	ChLA	chimpanzee leukocyte antigen (=CLA)
CHD	coronary heart disease	ChlB	chlorobutanol
Ch.D.	Chirurgiae Doctor (L); Doctor of Surgery (also: Chir.D.)	Ch.M.	Chirurgiae Magister (L); Master of Surgery (also: C.M.)
CHE	cholesterol esterase		
CHE, ChE	cholinesterase	CHN	Child Neurology
CHED	Community Hypertension Evaluation Clinic (cp. HDFP)	CHO	carbohydrate
		C_{H_2O}	free water clearance
CHEI	cholinesterase inhibitor	CHOP	cytotoxic combination therapy with cyclophosphamide, hydroxydaunomycin (adriamycin), Oncovin (vincristin), and prednisolone
ch$_{el}$	cheval vapeur électrique (F); electrical horse power		
CHEOPS	Chemistry of Ozone in the Polar Stratosphere (research program)		
		CHP	chemoprevention
		CHP	Child Psychiatry
ChES	cholinergic excitatory system	CHP	chronic hepatic porphyria

CHR	Centre Hospitalier de Réanimation (F); Resuscitation Center
chromat.	chromatographical
CHS	cyclohexasulfonamide
CHSA	Chest, Heart, and Stroke Association
CHSS	Cooperative Health Statistics System
CHT	chemotherapy
ChTr	chymotrypsin
CHU	centigrade heat unit
CHU	Centre Hospitalier Universitaire (F); University Hospital
CHX	chlorhexidene gluconate
CI	capacité inspiratoire (F); inspiratory capacity ($=$IC)
CI (anat)	capsula interna
CI	cardiac index
CI	cardiac infarction (usually: MI)
CI	Caritas Internationalis (L); International Charity
CI	chemotherapeutic index
CI	clonus index
CI (psych)	coefficient of intelligence
CI	color index
CI (stat)	confidence interval
CI	contamination index
CI (card)	contractility index
CI	contre-indication (F); contraindication
CI	coronary insufficiency
CI (rad)	cortical index
CI	crystalline insulin
Ci	curie
CIB	Centre Interaméricaine de Biostatistique (F); Interamerican Center of Biostatistics
CIB	International Council for Building Research Studies and Documentation
CIBHA	congenital inclusion body hemolytic anemia
CIC	cardiac inhibitor center

CIC	Centro Internazionale Congressi (Rome); International Convention Center
CIC	circulating immune complex
CICR	Comité International de Croix Rouge (F); Comité Internacional de la Cruz Roja (S); International Committee of the Red Cross (Geneva) ($=$ICRC)
CICS	Customer Information Control System
CICU	Coronary Intensive Care Unit ($=$CCU))
CID	cytomegalic inclusion disease
CIE	cellulose ion exchanger
CIE	counterimmunoelectrophoresis
CIF	cellular interfering factor
CIF	cloning inhibitory factor
CIF	colony inhibiting factor
CIFC	Council for the Investigation of Fertility Control
CIF test	candida immunofluorescence test
CIG	cold-insoluble globulin
CIH	carbohydrate-induced hypertriglyceridemia
CIHD	chronic ischemic heart disease
CIIA	Commisssion Internationale des Industries Agricoles (F); International Commission of Agricultural Industries (Paris)
CIIS	Cardiac Infarction Injury Score
CIM	Center for International Migration and Development
CIM (bact)	concentration inhibitrice minimale (F); minimal inhibitory concentration ($=$MHK, MIC)

CIM	cortically induced movement	CIQ	Confoederatio Internationalis ad Qualitates Plantarum Edulium (L); International Federation for the Study of Edible Plants
CIMII	continuous intramuscular insulin infusion		
cIMP	cyclic inosine-5'-monophosphate		
CIMTP	Congrès International de Médecine Tropicale et de Paludisme (F); Congreso Internacional de Medicina Tropical y Paludismo (S); International Congress of Tropical Medicine and Paludism (Malaria)	CIRM	Centro Internazionale Radio-Medico (I); International Radio-Medical Center
		CIS	carcinoma in situ
		CIS	central inhibitory state
		CIS	Chemical Information System
		CIS	Condition Index Score (in Intensive Care)
CIN	cervical intraepithelial neoplasia	CISS	Conseil International des Sciences Sociales (F); International Council of Social Sciences
CIN	cinnarizin		
C_{in}	inulin clearance		
CINP	Collegium Internationale Neuro-Psychopharmacologicum (L); International College of Neuropsychopharmacology	CIT	California Institute of Technology
		CIT	characterological intelligence test
		CIT	conventional insulin therapy
CIOMS	Council for International Organizations of Medical Sciences (Geneva)	CIUS	Conseil International des Unions Scientifiques (Rome); International Council of Scientific Unions (= ICSU)
CIP	Commission Internationale de Phytopharmacie (F); International Commission of Phytopharmacy		
		CIVD	cold-induced vasodilation
CIP	Congrès International de Psychomotricité (F); International Congress of Psychomotoricity	CJD	Creutzfeldt-Jakob disease
		CK	creatine kinase (cp. CPK)
		CKG	cardiokymography
CIPE	Collège International de Phonologie Experimentale; International College of Experimental Phonology	CK-MB	creatine kinase muscle-brain (= MB-CK)
		CL	chest – left arm (ECG lead)
		CL	cholesterol-lecithin (test)
CIP-F	classical interstitial pneumonitis-fibrosis	CL	chronic lymphadenosis
		CL	citrate lyase
CIPM	Comité International de Poids et Mesures (F); International Committee of Weights and Measures	CL, C_L	compliance of the lungs
		CL	corpus luteum
		CL	critical list
		CL	cycle length
		Cl	clearance
		CLA	cationic leukocyte antigen

CLA	chimpanzee leukocyte antigen	CLT *(pharm)*	cephalotin
Cl[a] factor	Caldwell factor, antigen Cl[a]	CLT *(lab)*	clot lysis time
ClAc	chloroacetyl	CLV	cholera-like vibrios
CLAO	Contact Lens Association of Ophthalmologists	CM *(pharm)*	capreomycin
CLAS	clinical laboraty automation system	CM *(chem)*	carboxymethyl
C-LAV	Cambridge isolate of LAV (= HIV)	CM	cardiomegaly
CLBA	competitive ligand-binding assay	CM	cardiomyopathy (= CMP)
CLBBB	complete left bundle branch block	CM	carpometacarpal (= CMC)
CLC syndrome	Clerc-Lévy-Christescu syndrome	CM	causa mortis (L); cause of death
CLE	cellule lupus érythémateux (F); LE cell	CM	Chick-Martin (test)
CLED agar	cystine lactose electrolyte-deficient agar	CM	circular muscle
CLH	corpus luteum hormone	CM *(otorhin)*	cochlear microphonics (Bray-Wever phenomenon)
CLI *(gyn)*	corpus luteum insufficiency	CM	colored male
CLIP	corticotrophin-like intermediate lobe peptide	CM	Compendium Medicamentorum (L); Drug Compendium
CLIS	carcinoma lobatum in situ (L)	CM	congenital malformation
CLL	cholesterol lowering lipid	CM *(rad)*	contrast medium
CLL	chronic lymphatic leukemia	CM	copulatory mechanism
CLM *(pharm)*	clindamycin	CM	costal margin
Cl₂MDP *(biochem)*	dichlormethylene diphosphonate	Cm	clearance maximum (of urea)
CLML	Current List of Medical Literature	C.M.	Chirurgiae Magister (L); Master of Surgery (also: Ch.M.)
CLO *(bact)*	campylobacter-like organisms	CMA	Canadian Medical Association
CLO	cod liver oil	CMA	candida microagglutination (test)
Clo unit	clothing unit	CMA	Chinese Medical Association
CLP	collagen-like protein	CMACP	Conseil Mondial pour l'Assemblée Constituante des Peuples (F); World Council for a Constituent Assembly of People
CLR *(dent)*	chloride test		
CLS	calcium lignosulfonate	CMAJ	Canadian Medical Association Journal (official abbreviation: Canad. med. Ass. J.)
CLSP	Cooperative Lipid Standardization Program (USA)	CMAP	clinical monophasic action potential
		CMAP	contrast medium appearance picture

CMB	carboxylic methylene blue	CMI	cell-mediated immunity
CMB	Central Midwives Board	CMI	Commonwealth Mycological Institute
CMB	chloromercuribenzoate		
CMC	carboxymethyl cellulose	CMI *(bact)*	concentration minimale inhibitrice (F); minimal inhibitory concentration (=CIM, MIC)
CMC	carpometacarpal		
CMC	closed mitral commissuro-tomy		
CMDNJ	College of Medicine and Dentistry of New Jersey (Newark)	CMI	Cornell Medical Index
		CMIT	Current Medical Information and Terminology
CME	Central Medical Establishment	CMK *(lab)*	cells of monkey kidney (also: cynomolgus kidney cells)
CME	Continuing Medical Education (US program)		
		CML	chronic myelocytic leukemia
C meiosis	colchicine meiosis		
CMF	chondromyxoid fibroma	CMLA *(card)*	catheter-mapped late activity
CMF	cytotoxic combination therapy with cyclophosphamide, methotrexate and 5-fluorouracil		
		CMLC	cardiac myosin light chain
		CMLD	Compendium Methodorum in Laboratoriis Diagnosticis (L); Compendium of Diagnostic Laboratory Methods
CMFP	cytotoxic combination therapy with cyclophosphamide, methotrexate, 5-fluorouracil, and prednisone		
		CMLT	continuous incrasing multiple load test
CMFT	cardiolipin microflocculation test (=CFT, VDRL)	CMM	Columbia Mental Maturity Scale
CMFV	cytotoxic combination therapy with cyclophosphamide, methotrexate, 5-fluorouracil, and vincristine	CMML	chronic myelomonocytic leukemia
		CMN	cystic medial necrosis (of the aorta)
CMFVP	cytotoxic combination therapy with cyclophosphamide, methotrexate, 5-fluorouracil, vincristine, and prednisone	CMO	cardiac minute output (=CO)
		CMOS	complementary metal oxide semiconductor
		CMP	cardiomyopathy (=CM)
CMG	chopped meat glucose (agar)	CMP	central monitoring position
CMGS	^{11}C-labelled methyl-D-glucose scanning	CMP	Centre de Médecine Préventive (F); Center of Preventive Medicine
CMH	congenital malformation of the heart	CMP	coal miners' pneumoconiosis
CMHC	Community Mental Health Center	CMP	cytidine monophosphate
		CMPS	chronic myeloproliferative syndrome
CMI	carbohydrate metabolism index	cmps	centimeters per second

CMPU (pharm)	3-chloromercuri-2-meth-oxypropyl-ureide	CNDC	chronic non-purulent destructive cholangitis
CMR	cerebral metabolic rate	CNE	chronic nervous exhaus-tion
CMR	Committee on Medical Research (USA)	CNF	congenital nephrosis (Fin-land)
CMRF (lab)	conditioned medium re-constituting factor	C.N.M.	Certified Nurse-Midwife
CMRG	cerebral metabolic rate of glucose	CNN	congenital nevomelano-cytic nevus
CMRO	Current Medical Research and Opinion (journal)	CNO	chronic non-infectious orchitis
$CMRO_2$	cerebral metabolic rate of oxygen	CNOC	Commission on the Nomenclature of Organic Chemistry
CMS	Codex Medicamentarius Scandinavicus (L); Scan-dinavian Drug Code	CNP	continuous negative pres-sure
CMT	California mastitis test	CNR	chronic non-responder
CMT	cardiolipin microfloccula-tion test (=CMFT)	CNR	Civil Nursing Reserve
CMT	catechol-o-methyl transfer-ase (=COMT)	CNRS	Centre National pour la Recherche Scientifique (F); National Center for Scientific Research
CMT	circus movement tachycar-dia	CNS	central nervous system
CMT	Current Medical Terminol-ogy	CNSD	chronic non-specific duo-denitis
CMU	complex motor unit	CNSHA	congenital non-spherocytic hemolytic anemia
CMU	concentration maximale d'urée (F); maximum con-centration of urea	CNSLD	chronic non-specific lung disease (=CNSRD)
CMV	cerebral minute volume	CNSRD	chronic non-specific re-spiratory disease (=CNSLD)
CMV	controlled mechanical ven-tilation		
CMV	cytomegalovirus	CNV (psych)	contingent negative varia-tion
cmW	centimeter wave (=SHF)	CO	cardiac output (=CMO)
CN (anat)	caudate nucleus	CO	castor oil
CN	cellulose nitrate	CO	Casualty Officer
CN	Charge Nurse	CO	centric occlusion
CN	chloro-acetophenone	CO (ophth)	corneal opacity
CN	clinical nursing	CO (gen)	crossover, crossing-over
CN (anat)	cranial nerve	Co I	codehydrase I (=DPN, NAD)
CN	cyanogen		
cn	common name	Co II	codehydrase II (=TPN, NADP)
CNA	Canadian Nurses' Associa-tion	COA	coarctation of the aorta
CNA	Central Neuropsychiatric Association (USA)	COA	condition on admission
		CoA	coenzyme A

COAD	chronic obstructive airway disease (=COLD, COPD)	COISM	Conseil des Organisations Internationales des Sciences Médicale (F); Council of International Organizations of Medical Sciences
COAP	cytotoxic combination therapy with cyclophosphamide, Oncovin (vincristine), ara-C (cytarabine), and prednisone		
		CoL	coenzyme L, biotin
COBP	chronic obstructive bronchial pneumopathy (=COAD, COLD, COPD)	COLD	chronic obstructive lung disease (=COPD)
		COM	College of Osteopathic Medicine
COBS	cesarian-obtained barrier-sustained (in experimental animals)	COMB	cytotoxic combination therapy with cyclophosphamide, Oncovin, methyl-CCNU, and bleomycin
COBT	chronic obstruction of biliary tract		
COC	cathodal opening contraction (=CaOC)	COMC	carboxymethyl cellulose (=CMC)
COC	cerebral oxygen consumption	comp.	compositus (L); composed
		COMT	catechol-o-methyl transferase
COC	oral contraceptive, combination type	CON	cyclopropane-oxygen-nitrogen (anesthesia)
CoC	coenzyme C		
COCl	cathodal opening clonus	ConA	concanavaline A
COCM	congestive cardiomyopathy	CONSEN-SUS	Cooperative North Scandinavian Enalapril Survival Study (in congestive heart failure)
COD	cause of death		
COD	chemical oxygen demand		
COD	Council of Deans		
Cod.Gall.	Codex Gallicus; French Pharmaceutical Code	COP	change of plaster
		COP	chemotherapeutic combination of cyclophosphamide, oncovin, and prednisone
CoE	coenzyme E		
COEB	chronic obstructive emphysematous bronchitis		
		COP	capillary osmotic pressure
COEPS	cortically originating extrapyramidal system	COP	colloid osmotic pressure
		COPD	chronic obstructive pulmonary disease (=COLD)
CoF	cobra factor		
CoF	coenzyme F	COPE	chronic obstructive pulmonary emphysema
COFAL	complement fixation avian leukosis (test)		
		COPP	cytotoxic combination therapy with cyclophosphamide, Oncovin, procarbazine, and prednisone (for lymphomas)
COG (SA)	College of Obstetricians and Gynaecologists (South Africa)		
COGTT	cortisone (primed) oral glucose tolerance test	COP	cytotoxic combination therapy with cyclophosphamide, vincristine (Oncovin), and prednisone
COH	carbohydrate (=CHO)		
CO-Hb	carbon monoxide hemoglobin, carboxyhemoglobin		
		CoQ	coenzyme Q, ubiquinone

COR	conditioned orientation reflex	CP	computerized programming
CoR	Congo red	CP	constant pressure
COS	Canadian Ophthalmological Society	CP	coproporphyrin
		CP *(card)*	cor pulmonale
COS	Charity Organization Society (USA)	CP *(lab)*	creatine phosphate
		CP	culture proven
COS	Clinical Orthopedic Society (USA)	Cp	plate capacitance
C_{osm}	osmolal clearance	cP	centipoise (1/100 of the viscosity unit poise)
C_{osmol}	osmolar clearance	cP	chronic polyarthritis
COSPAR	Committee on Space Research (Paris)	C.P.	Certified Prosthetist
		C/P	cholesterol-phosphatide ratio; lipolytic quotient (=CPQ)
COSS	Cooperative Osteosarcoma Study		
COSTEP	Commissioned Officer Student Training and Extern Program	C+P *(urol)*	cystoscopy and pyelogram
		CPA	Canadian Pharmaceutical Association
C.O.T.A.	Certified Occupational Therapy Assistant	CPA	Canadian Physiotherapy Association
COTe	cathodal opening tetanus		
COV	concentrated oil of vitriol	CPA	Canadian Psychological Association
COV *(gen)*	cross-over value		
COWS	Commission on World Standards	CPA	carboxypeptidase A
		CPA	Chinese Pharmaceutical Association
CP, c.p.	candle power (now: foot candle)		
		CPA	chlorophenylalanine
CP	capillary pressure	CPA	coeur pulmonaire aigu (F); acute right ventricular failure
CP *(neur)*	cerebral palsy		
CP	ceruloplasmin		
CP, cp	chemically pure	CPA	cyproterone acetate
CP	Child Psychiatry, Child Psychology (also: CHP)	CPAC	Collaborative Pesticides Analytical Committee
CP	chloroquine-primaquine (for malaria)	CPAF	chlorpropamide-induced alcohol flush
CP	chromosomal protein	C_{PAH}	p-aminohippuric acid clearance
CP	chronic pancreatitis		
CP	clearance period	$C_{Pa}O_2$	oxygen content of pulmonary arterial blood
CP	cleft palate		
CP	closing pressure, transpulmonary pressure	CPAP	continuous positive airway pressure
CP	cochlear potential	CPB	carboxypeptidase B
CP *(psych)*	combining power	CPB	cardiopulmonary bypass (=CPBP)
CP	Comité Permanent; Permanent Committee (of Physicians of the European Community)		
		CPB	cetylpyridinium bromide
		CPB	competitive protein-binding

CPBA	competitive protein-binding assay	CPI	California Psychological Inventory
CPBP	cardiopulmonary bypass (=CPB)	CPI	coronary prognostic index
CPC	carotid pulse curve	CPIB *(pharm)*	α-(p-chlorphenoxy)-isobutyrate; clofibrate
CPC	Cerebral Palsy Clinic	CPIP	chronic pulmonary insufficiency of prematurity
CPC	cetylpyridinium chloride		
CPC	chronic passive congestion	CPK *(lab)*	creatine phosphokinase
CPC	chronic cor pulmonale	CPK-MB	creatine phosphokinase isoenzyme muscle-brain
CPC	Clinical Pathological Conference	c_{Pl}	plasma concentration
CPC	cold potassium cardioplegia	CPLM	cysteine peptone liver methylene blue (culture medium for Trichomonas vaginalis)
CPCh	coeur pulmonaire chronique (F); chronic right ventricular failure	CPM	capreomycin
		CPM	cyclophosphamide
CPD	citrate phosphate dextrose	cpm *(phys)*	cycles per minute, counts per minute
CPD *(phys)*	contact potential difference	CPMG sequence	Carr-Purcell-Meiboom-Gill sequence (in NMR)
CPD *(vet)*	contagious pustular dermatitis; ecthyma contagiosum	CPN	chronic pyelonephritis
CPD	cyclopentadiene	CPP	cerebral perfusion pressure
cpd.	compound	CPP	chronic progressive polyarthritis
CPDG	Centre Pluridisciplinaire de Grenoble; Multidisciplinary Center of Grenoble (France)	CPP	Commission de Pharmacie Practique; Commission for Applied Pharmacy (Switzerland)
CPDS	carboxypyridine disulfide		
CPE	cytopathogenetic effect	CPP	coronary perfusion pressure
CPEO	chronic progressive external ophthalmoplegia	CPP	cyclopentophenanthrene
C peptide	connecting peptide	CPPB	continuous positive pressure breathing
CPF *(gen)*	competence provoking factor	CPPC *(card)*	corrected postpacing cycle
CPH	Children's Psychiatric Hospital	CPPD	calcium pyrophosphate dihydrate (arthropathy)
CPH	chronic paroxysmal hemicrania	CPPT	Coronary Primary Prevention Trial
CPH	chronic persistent hepatitis	CPPV	continuous positive pressure ventilation
CPH	Cutter protein hydrolysate		
C.P.H.	Certificate in Public Health	CPQ	cholesterol-phosphatide quotient (=C/P)
cph *(phys)*	counts per hour, cycles per hour	CPR	cardiac pulmonary reserve
		CPR	cardiopulmonary resuscitation
CPHA	Central Psychiatric Hospitals Association (USA)	CPR	centripetal rub

CPR	chlorphenol red	CR *(card)*	chest – right arm (ECG lead)
CPRD	Committe on Prosthetics Research and Development	CR	Clinical Records
		CR	clot retraction
CPRS	comprehensive Psychopathology Rating Scale	CR *(chir)*	colon resection
		CR *(clin)*	complete remission
CPRT *(card)*	corrected pacemaker recovery time	CR	computerized radiology
		CR *(physiol)*	conditioned reflex
CPS	carbamylphosphate synthetase	CR *(neur)*	corneal reflex
		CR	coronary reserve
CPS	Carr-Purcell series (in NMR testing)	CR	coronary resistance
		CR *(neur)*	cremasteric reflex (= CrR)
CPS	constitutional psychopathic state	CR	cresyl red
		CR	crown-rump (axis)
cps *(phys)*	cycles per second, counts per second	CR	erythrocyte receptor for complement (= ECR)
CPSA, CP(SA)	College of Physicians of South Africa	Cr	creatinine
		CRA	Canadian Rheumatism Association
CPT	capacité pulmonaire totale (F); total pulmonary capacity	CRA	cerebral radioisotope angiography
CPT *(card)*	carotid pulse tracing	CRA	chronic rheumatoid arthritis (= CRP)
CPT	choline phosphotransferase	CRABP	cellular retinoic acid binding protein
CPT	cold pressure test	cran.	cranial
CPT *(psych)*	combining power test	CR$_{ant}$	anterior regional coronary resistance
CPT *(psych)*	concentration performance test	CRAO	central retinal artery occlusion
CPT	Current Procedural Terminology	CRBBB	complete right bundle branch block
CPTPP	continuous positive transpulmonary pressure	Cr + Br *(dent)*	crown and bridge
CPU	central processing unit (of a computer)	CRC	Canadian Red Cross
CPUE	capacité pulmonaire utilisable à l'effort (F); usable lung capacity on exertion	CRCC	Canadian Red Cross Committee
		CRCL	corrected forced cycle length
CPVC	common pulmonary venous chamber	C.R.C.P.	Certificate of the Royal College of Physicians
C$_P$vO_2	oxygen content of pulmonary venous blood	CRCS	Canadian Red Cross Society
CPZ	chlorpromazine	CRD	cerebroretinal degeneration
CQ	chloroquine-quinine		
CQ	conceptual quotient	CRD	chronic renal disease
CR	cardiorespiratory		
CR	cathode ray		
CR *(rad)*	central ray	CRD	chronic respiratory disease

CRD	complete reaction of degeneration	CRM	capacité respiratoire maximale (F); maximum respiratory capacity
CRE	Cruz Roja Española; Spanish Red Cross	CRM	cross-reacting material
CRE	cumulative radiation effect	CRME	Committee on Research in Medical Economics (USA)
CREDOC	Centre de Recherches et Documentation sur la Consommation (F); Center for Research and Documentation of Consumption	C.R.N.A.	Certified Registered Nurse Anesthetist
		CRO	cathode ray oscillograph
		CROS	contralateral routing of signal (cp. IROS)
CRESI	complejo relacionado al SIDA (S); AIDS-related complex (=ARC)	CRP	chronic rheumatoid polyarthritis (=CRA)
		CRP	C-reactive protein
CREST	calcinosis, Raynaud's phenomenon, esophageal dysfunction, sclerodactyly, telangiectasia (syndrome); progressive systemic sclerosis	CRP	complete recovery period
		CrP	creatine phosphate (=CP)
		CRPA	C-reactive protein antiserum
		CrR	cremasteric reflex (=CR)
		CRS *(mil)*	Camp Reception Station
CRF	capacité résiduelle fonctionelle (F); functional residual capacity (=FRD)	CRS	"Chinese restaurant syndrome"
		CRS	colon and rectal surgery
CRF	chronic renal failure	CRS	congenital rubella syndrome
CRF	coagulase-reacting factor		
CRF	corticotrophin-releasing factor	CRS	Croix Rouge Suisse (F); Swiss Red Cross
CRF	Croix Rouge Française; French Red Cross	CRST	calcinosis cutis, Raynaud's phenomenon, sclerodactylia, telangiectasis (syndrome); progressive scleroderma; Thibierge-Weissenbach syndrome; Winterbauer syndrome
CRH	corticotrophin-releasing hormone		
CRI	chronic respiratory insufficiency		
CRI	Croce Rossa Italiana; Italian Red Cross		
CRI	Croix Rouge International (F); International Red Cross (cp. ICRC)	CRT	capillary resistance test
		CRT	cardiac resuscitation team
		CRT	cathode ray tube
		CRT	complete recovery time
CRIA	competitive radioimmunoassay	CRT *(psych)*	complex reaction time
		CR$_t$	total (left ventricular) coronary resistance
CRIE	crossed radioimmunoelectrophoresis	C.R.T.T.	Certified Respiratory Therapy Technician
CRL	complement receptor lymphocytes		
		CRU	Clinical Research Unit
CRL *(obst)*	crown-rump length	CRVS	California Relative Value Studies
C.R.L.	Certified Record Librarian		

CRVT	chronic recurrent ventricular tachycardia	CSC	coup sur coup (F); in small doses
CS	Central Supply	CSD	chronic specific duodenitis
CS	cerebrospinal	CSD	conduction system disease
CS *(obst)*	cesarian section	CSDH	chronic subdural hematoma
CS	chest strap		
CS	chondroitin sulfate	C-section	cesarian section (= CS)
CS *(biochem)*	citrate synthetase	CSF	cerebrospinal fluid
		CSF	colony stimulating factor
CS	clinical staging		
CS	completed stroke	CSF	coronary sinus flow
CS	concentrated strength (of a solution)	CSFP	cerebrospinal fluid pressure
CS	conditioned stimulus	CSF-WR	cerebrospinal fluid Wassermann reaction
CS	congenital syphilis		
CS	conscious	CSG	Clinical Study Group
CS	coronary sclerosis	CS gas	orthochlorobenzalmalonitrile (gas used in riot control, named after Corson and Stoughton)
CS *(pharm)*	corticosteroid		
CS	current strength		
CS	Cushing syndrome		
CS *(pharm)*	cycloserine	CSGUS	Clinical Society of Genito-Urinary Surgeons (USA)
cS	centistokes		
C + S *(bact)*	culture and sensitivity (test)	CSH	carotid sinus hypersensitivity
c/s	cycles per second (= cps)	CSHG	cardioscatter histography
C-4-S	chondroitin-4-sulfate (= CSA)	CSI	chemical shift imaging
		CSI	Convention Sanitaire Internationale (F); International Sanitary Convention
C-6-S	chondroitin-6-sulfate (= CSC)		
17-CS	17-ketosteroids		
CSA	chondroitin sulfate A (= C-4-S)	CSII	continuous subcutaneous insulin infusion
CSA	colony stimulating activity	CSIRO	Chemical Section of the International Research Organization
CSA	Council of Scientific Affairs (USA)		
CSA	cross-sectional area	CSL	Commonwealth Serum Laboratories (UK)
CSB	chondroitin sulfate B, dermatan sulfate		
		CSL	cornsteep liquor
CSB	plasma fraction consisting of convertin, Stuart-Prower factor, and AHG B (factor IX)	CSM	carotid sinus massage
		CSM	cerebrospinal meningitis
		CSM	Committee on Safety of Medicines
CSBF	coronary sinus blood flow	CSM	computer sonometry
CSC	chondroitin sulfate C (= C-6-S)	CSMC	chronic scalp muscle contraction (headache)
CSC *(ophth)*	cornea – sclera – conjunctiva	CSMI	cardiogenic shock after myocardial infarction

CSMMG	Chartered Society of Massage and Medical Gymnastics (UK)	CT	capacité totale (F); total capacity
CSM test	statistical test of Barnard (convexity, symmetry, maximum number of outcomes)	CT *(anat)*	carpal tunnel
		CT	cellular therapy
		CT	cerebral thrombosis
		CT	chemotherapy (=CHT)
CSN	carotid sinus nerves	CT	cholesterol total (F); total cholesterol
CSNRT *(card)*	corrected sinus node recovery time	CT	circulation time
CSNS	cardiac sympathetic nerve stimulation	CT	closed thoracotomy
		CT *(lab)*	clotting time, coagulation time
CSOM	chronic suppurative otitis media	CT *(pharm)*	coated tablet
		CT *(pharm)*	compressed tablet
CSP	cavum septi pellucidi	CT	computerized tomography (=CTM)
CSP	cell surface protein		
CSP	Chartered Society of Physiotherapists	CT	connective tissue
		CT	Coombs test
CSP, CS-P	chondroitin sulfate protein	CT	corneal transplant
		CT	coronary thrombosis
CSP *(gyn)*	Cooperative Statistical Program	CT	corrective therapy
		CT	cytological technician
C_{spec}	specific compliance	CTA	Canadian Tuberculosis Association
CSR	cadmium sulfate reaction		
CSR	caprine syncytial retrovirus	CTA	chymotrypsin activity
CSR	Cheyne-Stokes respiration	CTA *(stat)*	contingency table analysis
CSR	corrected sedimentation rate	CTA *(pharm)*	cyanotrimethyl androsterone
CSR	cortical secretion rate	CTA	cyproterone acetate
CSRT	corrected sinus node recovery time	CTA *(imm)*	(lympho-)cytotoxic assay
		CTAB	cetyltrimethylammonium bromide, cetrimide
CSS	carotid sinus syndrome		
CSSD	Central Sterile Supply Department	CTAC	Cancer Treatment Advisory Committee (USA)
CST	College of Speech Therapists (UK)	CTBT	carboxyl tolbutamide
		CTC	chlortetracycline
CST *(psych)*	convulsive shock therapy	CTCL	cutaneous T cell lymphoma
C_{st}	static compliance		
CSTI	Clearinghouse for Scientific and Technical Information	CTD	cardiac transverse diameter
		CTD	carpal tunnel decompression
CSU	catheter specimen urine	CTD	chlorthalidone
CSU	Central Statistical Unit	CTD	chemo-thermo-disinfecting (procedure)
C substance	complex carbohydrate (present in the cell wall of pneumococcal cells)		
		CTD	circulation time descending
CT	calcitonin	CTD	Cushing threshold dose

CTEM	conventional transmission electron microscope	cUMP	cyclic uridine-5-mono-phosphate
CTF	chemotactic factor	CUMS	Cornell University Medical School
CTF	Colorado tick fever		
CTFE	chlorotrifluoro-ethylene	CURS	chronic unspecific respira-tory syndrome (=CNSLD)
CTG *(obst)*	cardiotocogram		
CTg *(card)*	central terminal Gold-berger (ECG)	CUSA	Cavitron Ultrasonic Surgi-cal Aspirator
CTGA	corrected transposition of the great arteries	Cu-T	copper T (intrauterine con-traceptive device)
CTH	ceramide trihexoside	CV	capacité vitale (F); vital capacity
CTI	cardiothoracic index (=CTR)		
		CV, cv	cardiovascular
CTL	cytolytic T lymphocytes	CV	cardioversion
CTL	clotrimazole	CV	cavum Vergae
CTM	computerized tomography (=CT)	CV	cell volume
		CV	cerebrovascular
CTP	cytidine triphosphate	CV *(ophth)*	champ visuel (F); visual field
CTR	cardiothoracic ratio (=CTI)		
		CV, cv	cheval vapeur (F); horse power (=CH, ch)
CTS	carpal tunnel syndrome		
CTS	computerized topographic scanner	CV	closing volume
		CV *(stat)*	coefficient of variation
CTs	synthetic calcitonin	CV	colonne vertébrale (F); spinal column
CTSP	Cooperative Triglyceride Standardization Program (USA)		
		CV	color vision
		CV *(obst)*	conjugata vera (L); true conjugate (=CVO)
CTT	computerized transaxial (or transmission) tomogra-phy (=CT)		
		CV, cv *(rad)*	constant voltage
		CV	corpuscular volume
CTU, ctu	centigrade thermal unit	CV	cresyl violet
CTw *(card)*	central terminal Wilson (ECG)	CV	curriculum vitae
		CVA	cerebrovascular accident
CTX	cardiotoxin	CVA	chorioallantois vaccinia virus Ankara
CTX	cerebrotendinous xan-thomatosis		
		CVA	costovertebral angle
CTX	cyclophosphamide	CVBF	coronary venous blood flow
CTU	centigrade thermal unit		
CTZ	chemoreceptor trigger zone	CVD	cardiovascular disease
CU	clinical unit	CVD	cerebrovascular disease
CU	colitis ulcerosa (L); ulcera-tive colitis	CVD	color vision deviation
		CVG	cineventriculography
CU	contractions utérines (F); uterine contractions	CVI	cerebrovascular insuffi-ciency
C_u	urea clearance	CVI	chronic venous insuffi-ciency
CUC	chronic ulcerative colitis		
CUG	cysto-urethrogram	C virus	Coxsackie virus

CVLP	corona-virus-like particles	CXMD	canine X-linked muscular dystrophy
CVO	conjugata vera obstetrica (L); true conjugate (diameter of the pelvic outlet)	CXR	chest x-ray
		CyA	cyclosporin A
CVP	cell volume profile	CYC	cyclophosphamide
CVP	central venous pressure	CYC *(phys)*	cyclotron
CVPP	cytotoxic combination therapy with cyclophosphamide, vinblastine, procarbazine, and prednisone	Cyd	cytidine (according to IUPAC)
		CYL	casein yeast lactate (medium)
		cyl *(ophth)*	cylinder
CVR	cardiovascular renal disease	CYS	cystoscopy
		Cys-S	cystine
CVR	cardiovascular respiratory disease	Cys-SH	cysteine
		Cys-SO$_3$H	cysteic acid
CVR	cerebral vascular resistance	Cyt	cytochrome
CVR	coronary vascular resistance	Cyt-Fe$_2$	reduced cytochrome
		CZ	cephazotine
CVS	cardiovascular surgery	CZI	crystalline zinc insulin
CVS	cardiovascular system	CZ strain	Carr-Zilber strain (of Rous sarcoma virus)
CVS	clean voided specimen		
CVS	challenge virus standard (for rabies vaccine)		
CVTR	charcoal virus transport medium		
CW	cardiac work		
CW	chemical warfare		
CW	chest lead of Wilson (ECG)		
CW	chest wall		
CW	Children's Ward		
CW	clockwise		
CW	continuous wave		
CW	crutch walking		
CWBTS	capillary whole blood true sugar		
CWHB	citrated whole human blood		
CWI	cardiac work index ($=$CI)		
CWO	carrier wave oscillator		
CWOP	childbirth without pain		
CWS *(card)*	circumferential wall stress		
CWS	cold water soluble		
cwt	centweight, hundredweight (50,8 kg)		
CX	cefoxitin		
Cx	convex		

D

D, d *(phys)*	darcy (unit of mechanical permeability)
D	dead air space
D *(phys)*	debye (unit of dipole moment)
D	deciduous
D, d *(phys)*	density
D, d *(chem)*	deoxy-
D	dérivation (F); (ECG) lead
D	deviation
D, d	dexter (L); right
D	diameter
D	diastole
D	difference
D	diffusion capacity
D *(phys)*	diffusion coefficient
D *(ophth)*	diopter ($=$dpt)
D	displacement
D *(vet)*	dog

D	donor	DAB	4-dimethylamino-azoben-zene
D	dopamine		
D *(anat)*	dorsal segment	DAB	ductus arteriosus Botalli (L)
D *(pharm)*	dose		
D *(chem)*	stereoisomer of a chemical compound	DABA	p-dimethylaminobenzalde-hyde (=DMAB)
D. *(anat)*	ductus (L); duct	DA-ß-OH	dopamine beta-hydrox-ylase
D.,d. *(pharm)*	da, detur, divide (L); give, divide (Rx)	D.A.B.P.N.	Diplomate of the American Board of Psychiatry and Neurology
d	dies (L); day		
d- *(chem)*	dextrogyre; turning to the right	D.A.B.T.	Diplomate of the American Board of Toxicology
D+, d-	rhesus-positive, rhesus-negative	DAC	Deutscher Arzneimittel-Codex; German Drug Code
3D	three-dimensional		
2,4-D	2,4-dichlorophenoxyacetic acid	DAC	dialdehyde cellulose
DA	degenerative arthritis	DAC	digital analog converter (or compiler)
DA	delayed action (of a drug)		
DA	Dental Assistant	DACT *(pharm)*	actinomycin D
DA, dA	deoxyadenosine (=dAdo)		
DA	developmental age	DAD	delayed afterdepolariza-tion
DA	diagnostic arthrotomy		
DA	diphenylchlorarsine	DAD	dispense as directed (Rx)
DA	disability assistance	DADA	di-isopropylamine di-chloro-acetate (=DIPA)
DA	dopamine		
DA	drug abuser	DADAVS *(mil)*	Deputy Assistant Director of Army Veterinary Ser-vices
D.A.	Diploma in Anaesthetics (UK)		
D.a.	discus articularis (L); arti-cular disk	DADDS	diacetyl-diamino-diphenyl-sulfone
D4A	2',3'-didehydro-2',3'-dide-oxyadenosinene (=ddeAdo, DHA)	DADH *(mil)*	Deputy Assistant Director of Hygiene
		DADMS *(mil)*	Deputy Assistant Director of Medical Services
DAA	dihydroxyaluminum aminoacetate	dAdo	deoxyadenosine (=DA, dA)
DAA	ductus arteriosus apertus (L); patent ductus arterio-sus (=DAB, DBA)	DADP, dADP	deoxyadenosine diphos-phate
DAAD	Deutscher Akademischer Austauschdienst; German Academic Exchange Ser-vice	DADPS	diamino-diphenylsulfone (=DDS)
		DADS *(mil)*	Director of Army Dental Services
DAAO	d-amino-acid oxidase	DAdW	Deutsche Akademie der Wissenschaften; German Academy of Sciences (Ber-lin)
DAB	Deutsches Arzneibuch; German Pharmacopoeia		
DAB	α, γ-diaminobutyric acid		

DAE	diving air embolism	DAPI	Deutsches Arzneiprüfungs-institut (G); German Drug Evaluation Institute (Munich)
DAE	(mixture of) dimethylaceta-mide, acetone and ethanol		
DAF	delayed auditory feedback		
DAG	diacylglycerin	DAPI	4,6-diamidino-2-phenylin-dole
DAG	Deutsche Anatomische Gesellschaft; German Anatomical Society	DAPS	diazo-aminopolystyrene
		DAPT	2,4-diamino-5-phenylthia-zole, aminophenazole
DAGT	direct antiglobulin test (= DAT)	DAP test (psych)	draw-a-person test
DAH	disordered action of the heart	DAR (rad)	differential absorption ratio
DAI	death from accidental inju-ries	DAS	depressory active sub-stance
DAL, DALA	delta-aminolevulinic acid (= ALA)	DAS	dextroamphetamine sulfate
DALD	delta-aminolevulinic acid dehydrase	DAS	Direction des Affaires Sa-nitaires et Sociales; Managing Office of Sani-tary and Social Affairs (Paris)
DALS	delta-aminolevulinic acid synthetase		
DAM	degraded amyloid		
DAM	diacetylmonoxime	DASC	dehydroascorbic acid
DAM	diacetylmorphine	DASPMI	dimethylaminostyrene methylpyridine iodine
DAM	diethyl-aminomethyl		
DAMP, dAMP	deoxyadenosine mono-phosphate	DASS	defined antigen-substrate system
DANS	1-dimethylamino-naphtha-lene-5-sulfonic acid	DAT	(combination of) daunoru-bicin, cytarabine and 6-thi-oguanine
DANT	diallyl-nor-toxiferine, allo-ferine	DAT	delayed action tablet
DAO	diaminoxidase (= DO)	DAT	dementia of Alzheimer type
DAP	Deutsche Akademie für Psychoanalyse; German Academy of Psychoanaly-sis (Berlin/Munich)	DAT	diacetylthiamine
		DAT	differential agglutination test (Waaler-Rose)
DAP	diabetes-associated peptide	DAT	differential aptitude test
DAP	diallyl phthalate	DAT	direct antiglobulin test (= DAGT)
DAP	diamino-pimelinic acid		
DAP	diastolic aortic pressure (= DP$_{Ao}$)	DATC	diisoamyl oxythiocarbani-lide (= TC)
DAP	dihydrazinophthalazine	DATI	diastolic amplitude time index
DAP (biochem)	dihydroxy-acetone phos-phate (= DOAP)	DATP, dATP	deoxyadenosine triphos-phate
DAP	diphenylaminopropane		
DAP	direct latex agglutination	DAV	Deutscher Apotheker-Ver-ein; German Pharmacist Union
D.A.P.E.	Diploma in Applied Para-sitology and Entomology		

DAV	différence artério-veineuse (F); arteriovenous difference	DBPC	ditertiary butyl paracresol, butyl hydroxytoluene (= BHT)
D.Av.Med.	Diploma in Aviation Medicine	dB(PN)	perceived noise decibels
DAVN	dual AV-node pathway	DBS	deep brain stimulation
DAVRS *(mil)*	Director of Veterinary and Remount Services	DBS	despeciated bovine serum
		DBS *(pharm)*	dibromosalicylate
DAW *(card)*	distal anterior wall	DBS *(pharm)*	dibromosulfanilide
DB	dead space breathing	DBS	Division of Biological Standards
DB *(psych)*	digit span backward		
DB, db *(dent)*	distobuccal	DBS, DBT	double-blind study, ... trial
DB	Baudelocque's diameter; external conjugate diameter of the pelvis	DBW	desirable body weight
		DC	death certificate
		DC	débit cardiaque (F); cardiac output (= CO)
dB, db	decibel		
DBA	dibenzamine	DC	decarboxylase
DBA	dibenzanthracene	DC	Decimal Classification
DBA *(card)*	ductus Botalli apertus (L); patent ductus arteriosus	DC *(mil)*	Dental Corps
		DC	diagnostic center
DBC	differential blood count	DC	diphenylcyanoarsine
DBC	dye-binding capacity	DC, d.c.	direct current
DBCP	dibromochloropropane	DC, dc *(dent)*	distocervical
DBED	dibenzethylene diamine		
DBG	Deutsche Bunsen-Gesellschaft für Physikalische Chemie; German Bunsen Society of Physical Chemistry	DC	donor cell
		DC	dosis curativa (L) (= D_{cur}, Dos. cur.)
		DC	doxycycline
		dC	deoxycytidine, cytosine deoxyriboside (= dCR, dCyd)
DBH	dopamine ß-hydroxylase (= DA-ß-OH)		
DBI	development at birth index	D.C.	Doctor of Chiropractic
DBI	diazepam binding inhibitor	D + C *(gyn)*	dilation and curettage
DBL	distance between lenses	D + C	Drugs and Cosmetics
DBM	diabetic management	D4C	2',3'-didehydro-2',3'-dideoxycytidinene (= ddeCyd, DHC)
DBM	1,6-dibromo-1,6-dideoxy-D-mannitol		
DBMA	dibenzylmethylamine	DCA	deoxycholate citrate agar, Leifson's agar
DBO	demande biochimique en oxygène (F); biochemical oxygen demand (= BOD)		
		DCA	deoxycorticosterone acetate (= DOCA)
DBO, dbo *(dent)*	distobucco-occlusal	DCAD	documented coronary artery disease
DBP	diastolic blood pressure	DCAI	2-(2,6-dichlorophenyl-amino)-2-imidazoline
DBP	dibutylphthalate		
DBP, dbp *(dent)*	distobuccopulpal	DCBE	double-contrast barium enema

DCC	Day Care Center
DCC	dextrose coated charcoal (also: dextran-coated charcoal assay)
DCC	dicloxacillin
DCC	dicycloamino-hydrochloride
DCC	dicyclohexyl carbodiimide
DCc	double concave
DCCK	dihydroergocristine, dihydroergocornin, and dihydroergokryptin methane sulfonate
DCCV	direct current cardioversion (=DC shock)
DCDP, dCDP	deoxycytidine diphosphate (=deCDP)
D cells	delta cells (pancreas, anterior pituitary)
DCF	Dénominations Communes Françaises; French Common Denominations
DCF	direct centrifugal flotation
d.c.f.	detur cum formula (L); to be given with exact directions
DCG	dacryocystography
DCG	deoxycorticosterone glucoside (=DOCG)
DCG	dichloroglyoxin
D.C.H.	Diploma in Child Health
D.Ch.	Doctor Chirurgiae (L); Doctor of Surgery
DCHN	dicyclohexylamine nitrite
DCI	Dénominations Communes Internationales (F); International Common Denominations
DCI	dichloro-isoproterenol, dichloro-isoprenaline
DCIE	discontinuous counterimmunoelectrophoresis
DCIP	Dénominations Communes Internationales Proposées (F); Proposed International Common Denominations
DCIP	2,6-dichlorophenolindophenol (=DCPIP)
DCIR	Dénominations Communes Internationales Recommandées (F); Recommended International Common Denominations
DCL	diflucortolone
DCLS	deoxycholate citrate lactose saccharose (agar)
DCM	dilated cardiomyopathy
DCMP, dCMP	deoxycytidine monophosphate (=deCMP)
D.C.M.T.	Diploma in Clinical Medicine of Tropics
DCMX (pharm)	2,4-dichloro-3,5-m-xylenol
DCN	delayed conditioned necrosis
D.C.O.G.	Diploma of the College of Obstetricians and Gynaecologists (UK)
DCP	Data Collection Platform
DCP	dicalcium phosphate; Calcium phosphoricum
DCP	dicaprylphthalate
DCP	District Community Physician
D.C.P.	Diploma in Clinical Pathology (UK)
DCPA	dichlorphenamide, Daranide
D.C.Path.	Diploma of the College of Pathologists
DCPIP	2,6-dichlorophenolindophenol (=DCIP)
DCPM	di-(4-chlorophenoxy)-methane
DCR	direct cortical response
dCR	deoxycytidine, cytosine deoxyriboside (=dC, dCyd)
DCRV (card)	double-chambered right ventricle
DCS	decompression sickness
DCS	distal coronary sinus (electrogram)

DCS *(neur)*	dorsal column stimulation	ddCyd	2',3'-dideoxycytidine (=DDC, DOC)
DC shock	direct current shock, cardioversion	DDD	defined daily dose
DCT	distal convoluted tubule	DDD	Denver dialysis disease
Dct.	decoction	DDD	5,5-dichloro-2,2-dihydroxy-diphenylsulfide
DCTMA	deoxycorticosterone trimethylacetate	DDD	dichloro-diphenyl-dichloroethane (=TDE)
DCTP, dCTP	deoxycytidine triphosphate (=deCTP)	DDD	diet – digitalis – diuretics; classical therapy of heart failure
DCTPA	deoxycorticosterone triphenylacetate	DDD	dihydroxy-dinaphthyldisulfide
DCU	dichloral urea	ddDAPR	2',3'-dideoxy-2,6-diaminopurine
D$_{cur}$	dosis curativa (L) (=CD, DC, Dos. cur.)	DDD syndrome	diarrhée-douleur-diabète (F); diarrhea, pain, diabetes syndrome
DCV	desciclovir		
DCVO	Deputy Chief Veterinary Officer	DDE	1,1-dichloro-2,2-dichlorophenylethylene
d-c voltage	electrical potential in the cochlear duct	ddeAdo	2',3'-didehydro-2',3'-dideoxyadenosinene (=D4A, DHA)
DCX	dicloxacillin (=DCC)		
DCx	double convex	ddeCyd	2',3'-didehydro-2',3'-dideoxycytidinene (=D4C, DHC)
dCyd	deoxycytidine		
DD	dependent drainage	ddeN	2',3'-didehydro-2',3'-dideoxyribonucleoside (=DDN, DHN, D4N)
DD	developmental disability		
DD	diastolic diameter		
DD	diastolic duration	ddeThd	2',3'-didehydro-2',3'-dideoxythymidinene (=DHT, D4T)
DD	differential diagnosis		
DD	disc diameter		
DD	double diffusion	ddeUrd	2',3'-didehydro-2',3'-dideoxyuridinene (=DHU, D4U)
DD	dry dressing		
DD	duodenal diverticulum		
D$_d$ *(card)*	diameter (of left ventricle) in diastole	DDG	Deutsche Dermatologische Gesellschaft; German Dermatological Society
DDA	Dangerous Drugs Act (USA)		
DDA, ddAdo	2',3'-dideoxyadenosine	DDIB	Disease Detection Information Bureau
DDAVP	1-deamino-D-arginine[8] vasopressin	3D disease	pellagra (with dermatitis, diarrhea, and dementia)
DDB	dilatation des bronches (F); bronchial dilation		
DDC	2',3'-dideoxycytidine (=ddCyd, DOC)	D.D.M.	Diploma in Dermatological Medicine (UK)
DDC	(sodium) diethyldithiocarbamate (=DDTC, DTC)	DDMP	diamino-dichlorophenylmethylpyrimidine
DDC	direct digital control		

70

DDMS *(mil)* Deputy Director of Medical Services

DDN 2',3'-didehydro-2',3'-dideoxyribonucleoside (=ddeN, DHN, D4N)

dDNA denatured deoxyribonucleic acid

D.D.O. Diploma in Dental Orthopaedics (UK)

DDP dichloro-diamine-platinum; cisplatinum

DDPM dimethylamino-3,5-dinitrophenyl maleimide

DDPTI distal diastolic pressure-time index

DDR *(gyn)* date des dernières règles (F); date of last period

D.D.R. Diploma in Diagnostic Radiology (UK)

DDS dialysis disequilibrium syndrome

DDS diamino-diphenyl-sulfone, dapsone (=DADPS)

DDS directional Doppler sonography

D.D.S. Doctor of Dental Surgery

D.D.Sc. Doctor of Dental Science

DDSO diamino-diphenyl-sulfoxide

DDST Denver Developmental Screening Test

DDT dichlor-diphenyl-trichloroethane

DDT 2',3'-dideoxythymidine

DDTC (sodium) diethyldithiocarbamate (=DDC, DTC)

DDVP O,O-dimethyl-O-(2,2-dichlorovinyl)-phosphate

DE dosis effectiva (L) (=ED)

DE_{50} dosis effectiva media (L); mean effective dose (=ED_{50})

D+E *(gyn)* dilation and evacuation

DEA dehydroepiandrosterone (=DHA, DHE, DHEA)

DEA diethanolamine

DEA Drug Enforcement Administration

deA, deADO deoxyadenosine (=DA)

DEAE diethylaminoethanol

DEAEC diethylaminoethyl cellulose

DEAED diethylaminoethyl dextrane

DEB diethylbutanediol

DEC diethylcarbamazine

deCDP deoxycytidine diphosphate (usually: DCDP, dCDP)

deCMP deoxycytidine monophosphate (usually: DCMP, dCMP)

deCTP deoxycytidine triphosphate (usually: DCTP, dCTP)

DED declared dead

DED *(rad)* delayed erythema dose

DEF dental "extraction and filling" formula

DEG diethylene glycol

DEGAM Deutsche Gesellschaft für Allgemeinmedizin; German Society of General Medicine

deGDP deoxyguanosine diphosphate (usually: DGMP, dGMP)

DeGMP deoxyguanosine monophosphate (usually: DGTP, dGTP)

DEGS diethylene glycolsuccinate

DEHP di-2-ethylhexylphthalate

DEHS Division of Emergency Health Services

DEJ *(dent)* dento-enamel junction

DEJ *(derm)* dermal-epidermal junction

DEMA dichloroethylmethylamine

DEMS débit expiratoire maximum seconde (F); forced expiratory volume (=FEV)

DENA diethylnitrosamine

D enzyme dextrin transglycosylase

DEP diethylpropanediol

DEPA diethylene phosphoramide

DEPC	diethylpyrocarbonate (=DPC)	DFH	Danmarks Farmaceutiske Hojskole; Danish Pharmaceutical Academy
DeR	reaction of degeneration (=CRD, DR)	D.F.Hom.	Diploma of the Faculty of Homeopathy
DERP-NIMH	Drug Evaluation Rating Program (of the National Institute of Mental Health)	DFID	dual-flame ionization detector
DES	diethylstilbestrol	DFM *(obst)*	decreased fetal movement
DES	Doctor's Emergency Service	DFMO	difluoromethylornithine
DET	detector	DFMR *(obst)*	daily fetal movement recording
DET	N,N-diethyl-m-toluamide	DFO	desferrioxamine, deferoxamine
DET	diethyltryptamine		
DETM	dihydroergotamine (=DHE)	DFP	diastolic filling phase
DEV	deep epithelial volume	DFP	diisopropylfluorophosphate, fluostigmine
DEV	duck egg (or embryo) virus		
DE value	dextrose equivalent value	D.F.P.	Diploma in Family Practice
DEX	dextrothyroxine		
Dex	dexamethasone	DFPase	dialcylfluorophosphatase
DF	decapacitation factor (of sperms)	DFS	disease-free survival
		DFSP	dermatofibrosarcoma protuberans
DF *(dent)*	decayed and filled		
		DFSS	discrete fibromuscular aortic stenosis
DF *(orth)*	degree of freedom		
		DFT	defibrillation threshold
DF	dialysable fraction	DFT	difluorodiphenyltrichloromethane
DF *(psych)*	digit span forward (test)		
DF	dorsiflexion	5-DFUR	5'-deoxy-5-fluorouridine
dF	daily feces	DG	diffuse gastritis
df *(stat)*	degree of freedom	DG	diglyceride
D.f.	dientamoeba fragilis	DG, dg *(dent)*	distogingival
DFA	difluoroadrenaline		
DFA	fructose-1,6-diphosphate aldolase	dG	deoxyguanosine, guanosine deoxyriboside (=dGuo)
DFADL	developmental functional activities of daily living score	DGAMS	Director General of Army Medical Services
		DGC	depth-gain compensation (ECG)
DFB *(rad)*	direct fan beam reconstruction	DGC	Deutsche Gesellschaft für Chirurgie; German Society of Surgery
DFC	dry-filled capsules		
DFDT	difluoro-diphenyl-trichloro-ethane	DGDP, dGDP	deoxyguanosine diphosphate (=deGDP)
DFG	Deutsche Forschungsgemeinschaft; German Research Association (Bonn)	DGE	Deutsche Gesellschaft für Ernährung; German Society for Nutrition

DGF *(gyn)*	duct growth factor	DGTP, dGTP	deoxyguanosine triphosphate (=deGTP)
DGGG	Deutsche Gesellschaft für Gynäkologie und Geburtshilfe; German Society of Gynecology and Obstetrics	dGTPase	deoxyguanosine triphosphatase
DGHM	Deutsche Gesellschaft für Hygiene und Mikrobiologie; German Society of Hygiene and Microbiology	DGUM	Deutsche Gesellschaft für Ultraschall in der Medizin; German Society for Ultrasound in Medicine
DGK	Deutsche Gesellschaft für Kreislaufforschung; German Society of Circulation Research	dGUO	deoxyguanosine, guanosine deoxyriboside (=dG)
		DH	Day Hospital
		DH	dehydrocholic acid
		DH	dehydrogenase
DGMP, dDMP	deoxyguanosine monophosphate (=deGMP)	DH	delayed hypersensitivity
DGMS *(mil)*	Director General of Medical Services	DH	Document Handling
		DH	dorsal hippocampus
DGN	Deutsche Gesellschaft für Neurochirurgie; German Society of Neurosurgery	D.H. *(mil)*	Director of Hygiene
		DHA	dehydro-ascorbic acid
DGN	Deutsche Gesellschaft für Neurologie; German Society of Neurology	DHA	dehydroepiandrosterone (=DEA, DHE, DHEA)
D.G.O.	Diploma in Gynaecology and Obstetrics (UK)	DHA	2',3'-didehydro-2',3'-dideoxyadenosinene (=D4A, ddeAdo)
DGOT	Deutsche Gesellschaft für Orthopädie und Traumatologie; German Society of Orthopedic Surgery and Traumatology	DHAP	dihydroxyacetone phosphate
		DHAS	dehydroepiandrosterone sulfate
DGPM	Deutsche Gesellschaft für Perinatale Medizin; German Society of Perinatal Medicine	DHB, DHBP	dehydrobenzperidol
		DHC	2',3'-didehydro-2',3'-dideoxycytidinene (=D4C, ddeCyd)
DGPN	Deutsche Gesellschaft für Psychiatrie und Nervenheilkunde; German Society of Psychiatry and Neurology	DHC	dihydroheptachlorine
		DHCC	1,25-dihydroxycholecalciferol
		DHD	dermatitis herpetiformis Duhring
DGR	duodenogastric reflux	DHE, DHEA	dehydroepiandrosterone (=DEA, DHA)
DGRST	Délégation Générale à la Recherche Scientifique et Technique (F); General Delegation for Scientific and Technical Research	DHE	dihydroergotamine (=DETM)
		DHEAS	dehydroepiandrosterone sulfate
DGSS	Darier-Groenblad-Strandberg syndrome	DHEW	Department of Health, Education, and Welfare (Washington/USA)

DHF	dihydroxyfumaric acid	DHT	2',3'-didehydro-2',3'-dide-oxythymidinene (= ddeThd, D4T)
DHFR	dihydrofolate reductase		
D.Hg.	Doctor of Hygiene (= D.Hyg.)	DHT	dihydrotachysterol
DHHS	Department of Health and Human Services (USA)	DHT	dihydrotestosterone
		DHT	dihydrothymine
DHI	decompensated heart insufficiency (= CCF, CHF)	DHT	dihydroxypropyltheophyl-line
		DHT	dihydroxytryptamine
DHIA	dehydroisoandrosterone (= DEA, DHA, DHE, DHEA)	DHU	2',3'-didehydro-2',3'-dide-oxyuridinene (= ddeUrd, D4U)
DHIC	dihydroisocodeine	DHVD	Divison of Heart and Vas-cular Diseases (of the NHLBI)
DHMA	dehydroxymandelic acid;		
DHMCMP, dHMCMP	deoxy-5-hydroxymethyl-cytidine monophosphate	D.Hyg.	Doctor of Hygiene (= D. Hg.)
D.H.M.S.A.	Diploma in History of Medicine and Scientific Arts	DHZ	Deutsches Herzzentrum; German Heart Center (Munich/Berlin)
DHN	2',3'-didehydro-2',3'-dide-oxyribonucleoside (= DDN, ddeN, D4N)	DI (clin)	deterioration index
		DI	diabetes insipidus
		DI, di (dent)	distoincisal
DHO	deuterium hydrogen oxide	DI	dosing interval
DHODP	di-n-octyl-n-decylphthalate	DI	dyspnea index
DHP	Deutsche Herz-Kreislauf-Präventionsstudie (G); German Cardiocirculatory Prevention Study	DI	indicator dose
		DI	initial dose
		Di	diphtheria
		dI	deoxyinosine, inosine deoxyriboside (= dIno)
DHP	dehydrobenzperidol	DIA (mil)	death in action
DHP	dihydropteridine	DIAC	diiodothyroacetic acid
DHP	dihydropyridines	Di^a factor	Diego factor, antigen Di^a
DHP	dinonylphthalate	DIAR	dextran-induced anaphy-lactoid reaction
DHPG	dihydroxyphenylglycol		
DHPG	9[(1,3-dihydroxy-2-prop-oxy)methyl]guanine	DIB	butyl-3,5-diiodo-4-hydroxy-benzoate
DHPR	dihydropteridine reductase	DIB	dot immunobinding
DHR	delayed hypersensitivity reaction	DIC	disseminated intravascular coagulation
DHR	Department of Health Regulations (USA)	DIDA	diisodecyladipinate
DHS	delayed-type hypersensi-tivity (response)	DIDMOAD	diabetes insipidus, diabetes mellitus, optic nerve atro-phy, deafness (syndrome)
DHSM	dihydrostreptomycin (= DSM, DST)	DIDP, dIDP	deoxyinosine diphosphate
DHSS	Department of Health and Social Security (UK)	DIDP	diisodecylphthalate

dieb.alt.	diebus alternis (L); every other day (Rx)
dieb.tert.	diebus tertiis (L); every third day (Rx)
DIF	differentiation inducing factor
DIF	direct immunofluorescence
DIFP	diisopropylfluorophosphate, fluostigmine (=DFP)
DIGLYME	diethyleneglycoldimethylether
D.I.H.	Diploma in Industrial Health (UK)
DIHPPA	diiohydroxyphenylpyruvic acid
dil.	dilutus (L); diluted
DILE	drug induced lupus erythematosus
DILF	diffuse interstitial lung fibrosis
DIM	Departement Innere Medizin; Department of Internal Medicine (in Swiss hospitals)
DIM	Dosis infectiosa media; median infectious dose (=ID$_{50}$)
dim. *(pharm)*	dimidium (L); one-half
DIMDI	Deutsches Institut für Medizinische Dokumentation und Information; German Institute of Documentation and Information (Cologne)
DIMP, dIMP	deoxyinosine monophosphate
DIMHS *(psych)*	Davis Institute Modification of Hamilton Scale
DIN	Deutsches Institut für Normung; German Institute for Standardization (Berlin)
DINA	diisonitrose acetone
dIno	deoxyinosine, inosine deoxyriboside (=dI)

d.in p.aeq.	divide in partes aequales (L); divide in equal parts (Rx)
DIOA	diisooctylphthalate
DIP	desquamative interstitial pneumonia
DIP	2,6-dichlorophenolindophenol (=DCIP, DCPIP)
DIP	distal interphalangeal (joint)
DIPA	diisopropylaminodichloroacetate (=DADA)
Dip.Am.Bd. P.N.	Diplomate of the American Board of Psychiatry and Neurology
Dip.Bact.	Diploma in Bacteriology
DIPC	diffuse interstitial pulmonary calcification
DIPG, DiPG	diphosphoglyceric acid
Dip.Micr.	Diploma in Microbiology
DIQ	direct/indirect quotient (bilirubin)
dir.prop.	directione propria (L); with proper direction
DIS	Diagnostic Information System
DIS	diagnostic interview schedule
DIS	disorientation
DIT	diiodotyrosine
Di-Te-Pe-Pol	vaccine against diphtheria, tetanus, pertussis, and poliomyelitis
DITP, dITP	deoxyinosine triphosphate
DIU	dispositif intra-utérin (F); intrauterine contraceptive device (=IUD, IUCD, IUP)
DIU	drug induced ulcer
DIVA	digital intravenous angiography
DIVSA	digital intravenous subtraction angiography
DIW *(card)*	distal inferior wall

DJD	degenerative joint disease	DLP, dlp *(dent)*	distolinguopulpal
DKA	diabetic ketoacidosis	DLP	dose liminaire de poussières (F); pollen threshold dose
DKFZ	Deutsches Krebsforschungszentrum; German Cancer Research Center (Heidelberg)	DLR	Donath-Landsteiner reaction
DL	danger list	DLS	d-lysergic acid diethylamide
D_L	diffusion capacity of the lungs	DM	dexamethasone
DL, dl *(dent)*	distolingual	DM	diabetes mellitus
		DM *(card)*	diastolic murmur
DL	Donath-Landsteiner (test)	DM	diphenylaminearsine chloride, Adamsite
DL	dosis letalis (L); lethal dose (= LD)	DM	dopamine (= DA)
		dm	decimeter
DL_{50}	dosis letalis media (L); median lethal dose (= LD_{50})	D_M	membrane diffusion
		D.M.	Docteur en Médicine (F); Doctor of Medicine (also: M.D.)
dl	deciliter, 100 ml	DMA	dimethylamine
DLa, dla *(dent)*	distolabial	DMAB	p-dimethylaminobenzaldehyde (= DMBA)
DLAC	dose liminaire d'acétylcholine (F); acetylcholine threshold dose	DMAC	dimethylacetamide
		DMAE	ß-dimethylaminoethanol
DLaL, dlal *(dent)*	distolabioincisal	DMAP	3-deoxy-alpha-methyl-17-alpha-acetoxyprogesterone
DLaP, dlap *(dent)*	distolabiopulpal		
		4-DMAP	4-dimethylaminophenol
DLC	dynamic lung compliance	DMAPN	dimethylaminopropionitrile
DLE	dialysable leukocyte extract	DMARD	disease modifying antirheumatic drugs
DLE	disseminated lupus erythematosus	DMASt	4-dimethylaminostilbene (= DMST, DS)
DLF	digitalis-like factor	DMBA	p-dimethylaminobenzaldehyde (= DMAB)
DLF	Disabled Living Foundation		
DLI, dli *(dent)*	distolinguoincisal	DMBA	7,12-dimethylbenzanthracene
DLLI	dulcitol lysine lactose iron (agar)	DMBC	dimethylbenzylchloride
		DMC	dimethylcarbinol
DLM	dosis letalis minima (L); minimum lethal dose	DMCMP, dMCMP	deoxymethylcytidine monophosphate
DLO, dlo *(dent)*	distolinguoocclusal	DMCT, DMCTC	6-demethyl-7-chlortetracycline (demeclocycline)
D.L.O.	Diploma in Laryngology and Otology (UK)	DMD	Duchenne muscular dystrophy

D.M.D.	Dentariae Medicinae Doctor (L); Doctor of Dental Medicine	D.M.R.E.	Diploma in Medical Radiology and Electrology
DMDT	4,4-dimethoxydiphenyl-trichloroethane	D.M.R.T.	Diploma in Medical Radiotherapy (UK)
DMDTC	(zinc) dimethyldithiocarbamate	DMS	dermatomyositis
		DMS	dexamethasone
DMDTH	5,5-dimethyl-2,4-dithiohydantoine	DMS	dimercaptosuccinate
		D.M.S. (mil)	Directof of Medical Services
DME	dimethyltubocurarine		
D.M.E.	Director of Medical Education	D.M.S.	Doctor of Medical Science
		DMSA	dimercapto-succinic acid
DMF, DMFA	dimethylformamide	D.M.S.A.	Diploma in Medical Services Administration
DMF (dent)	diseased, missing, filled teeth (index)	DMSO	dimethylsulfoxide
		DMSS	discrete membranous sub-aortic stenosis
DMG	dimethylglyoxin		
D-MGA	dextro-malposition of the great arteries	D.M.S.S.	Director of Medical and Sanitary Services
D.M.H.S.	Director of Medical and Health Services	DMST	dimethylaminostilbene (= DMASt)
DMI	dimethylimipramine	DMT	N,N-dimethyltryptamine
D.M.J.	Diploma in Medical Jurisprudence	DMTC	demethyltetracycline
		DMU	dwarf mouse unit
DMNA	dimethylnitrosamine	D.M.V.	Doctor of Veterinary Medicine (also: D.V.M.)
DMO	dimethyloxazolidine		
DMP	dimercaprol	dmW	decimeter wave (= UHF)
DMP	dimethylphthalate	DN	dibucaine number
DMP	dimethylpolysiloxane	DN	dicrotic notch
DMP	dystrophia musculorum progressiva (L); progressive muscular dystrophy	DN	District Nurse
		D.N.	Diploma in Nursing
		D/N	dextrose-nitrogen ratio (= D-N ratio, G/N)
DMPA	depo-medroxyprogesterone acetate	D4N	2',3'-didehydro-2',3'-dideoxyribonucleoside (= ddeN, DDN, DHN)
DMPE	3,4-dimethoxyphenylethylamine		
		DNA	deoxyribonucleic acid
DMPP	1,1-dimethyl-4-phenylpiperazine	DNAP	deoxyribonucleic acid polymerase
DMPS	dimercaptopropane sulfonate	DNase	deoxyribonuclease
		DNB	dinitrobenzene
DMR	Department of Medical Radiology	D.N.B.	Diplomate of the National Board (of Medical Examiners)
D.M.R.	Diploma in Medical Radiology (UK)	DNBP	2,4-dinitro-6-butylphenol
D.M.R.D.	Diploma in Medical Radiodiagnosis (UK)	DNCB	dinitrochlorobenzene, 1-chloro-2,4-dinitrobenzene

DNCG	disodium cromoglycate (=DSCG)	DOB	date of birth
DNCM	dilatative non-obstructive cardiomyopathy	D.Obst.R.C. O.G.	Diploma in Obstetrics of the Royal College of Obstetricians and Gynae-
DND	double needle dialysis		cologists
DNE	Director of Nursing Edu-	DOC *(obst)*	date of conception
	cation	DOC	deoxycholate
DNFB	2,4-dinitro-1-fluorobenzene	DOC	deoxycortone, deoxycorti-
DNM	dosis necroticans minima		costerone
	(L); minimum necrotizing dose	DOC	2',3'-dideoxycytidine (=DDC, ddCyd)
DNN	dinitronaphthol	DOCA	deoxycorticosterone ace-
DNO	District Nursing Officer		tate (=DCA)
DNOC	4,6-dinitro-o-cresol	DOCG	deoxycorticosterone gluco-
DNP	deoxypentose nucleopro-		side (=DCG)
	teide	DOCM	dilatative obstructive car-
DNP	deoxyribonucleoproteide		diomyopathy
DNP	2,4-dinitrophenol	DOD	Department of Defense;
DNPH	2,4-dinitrophenyl hydra-		"Pentagon"
	zine	DOD	dopamine decarboxylase
DNPM	dinitrophenylmorphine	DOE	deoxyephedrine
D-N ratio	dextrose-nitrogen ratio	DOE	dyspnea on exertion
	(=D/N, G/N)	DOG	2-deoxy-D-glucose
DNS	Desoxyribonukleinsäure	DOG	Deutsche Ophthalmolo-
	(G); deoxyribonucleic acid (=DNA)		gische Gesellschaft; Ger- man Ophthalmologic
DNTP	diethyl-p-nitrophenyl-thio-		Society
	phosphate, parathion, E 605	DOG	Deutsche Orthopädische Gesellschaft; German
DO	densité optique (F); optical		Orthopedic Society
	density	DOGP	2-deoxy-d-glucose-6-phos-
DO	diamine oxidase		phate
DO, do *(dent)*	disto-occlusal	DOLV	double outlet left ventricle
		DOM	dimethoxy-4 -dimethyl-
D.O.	Diploma in Ophthalmol-		phenethylamine
	ogy (UK)	DOM	2,5-dimethoxy-4-methyl-
D.O.	Diploma in Optometry		amphetamine
D.O.	Doctor of Ophthalmology	DOMA	3,4-dihydroxymandelic
D.O.	Doctor of Osteopathy		acid
DOA	dead on arrival	DOMF	2,7-dibromo-4-hydroxy-
DOA	dioctyladipinate		mercurifluorescein
DO[a]	Dombrock factor, antigen Do[a]	D.O.M.S.	Diploma in Ophthalmic Medicine and Surgery
DOAC *(bact)*	Dubois oleic albumin com- plex		(UK)
		DON	6-diazo-5-oxo-L-norleucine
DOAP	dihydroxyacetone phos- phate (=DAP)	DOP	dihydroxyacetone phos- phate (=DOAP)

DOP	dioctylphthalate	DP	diffusion pressure
DOPA, Dopa	3,4-dioxyphenylalanine	DP	digestible protein
		DP	diphosgene
DOPAC	3,4-dihydroxyphenylacetic acid	DP	diphosphate
		DP	dipropionate
DOPA-DC	dioxyphenylalanine decarboxylase	DP	dispensing (or dosing) pump
Dopamine	dihydroxyphenylethylamine	DP	displaced person
		DP,dp (dent)	distopulpal
DOPET	Doppler-echocardiographic systolic ejection time	DP	donor plasma
		DP	dorsal pulse
D.Oph.	Doctor of Ophthalmology (=D.O.)	DP (card)	double product, pressure-rate index (=PRI)
DOPS	dihydroxyphenylserine	D.P.	Doctor of Pharmacy
DOR (gyn)	decreased ovarian reserve (cp. AOR)	d.p.	directione propria (L); with proper directions (=dir.prop.)
DOR	Digital Optical Recording		
-dornase	-deoxyribonuclease (e.g. streptodornase)	d.p. (rad)	dorso-plantar
		d.p.	dry pint (USA)
D.Orth.	Diploma in Orthodontics (UK)	DPA	diphenylamine
		DPA	dipicolinic acid
DORV	double outlet right ventricle	DPA (pharm)	dipropylacetate
DORV-TB	DORV Taussig-Bing type	DPA	D-penicillamine, 3-mercapto-D-valine
D.Orth.	Diploma in Orthodontics		
DOS	dioctylsebacate	DPA	dual-photon absorptiometry
DOS	Disk Operating System		
dos.	dose, dosage (=D.)	D.P.A.	Diploma in Public Administration
D.O.S.	Doctor of Ocular Science; Doctor of Optometric Science	DPAI	drug protein activity index
DOSC (bact)	Dubois oleic serum complex	DP$_{AO}$	diastolic aortic pressure
		DPAP	diastolic pulmonary artery pressure
DOSS	dioctylsodium sulfosuccinate (=DSS)	DPAR	diphenylamine reaction
DOSS	distal over-shoulder strap	DPAR	direct passive Arthus reaction
dos.tol.	dosis tolerata (L); tolerated dose	DPC	diethylpyrocarbonate (=DEPC)
dos.tox.	dosis toxica (L); toxic dose	DPD	Department of Public Dispensary
DOTC	6D-deoxy-5A-hydroxytetracycline (doxycycline)	DPD	diphenamide
DOX	digoxin	DPD	3,3-diphosphono-1,2-propane-dicarboxylic acid
DOX	doxephrine		
DOZ	dioctylazelate	D.P.D.	Diploma in Public Dentistry
DP	deep pulse		
DP	dementia praecox (L)		
DP	diastolic pressure		

dp/dt	differential quotient of pressure change against time	DPLa, dpla *(dent)*	distopulpolabial
dp/dv	volume elasticity coefficient	DPM	dipyramidole
		DPM	dipyrromethene
DPF	Dental Practitioners' Formulary	DPM	discontinue previous medication
DPF	diisopropylfluorophosphate (= DFP),	dpm, DPM	disintegrations per minute
DPG	Deutsche Pathologische (Physikalische, Physiologische, Psychoanalytische) Gesellschaft; German Society of Pathology (Physics, Physiology, Psychoanalytics)	D.P.M.	Doctor of Podiatric Medicine
		DPN	diphosphopyridine nucleotide (see NAD)
		DPND	diphosphopyridine nucleotide diaphorase
		DPNH	reduced form of DPN (see NADH)
DPG	2,3-diphosphoglycerate	DPNM	diphenylnaphthylmethane
DPGM	diphosphoglyceromutase	DPOx	diphenol oxidase
DPH	Department of Public Health	DPP	differential pulse polarography
DPH	diphenylhydantoin, phenytoin	DPPD	diphenyl-p-phenylenediamine
D.P.H.	Diploma in Public Health (UK)	DPPH	diphenylpicrylhydrazyl
D.P.H.	Doctor of Public Health (USA)	DPPK	dephospho-phosphorylase kinase
D.Ph.	Doctor of Philosophy (usually: Ph.D.)	DPR *(gyn)*	date premières règles (F); date of first menstrual period, menarche
DPhG	Deutsche Pharmakologische Gesellschaft; German Pharmacological Society	DPR	diaminopropionic acid
		DPS *(chir)*	delayed primary suture
		dps, DPS	disintegrations per second
DPhG	Deutsche Pharmazeutische Gesellschaft; German Pharmaceutical Society	DPSM *(card)*	diastolic posterior septal motion
		DPT	diphenylthiourea
D.Ph.M.	Diploma in Pharmaceutical Medicine	DPT	diphosphothiamine
		DPT	diphtheria-pertussis-tetanus (vaccine)
DPHR	dihydropteridine reductase	DPT	dipropyltryptamine
D.Phys. Med.	Diploma in Physical Medicine	dpt	diopter (= D)
		DPTI *(card)*	diastolic pressure time index
DPIA	dimethoxyphenylisopropylamine	DPTI/TTI	diastolic pressure time index/tension time index
DPIP	dichlorophenolindophenol (= DCPIP)	DQ	deterioration quotient
		DQ	development quotient
DPL, dpl *(dent)*	distopulpolingual	Dq	equivalent dose
		d.q.	dry quart (USA)

DQE *(rad)*	detective quantum efficiency	DS	dehydroepiandrosterone sulfate
DR	degeneration reaction (=CRD, DeR)	DS	density standard
		DS	desmosome
DR *(obst)*	Delivery Room	DS	diabetic serum factors
DR *(gyn)*	dernières règles (F); last menstrual period	DS	dilute strength
		DS	dimethylaminostilbene (=DMASt, DMST)
DR	diabetic retinopathy		
DR	diagnostic radiology	DS	dioptric strength
DR	dihydrofolic acid reductase	DS	disseminated sclerosis
DR	dorsal root	DS	donor serum
dR	deoxyribose (=dRib)	DS, ds	double-stranded (DNA)
dr	dram, drachm	DS	double strength
D.R.	Diploma in Radiology (UK)	DS	Down syndrome
drag.	dragée (F); sugar-coated tablet	DS	dumping syndrome
		DS	systolic diameter (of the heart)
DRC	dynamic range compression		
		D.S.	Doctor of Sciences
D.R.C.O.G.	Diplomate of the Royal College of Obstetricians and Gynaecologists	D/S	dextrose in saline
		D/S *(psych)*	dominance and submission
		DSA	digital subtraction angiography
DRF *(phys)*	dose reduction factor		
DRG	Deutsche Röntgen Gesellschaft; German Röntgen Society	DSA$_{IA}$	intra-arterial digital subtraction angiography
		DSAS	discrete subaortic stenosis (=DMSS)
DRG	dynamic radiography		
dRib	deoxyribose (=dR)	DSC	disodium cromoglycate (=DNCG, DSCG)
DRK	Deutsches Rotes Kreuz; German Red Cross		
		D.S.C.	Doctor of Surgical Chiropody
DRM	dosis reagens minima (L); minimum reacting dose		
		D.Sc.	Doctor of Sciences
DRNA	deoxyribonucleic acid (=DNA)	DSCG	disodium cromoglycate (=DNCG, DSC)
DRO	Disablement Resettlement Officer	DSD	dry sterile dressing
		dsDNA	double-stranded DNA
DRP	deoxyribophosphate	DSFI *(psych)*	Derogatis Sexual Functioning Inventory
DRP *(neur)*	dorsal root potential (=DRR)		
		DSI	dermatitis seborrhoides infantum (L); seborrhoic dermatitis of infants
Dr.P.H.	Doctor of Public Health (=D.P.H.)		
DRQ	discomfort relief quotient	DSI	Digital Speech Interpolation
DRR *(neur)*	dorsal root reflex (=DRP)		
DRS	Diabetic Retinopathy Study (USA)	DSIP	delta sleep inducing peptide
D.R.V.O.	Deputy Regional Veterinary Officer	DSM	Diagnostic and Statistical Manual (of Mental Disorders)
DS	dead (air) space (=D)		

DSM	dihydrostreptomycin (=DHSM, DST)	DT	diphtheria-tetanus vaccine
DSMR	digital-subtracted magnetic resonance	DT	distance test
		DT	duration of tetany
d.s.n.	detur suo nomine (L); label with patient's name	dT	deoxythymidine (=dThd)
		D/T	deaths – total ratio
DSP	digital subtraction phlebography	D4T	2',3'-didehydro-2',3'-dideoxythymidinene (=ddeThd, DHT)
DSP	disulfanilamidophenolphthalein	DTA	descending thoracic aorta
		DTA	differential thermoanalysis
DSPECT	dynamic single photon emission computerized tomography	DTC	(sodium) diethyldithiocarbamate (=DDC, DDTC)
DS prosthesis	drum-to-stapes prosthesis	DTDP, dTDP	deoxythymidine diphosphate
DSPS	delayed sleep phase syndrome	DTE	dithioerythritol
		DTG	differential thermogravimetry
DSR	diastolic synchronized retroperfusion	d-TGA	dextro-transposition of the great arteries (cp. l-TGA)
DSRS	Dynamic Spatial Reconstruction System	DTH	delayed-type hypersensitivity
DSS	dioctylsodium sulfosuccinate (=DOSS)	D.T.H.	Diploma in Tropical Hygiene (UK)
DSS	discrete subaortic stenosis (=DSAS, DMSS)	dThd	deoxythymidine (=dT)
DSS agar	dextrose-starch-saccharose agar	3-D therapy	classical therapy of heart failure with digitalis, diuretics, and diet (=DDD)
D.S.Sc.	Diploma in Sanitary Science (UK)		
DST	Daylight Saving Time	DTI	diastolic time interval
DST (psych)	desensitization time	DTIC	5-(3,3-dimethyl-1-triazeno)-imidazole-4-carboxamide
DST	dexamethasone suppression test		
DST	dihydrostreptomycin (=DHSM, DSM)	D.T.M.	Diploma in Tropical Medicine (UK)
DST agar	diagnostic sensitivity test agar	D.T.M.	Doctor of Tropical Medicine
DSTE	diethylstilbestrol	D.T.M.H.	Diplomate of Tropical Medicine and Hygiene (UK)
DS test	digit symbol test		
DSUH	direct suggestion under hypnosis	DTMP, dTMP	deoxythymidine monophosphate
DSV	digital subtraction ventriculography	DTN	diphtheria toxin normal (Schick test)
DT	delirium tremens		
DT	deoxyribosylthymine	DTNB	5,5-dithionitrobenzene
DT	diastolic (filling) time	DTNB	5,5'-dithio-bis(2-nitrobenzoic acid)
DT	digitoxin (=DTX)		

D_{tox}	Dosis toxica (L); toxic dose (=dos.tox.)	DUS	Doppler ultrasound (flow detector)
DTP	Desktop Publishing	DUTP,	deoxyuridine triphosphate
DTP	diphtheria-tetanus-pertussis vaccine	dUTP	
		DV	dependant variable
DTP	distal tingling on percussion	DV	dilute volume
		DV	direct voltage
DTPA	diethylene triamine penta-acetate	DV *(vet)*	distemper virus
		DV	double vibrations
DTPT	dithiopropylthiamine	d.v. *(rad)*	dorso-ventral
DTR	deep tendon reflex	d.v. *(rad)*	dorso-volar
DTR	diagnostic thyroxine ratio	D+V	diarrhea and vomiting
DTT	diphtheria-tetanus toxoid	DVA	duration of voluntary apnea (test)
DTT	dithiothreitole		
DTTAB	vaccin antidiphthérique, antitétanique, antitypho-parathyphoidique A et B (F); vaccine for diphtheria, tetanus, typhoid and paratyphoid fever type A and B	DVD	double vessel disease (of the heart)
		D.V.H.	Diploma in Veterinary Hygiene
		DVI *(rad)*	digital vascular imaging
		D.V.M.	Doctor of Veterinary Medicine (USA)
DTTP,	deoxythymidine triphosphate		
dTTP		D.V.M.S.	Doctor of Veterinary Medicine and Surgery
D.T.V.M.	Diploma in Tropical Veterinary Medicine	DVOR	Doppler very high frequency omni-range
D type *(psych)*	disintegration type		
		DVR	Department of Vocational Rehabilitation
DTX	digitoxin		
DU	density unknown	DVR *(chir)*	double valve replacement
DU	diagnosis undetermined	D.V.S.	Doctor of Veterinary Surgery (USA)
DU	dog unit		
DU	duodenal ulcer	D.V.S.	Doctor of Veterinary Science (also: D.V.Sc.)
dU	deoxyuridine, uridine deoxyriboside (=dUrd)		
		DVSA	digital video subtraction angiography
dU	daily urine, 24-h urine		
D4U	2',3'-didehydro-2',3'-dideoxyuridinene (=ddeUrd, DHU)	D.V.Sc.	Doctor of Veterinary Science (also: D.V.S.)
		D.V.S.M.	Diploma in Veterinary State Medicine
DUB	dysfunctional uterine bleeding		
		DVSP	digital video subtraction phlebography
DUDP,	deoxyuridine diphosphate		
dUDP		DVT	deep vein thrombosis
DUMP,	deoxyuridine monophosphate	DVV	diastolic ventricular volume
dUMP			
DUNHL	diffuse undifferentiated non-Hodgkin lymphoma	DW	distilled water (=Aq.dest.)
		D/W	dextrose in water
dURD	deoxyuridine, uridine deoxyriboside (=dU)	DWT	diastolic wall thickness
		Dx	diagnosis

dX, dXao	deoxyxanthosine, xanthosine deoxyriboside
DXM	dexamethasone (test)
DXRT	deep x-ray therapy
DZ	dizygotic
dz.	dozen
D.Z.	Doctor of Zoology

E

E	Einheit (G); unit
E	Einstein (photochemical unit)
E *(card)*	ejection click
E	ectropion
E	elasticity modulus (of vessels)
E *(phys)*	electromotive force
E	electron ($= e^-$)
E *(ophth)*	emmetropia ($=$ Em.)
E *(phys)*	energy
E	enzyme
E	epinephrine (adrenaline)
E	erythema
E	erythrocyte
E *(bact)*	Escherichia
E *(chem)*	ester
E	extinction coefficient
e *(phys)*	electric elementary loading
e$^+$	positron
e$^-$	electron ($=$ E)
EA	early antigens
EA	educational age
EA *(chir)*	enteroanastomosis
EA	epiandrosterone
EA	erythrocyte antibody
EA	estivo-autumnal (type of malaria caused by Plasmodium falciparum)
EA	ethyl alcohol, ethanol
EA	extralemniscal myelotomy
EAA	essential amino acids

EAA	European Academy of Anaesthesiology
EAACI	European Academy of Allergology and Clinical Immunology
EABF	efferent arteriole blood flow
EAC	erythrocyte antibody complement
EAC	external auditory canal ($=$ EAM)
EACA	epsilon-aminocaproic acid
EACD	eczematous allergic contact dermatitis
EACR	European Association of Cancer Research
EAD *(phys)*	electron attachment detector
EAE	experimental allergic encephalomyelitis
EAEC *(bact)*	enteroadherent Escherichia coli
EAEM	experimental allergic encephalomyelitis
EAES	European Atomic Energy Society
EAG, Eag	electroatriogram
EAHF	eczema, asthma, hay fever complex
EAI	erythrocyte aggregation index
EAI	erythrocyte antibody rosette inhibition
EAM	external acoustic meatus ($=$ EAC)
EAMF	Europäische Akademie für Medizinische Fortbildung (G); European Academy of Medical Education
EAMFS	European Association for Maxillo-Facial Surgery
EAN	European Article Number
EAN	experimental allergic neuritis
EANM	European Association of Nuclear Medicine

EAO	European Association of Orthodontists	EBB	endobronchial biopsy
EAO	experimental allergic orchitis	EBC	ethylbenzyl chloride
		EBF	erythroblastosis fetalis
EAOS	European Association of Oral Surgeons	EBF	estimated blood flow
		EBI	emetine bismuth iodide
EAP	electro-acupuncture	EBI	ergosterol biosynthesis inhibition
EAP	epiallopregnanolone		
EAP	ß-ethanolamino-phosphoric acid	EBL	estimated blood loss
		EBM	expressed breast milk
EAP	(combination of) etoposide, adriamycin, and cis-platinum	EBMT	European Cooperative Group for Bone Marrow Transplantation
EAP	evoked action potential	EBNA	Epstein-Barr nucleotide antigen
EAR, EaR	Entartungsreaktion (G); reaction of degeneration	EBS	electric brain stimulator
EART	early apex-cardiographic relaxation time	EBS	Emergency Bed Service
		EBT	p-ethylsulfonyl benzalde-hyde thiosemicarbazone
EAS	European Atherosclerosis Society	EBV	Epstein-Barr virus
EASD	European Association for the Study of Diabetes (London)	EC	eclampsia convulsiva
		EC	effective concentration
		EC (lab)	egg culture
		EC	electron capture
EASL	European Association for the Study of the Liver	EC (pharm)	enteric-coated
		EC	entering complaint
EAT	Ehrlich ascites tumor	EC, E.C.	Enzyme Commission (of IUB)
EAT	enzyme antibody technique		
		EC	ethyl cellulose
EAT	epidermolysis acuta toxica	EC	expiratory center
EATA	European Association for Transactional Analysis	EC	extracellular
		E/C	estrogen-creatinine ratio
EAV	electro-acupuncture according to Voll	ECA	electrical control activity
		ECAO	enteric cytopathogenic avian orphan (virus)
EAVNC	enhanced atrioventricular nodal conduction		
		ECAT	emission computerized axial tomography
EB	ectopic beat		
EB	elementary body	ECbG	electrocerebellogram
EB	endoplasmic bubble	ECBO	European Cell Biology Organization
EB	Epstein-Barr (virus) (=EBV)		
		ECBO	enteric cytopathogenic bovine orphan (virus)
EB	erythroblast		
EB (pharm)	estradiol benzoate	ECC	electrocorticogram
EB (pharm)	ethidium bromide	ECC	emergency cardiac care
EBA	ethoxy-benzoic acid	ECC	external cardiac compression
EBAB	Epstein-Barr antibodies		
EBAD, Ebad	exfoliative broncho-alveolar disease	ECC	extracorporeal circulation

ECCE	Exposiciones Congresos y Convenciones de Espana (S); Congress and Convention Exposition Service of Spain (Madrid)	ECHO	echoencephalogram (ultrasound technique)
ECCE *(ophth)*	extra-capsular cataract extraction	ECHO	enteric cytopathogenic human orphan (virus)
EC cells	enterochromaffin cells	ECI	echoventriculographic contraction index
ECCO	enteric cytopathogenic cat orphan (virus)	ECI	effective conductivity index
ECCO	European Cardiology Congress Organization	ECI	extracorporeal irradiation
ECCO$_2$R	extracorporeal CO$_2$ removal	ECL cells	enterochromaffin-like cells
ECD	echocardiographic contrast defect	ECLSO	European Contact Lens Society of Ophthalmologists
ECD	electron capture detector (gas chromatography)	ECM	erythema chronicum migrans
ECD	endocardial cushion defect	EC mixture	ether-chloroform mixture
ECDEU	Early Clinical Drug Evaluation Units	ECMO	enteric cytopathogenic monkey orphan (virus)
ECDO	enteric cytopathogenic dog orphan (virus)	ECMO	extracorporeal membrane oxygenation
E cell	epsilon cell (of the anterior pituitary)	ECO	electron-coupled oscillator
E cell	erythematosus cell (= LE cell)	ECOAA	European Congress on Obstetrical Anaesthesia and Analgesia
ECEO	enteric cytopathogenic equine orphan (virus)	ECOC	European Congress on Optical Communication
ECF	eosinophil chemotactic factor (cp. ECFA)	ECochG	electrocochleography
ECF	Extended Care Facility	ECoG	electrocorticography (= ECC, ECG)
ECF	extracellular fluid	ECO mixture	mixture of ethylesters of chaulmoogra oil, camphor, creosote, and olive oil
ECFA	eosinophil chemotactic factor of anaphylaxis	ECP	emergency charge potential
ECFMG	Educational Council for Foreign Medical Graduates (USA)	ECP	erythropoietic coproporphyria
ECFMS	Educational Commission for Foreign Medical Students (USA)	ECP	estradiol cyclopentane propionate
ECFV	extracellular fluid volume	ECP	external counter pulsation
ECG	electrocorticogram (= ECC, ECoG)	ECP	(free) cytoporphyrin in erythrocytes
ECG, E.C.G.	electrocardiogram, electrocardiography	ECPG	electrochemical potential gradient (= ECPOG)
		ECPO	enteric cytopathogenic porcine orphan (virus) (= ECSO)

ECPOG	electrochemical potential gradient ($=$ECPG)	EDC	ethylene dichloride
E-CR *(imm)*	erythrocyte receptor for complement ($=$CR)	EDC	expected date of confinement
ECRO	enteric cytopathogenic rodent orphan (virus)	EDCF	endothelium-derived constricting factor
ECS	electroconvulsive shock	EDCR	end-diastolic count rate
ECS	extracellular space	EDD	end-diastolic diameter
ECSO	enteric cytopathogenic swine (suis) orphan ($=$ECPO)	EDD *(obst)*	expected date of delivery
		EDDHA	ethylenediamine-di-(ortho)-hydroxyphenylacetate
ECSS	European Coronary Surgery Study	EDFL	end-diastolic fiber length ($=$EDL)
ECT	electroconvulsive therapy ($=$EST)	EDG	electrodermatogram
ECT	emission computer tomography	EDG	electrodurogram
		EDH	epidural hematoma
ECT	enteric coated tablet	EDI	eosinophil-derived inhibitor (of histamine release), prostaglandin E
ECTA	European Conference on Thermal Analyses		
ECTEOLA	epichlorhydrine triethanolamine	EDL	end-diastolic length ($=$EDFL)
ECU, Ecu	environmental control unit	EDN	electrodesiccation
ECU	European Chiropractic Union	EDP	electronic data processing
		EDP	end-diastolic pressure
ECU	European Currency Unit	EDPAP	end-diastolic pulmonary artery pressure
ECV	electro-cardioversion		
ECV	extracellular volume	EDPM	electronic data processing machine
ECW	extracellular water		
ED *(pharm)*	effective dose	EDR	effective direct radiation
ED	electrodiagnosis ($=$EDx)	EDR	electrodermal response
ED *(pharm)*	emetic dose	EDRF	endothelium-derived relaxing factor
ED *(biochem)*	Entner-Doudoroff (pathway)		
ED	epidural	EDS	Ehlers-Danlos syndrome
ED *(rad)*	erythema dose	EDS *(psych)*	Erlangen Depression Scale
ED *(chem)*	ethyl dichlorarsine	EDSL	end-diastolic segment length
Ed., Eds.	editor(s)		
ED$_{50}$	mean effective dose	EDTA	ethylene diamine tetraacetate
EDA	electrodermal activity		
EDA	end-diastolic activity	EDTA	European Dialysis and Transplant Association
EDAP	end-diastolic aortic pressure		
		EDTNA	European Dialysis and Transplant Nurses Association
EDAS	early detectable arteriosclerosis		
EDB *(clin)*	early dry breakfast	EDV	elektronische Datenverarbeitung (G); electronic data processing ($=$EDP)
EDB	ethylene dibromide		
		EDV	end-diastolic volume

EDVI	end-diastolic volume index	EF *(pharm)*	etafenone
EDWS	end-diastolic wall stress	EF	excretion fraction (of the kidney)
EDWT	end-diastolic wall thickness	EF	exophthalmogenic factor (= EPA, EPF, EPS)
EDx	electrodiagnosis (= ED)	EF	extrinsic factor
EDXA	energy dispersive x-ray analysis	eF	elastic fiber
EE	embryo extract	EFA	essential fatty acids
EE	endogenous eczema	EFA	euglobulin fibrinolytic activity
EE	equine encephalitis	E factor	erythematosus factor (= LE factor)
EE	exudative enteropathy	EFC	endogenous fecal calcium
EE	eye and ear	EFE	endocardial fibroelastosis
E-E	erythematous-edematous (reaction)	EFI	extended field irradiation
EEA *(chir)*	end-end anastomosis	EFM	electronic fetal monitoring
EEC	European Economic Community	EFMI	European Federation of Medical Information (= FEIM)
EEC	European Endometriosis Classification	EFMK	European Federation of Masseurs and Kinesitherapists
EECO	European Endoscopy Congress	EFP	effective filtration pressure
EEC syndrome	ectrodactylism, ectodermal dysplasia, clefting	EFPIA	European Federation of Pharmaceutical Industry Associations
EEDTA	2,2'-bis-(diacetylamino)-diethylether (= BAETA)	EFPW	European Federation for the Protection of Waters
EEE	eastern equine encephalomyelitis	EFR	effective filtration rate
EEG	electroencephalogram	EFR	examen (épreuve) de la fonction respiratoire (F); respiratory function test
EEL	emergency exposure limits	EG	echinococcus granulosus
EEM	erythema exsudativum multiforme	e.g.	exempli gratia (L); for instance, for example
EE3ME	ethinylestradiol-3-methylether	EGA	elephantiasis genito-anorectalis, elephantiasis venerea, "esthiomène"
EENT	eye, ear, nose, and throat	EGA	error grid analysis
EE plasmodia	exoerythrocytic plasmodia (malaria)	EGB	endothelium glia barrier
EES	Electroencephalographic Society	EGEG	electrogastroenterogram
EES	ethyl ethanesulfate	EGF	epidermal growth factor
EEV *(chir)*	encircling endocardial ventriculotomy	EGFR	epidermal growth factor receptor
EF	edema factor	EGG	electrogastrogram
EF *(card)*	ejection fraction	EGMA	eosinophil growth and maturation activity
EF *(gen)*	elongation factor		
EF	encephalitogenic factor		
EF	equivalent focus		
EF	essential fructosuria		

EGOT	erythrocyte glutamate oxal-acetate transaminase		EHP	extra high potency
EGPC	Europäische Gesellschaft für plastische Chirurgie (G); European Society of Plastic Surgery		EHPF	estimated hepatic plasma flow
			EHPT	Eddy hot plate test
			EHR	evoked heart rate response
EGT	euglobulin test		EHSDS	Experimental Health Service Delivery System
EGTA	ethyleneglycol-bis-ß-ami-noethylether-N,N,N',N'-tetraacetic acid		EHTC	electro-hydro-thermo-coagulation
EH	enlarged heart		EI	eccentricity index
EH	entameba histolytica		EI	excretion index
EH	eosin-hematoxylin (stain-ing) (=HE)		EI	imminent eclampsia
			E/I	expiration/inspiration
EH	essential hypertension		EIA	enzyme immunoassay
E+H *(psych)*	environment and heredity		EIA	equine infectious anemia (virus)
EHA	encéphalite humaine aigue (F); acute human ence-phalomyelitis		EIA	exercise-induced asthma
			EIAB	extra-intracranial arterial bypass
EHAA	epidemic hepatitis asso-ciated antigen		EIC	espace intercostal (F); intercostal space
EHBF	estimated hepatic blood flow		EICT	external isovolumic con-traction time
EHBF	extrahepatic blood flow		EID	electro-immunodiffusion
EHC	enterohepatic circulation		EIEC *(bact)*	enteroinvasive Escherichia coli
EHC	enterophepatic clearance			
EHD *(vet)*	epizootic hemorrhagic dis-ease (of poultry)		EIF	erythropoiesis inhibiting factor
EHDP	ethylidene-1-hydroxy-1,1-diphosphonate		EIM	excitability inducing mate-rial
EHEC *(bact)*	enterohemorrhagic Esche-richia coli		EIN	excitatory interneuron
			EIP	end-expiratory plateau
EHF	epidemic hemorrhagic fever		EIRnv	extra incidence rate in non-vaccinated groups
EHF	exophthalmus hyperthy-roid factor		EIRv	extra incidence rate in vac-cinated groups
EHF	extremely high frequency (in electrotherapy) (=mmW)		EIS	Epidemiological Investiga-tional Service
			EISA	EEG-interval spectrum analysis
EHL	effective half-life		EIT	erythrocyte incorporation test
EHL	essential hyperlipidemia, Bürger-Grütz syndrome			
			EIT	erythroid iron turnover
EHP, ehp	effective horse power		EITB *(lab)*	enzyme-linked immuno-electric transfer blot
EHP	di-(2-ethylhexyl) hydrogen phosphate		EIVA	exercise-induced ventricu-lar arrhythmia

EJ	elbow jerk
EJC	epitheloid juxtaglomerular cells
EJC	European Journal of Cardiology (official abbreviation: Eur. J. Card.)
EJP	excitatory junction potential
EKC	epidemic keratoconjunctivitis
EKG	Elektrokardiogramm (G); ECG
EKY, EKyG	electrokymogram
EL	erythroleukemia
EL	exercise limit
e_L	lysine exponent (bacteriophage titer)
ELAS	extended lymphadenopathy syndrome
ELAVIA	enzyme-linked LAV-immunoassay
ELB (clin)	early light breakfast
ELC	electrocoagulation
ELC system	encapsulated liquid crystals system
ELDOR (phys)	electron-electron double resonance
ELIEDA	enzyme-linked immuno-electrodiffusion assay
ELISA	enzyme-linked immunosorbent assay (= EIA)
Elphor	electrophoresis
ELR	epidermis/lymphocyte reaction
ELRT	endolymphatic radionuclide therapy
ELVP	external left ventricular pressure
ELW	extravascular lung water
EM	elasticity modulus (= E)
EM	electrometer
EM	electron microscopy
EM	electrophoretic mobility
EM (biochem)	Embden-Meyerhof (glycolytic pathway) (see also: EMP)
EM	endomyocardium
EM (mil)	enlisted men (of US Army)
EM	enterovirus meningitis
EM	erythema multiforme
EM	erythromycin
Em	emanation
Em.	emmetropia (= E)
E + M	endocrine and metabolism
EMA	exophthalmus-myxedema-acropachy (syndrome)
EMAT cells	Ehrlich mouse ascites tumor cells
EMB	endomyocardial biopsy
EMB	eosin-methylene blue (agar)
EMB	ethambutol
EMBL	European Molecular Biology Laboratory (Heidelberg/Germany)
EMBO	European Molecular Biology Organization
EMC	encephalomyocarditis
EMC	erythromycin
EMCRO	Experimental Medical Care Review Organization
EMCU	excretion micturition cysto-urethrogram
EMD	erythema migrans disease
EME	elektromagnetische Einheit (G); electromagnetic unit (= EMU)
EMERA	Estudio Multicentrico Estreptoquinasa – Republica Argentina (S); Multicenter Streptokinase Study – Republic of Argentina
EMF	electromagnetic field
EMF	electromagnetic flowmeter
EMF	electromotive force
EMF	endomyocardial fibrosis
EMF	erythrocyte maturation factor
EMFRPT	European Multifactorial Risk Prevention Trial
EMG	electromyogram
EMG	exomphalos-macroglossia-gigantism (syndrome)

EMI	electromagnetic interference
EMI	electromechanical interval
EMI	electro-myointegral
EMIC *(obst)*	Emergency Maternity and Infant Care
EMIP	European Myocardial Infarction Project
EMIT	enzyme-multiplied immunotechnique
EMIT	erythrocyte migration inhibition test
EML, emL	electromagnetic loading unit
EMMA	electron microscope and microprobe analysis
EMMA	Engström Multigas Monitor for Anesthesia
EMMV	extended mandatory minute volume
EMO	Epstein-MacIntosh-Oxford (inhalation device) (cp. Emotril)
EMO	thyroid-pituitary syndrome (with exophthalmus, myxedema, and hypertrophic osteoarthropathy
Emotril	Epstein-MacIntosh-Oxford (inhaler for anesthesia with trichloroethylene = Trilene) (cp. EMO device)
EMP	electromagnetic pulse
Empl.	emplastrum (L); plaster
EMP	Embden-Meyerhof-Parnas (glycolysis scheme)
EMP	encephalitogenic myelin protein
EMRO	European Media Research Organization
EMS	early morning specimen
EMS *(card)*	electromechanical systole
EMS	Emergency Medical Service (UK)
EMS	ethylmethane sulfonate
EMSA	Electron Microscopy Society of America

EMT	electrophoretic mobility test
EMT	Emergency Medical Technician
EMU, emu	electromagnetic unit
EMV	endomyocardial ventriculotomy (= EEV)
EMV	extended mandatory ventilation
EMW	electromagnetic wave
EN	efferent neuron
EN	enolase (= Eno, ENOL)
EN	erythema nodosum
en	enema
ENA	European Neuroscience Associations
ENA	extractable nuclear antigen
END	enhancement Newcastle disease
ENDOR	electron-nuclear double resonance
ENE	ethylnorepinephrine
ENEA	European Neuroendocrine Association
ENEA	European Nuclear Energy Agency
ENG	electroneurogram
ENG	electronystagmogram
ENG	N-ethyl-N-nitroso-N-nitroguanidine
ENI	Electro-Nucleonics Industry
ENK	enkephalin
ENL	erythema nodosum leprosum
ENM	electronystagmometer
ENMS	European Nuclear Medicine Society
Eno, ENOL	enolase (= EN)
ENP	ethyl-p-nitrophenylthiobenzene phosphate
ENR	extrathyroidal neck radioactivity
ENT	Ears, Nose, and Throat
env *(gen)*	envelope
EO	ethylene oxide
EOA	epidural opiate anesthesia

91

EOA *(clin)*	examination, opinion, advice	EPA	exophthalmus-producing activity (= EF, EPF, EPS)
EOAS	esophageal obturator airway system	EPAP	expiratory positive airway pressure
EOCCD	European Organization for the Control of Circulatory Diseases	EPC	epilepsia partialis continua (Kojewnikoff)
E of M	error of measurement	EPCL	ectopic pacemaker cycle length
EOG	electro-oculogram	EPE	empirical parameter evaluation
EOG	electro-olfactogram		
EOL	end of life (of a cardiac pacemaker)	EPEC *(bact)*	enteropathogenic Escherichia coli
EOLI	end of life indicator	EPF	early pregnancy factor
EOM	external ocular muscles	EPF	endocarditis parietalis fibroplastica
EOM	extraocular movement		
EOP	early onset pneumonia	EPF	exophthalmus-producing factor (= EF, EPA, EPS)
EOP	endogenous opioid peptide		
EOQC	European Organization for Quality Control	EPF	expiratory peak flow
		EPG	eggs per gram (parasitology)
EORBS	earth orbiting recoverable biological satellite	EPG	electropherogram
EORTC	European Organization for Research and Treatment of Cancer	EPG	electropupillography
		E phenomenon	erythematosus phenomenon (= LE phenomenon)
EOS	European Orthodontic Society	EPH	essential pulmonary hemosiderosis
Eos.	eosinophils	EPH	toxemia of pregnancy with edema, proteinuria, and hypertension
EOTA	ethylene-bis-(hydroxyethylene-nitrilo)tetra-acetate		
EOU	epidemic observation unit	Ephoresis	electrophoresis
EP	ectopic pregnancy (= EU)	EPI *(psych)*	Eysenck Personality Inventory
EP	electrophoresis		
EP	endogenous pyrogen, endotoxin	EPL	essential phospholipids
		E plasmodia	exoerythrocytic plasmodia in malaria (= EE plasmodia)
EP	endpoint		
EP	epoxide		
EP	erythropoietin (= ESF)	EPMS	extrapyramidal motor system
EP	evoked potential		
EP	extreme pressure	EPO	erythropoietin
EP	exudative pericarditis	EPP	end-plate potential
E-4-P	D-erythrose-4-phosphate	EPP	equal pressure point
EPA	eicosapentaenoic acid	EPP	erythropoietic protoporphyria
EPA	Environmental Protection Agency (USA)	EPPS *(psych)*	Edwards Personal Preference Schedule
EPA *(rad)*	erect posterior-anterior	EPR	electron paramagnetic resonance (= ESR, RPE)
EPA	European Patent Agency (Munich/Germany)		

EPR	electrophrenic respiration	ERBF	effective renal blood flow
EPRS	European Paediatric Respiratory Society	ERC	ECHO-rhino-coryza (viruses)
EPS	Elementary Psychology	ERC	endoscopic retrograde cholangiography
EPS	exophthalmus-producing substance (= EF, EPA, EPF)	ERC	erythropoietic responsive cell
EPS	extracellular polymeric substances	ERC	expiratory reserve capacity (= ERV)
EPS	extrapyramidal side-effects	ERCP	elective retrograde cholangiopancreatography
EPS	extrapyramidal system	ERCP	endoscopic retrograde cannulation of the papilla (Vateri)
EPSDT	early and periodical screening, diagnosis, and treatment	ERCS	endoscopic retrograde cholangioscopy
EPSIM	Enquète de Prévention Secondaire de l'Infarctus de Myocarde (F); Secondary Prevention of Myocardial Infarction Research Group	ERD	evoked response detector
		ERDA	Energy Research and Development Administration
EPSP	excitatory post-synaptic potential	E reaction	elimination reaction
EPSS (card)	E-point septal separation	EREIA (imm)	estrogen receptor enzyme-linked immunoassay
EPT	endoscopic papillotomy	ERF	Education and Research Foundation (of the AMA)
EPTS	existing prior to service		
EPV, Epv	encephalitis postvaccinalis	ERG	electroretinogram
EQ	educational quotient	ERI	elective replacement indicator (for pacemaker change)
EQ	energy quotient		
EQ	excitability quotient		
eq	equivalent	ERIA	electroradio-immuno assay
ER	ejection rate	ERICA	Engström Respirator for Intensive Care
ER	electroresection		
ER	Emergency Room	ERICA (imm)	estrogen receptor immuno-cytochemical assay
ER	endoplasmic reticulum		
ER	epigastric region	ERNA	equilibrium radionuclide angiocardiography
ER	equivalent roentgen		
ER	estrogen receptor (ER+, ER-)	ERP (card)	effective refractory period
		ERP	endoscopic radiological pancreaticography
ER	evoked response		
ER	extended release	ERP-AVN	effective refractory period of the AV node
ER	external resistance		
ERA	effective radiating area (of medical devices)	ERPC	endoscopic retrograde pancreatocholangiography (= ERCP)
ERA	Electroshock Research Association		
		ERPF	effective renal plasma flow
ERA (otol)	electric response audiometry (cp. BERA)	ERRT	escape rhythm recovery time

ERT *(card)*	elective replacement time (of a pacemaker)	ESC	Entomological Society of Canada
ERT	Emergency Room Technician	ESC	European Society of Cardiology
ERT	endolymphatic radionuclide therapy	ESCC	electrolyte-steroid cardiopathy by calcification
ERTS	Earth Resources Technology Satellite	ESCH	electrolyte-steroid cardiopathy by hyalinization
ERV, erv	endogenous retrovirus	ESCI	European Society of Clinical Investigation
ERV	expiratory reserve volume ($=$ERC)	ESCN	electrolyte-steroid cardiopathy by necrosis
ERY	erysipelothrix (gram-positive bacteria)	ESCO	European Sterility Congress Organization
Ery	erythrocyte(s)	ESCPB	European Society for Comparative Physiology and Biochemistry
ES	elastic suspensor		
ES	electrical stimulation		
ES	Emergency Service	ESCVS	European Society of Cardiovascular Surgery
ES	endoscopic sphincterotomy	ESD *(card)*	end-systolic (left ventricular) diameter ($=$LVED)
ES	enema saponis (L); soap enema	ESDAC	European Space Data Center (Department of the ESRO, Darmstadt/Germany)
ES	entoderm sinus		
ES	Entomological Society (UK)		
ES	enzyme substrate	ESDR	European Society for Dermatological Research
ES	extrasystole, ectopic beat		
ESA	electrostimulation anesthesia	ESE	elektrostatische Einheit (G); electrostatic unit ($=$ESU)
ESA *(chir)*	end-to-side anastomosis		
		ESF	erythropoiesis-stimulating factor, erythropoietin ($=$EMF)
ESA	Entomological Society of America (USA)		
ESA	European Space Agency	ESG	Europäische Strahlenschutz-Gesellschaft (G); European Society of Radiation Protection
ESA	European Strabismological Association ($=$CESSD)		
ESACT	European Society of Animal Cell Technology		
		ESGCP	European Study Group for Cell Proliferation
ESAO	European Society for Artificial Organs		
ESA test	embryo sinapis alba test	ESH	European Society of Haematology
ESB	electrical stimulation to the brain	ESHRE	European Society of Human Reproduction and Embryology
ESBP	European Society of Biochemical Pharmacology		
ESC	early systolic (aortic valve) closure	ESIMV	expiration synchronized intermittent mandatory ventilation

ESIS	electrical status induced by sleep (electroencephalographic epileptic state)	ESRD	end-stage renal disease
		ESRF	end-stage renal failure
ESL, esL	electrostatic loading unit	ESRIN	European Space Research Institute (Department of the ESRO, Frascati/Italy)
ESL	end-systolic length		
ESLAB	European Space Research Laboratory	ESRO	European Space Research Organization (Paris)
ESN *(psych)*	educationally subnormal	ESRP	European Society of Radiation Protection
ESOC	European Space Operation Center (Darmstadt/Germany)	ESS	electronic switching system
		ESS	end-systolic shoulder (point)
ESP	electrostatic potential		
ESP *(card)*	end-systolic pressure	ESS	end-systolic stress
ESP	eosinophil stimulation promotor	ESSR	European Society for Sleep Research
ESP	extrasensory perception	ESSR	European Society for Surgical Research
ESPE	European Society for Paediatric Endocrinology	EST	electroshock therapy ($=$ ECT)
ESPEN	European Society of Parenteral and Enteral Nutrition	EST	endoscopic sphincterotomy (of the papilla Vateri) ($=$ ES, EPT)
ESPGA	European Society of Paediatric Gastroenterology	EST	European Society of Toxicology
ESPHI	European Society of Paediatric Haematology and Immunology	E stage	exoerythrocytic form of malaria plasmodia ($=$ E plasmodia, EE plasmodia)
ESPID	European Society of Parasitic and Infectious Diseases	ESTEC	European Space Technology Centre
ESPR	European Society of Paediatric Radiology	ESTRO	European Society for Therapeutic Radiology and Oncology
ESPR	European Society for Paediatric Research	ESU, esu	electrostatic unit ($=$ ESE)
ESPVR	end-systolic pressure/volume relation	ESUT	ejectional systolic upstroke time
ESPS	European Society of Plastic Surgery	ESV	end-systolic volume
		ESVI	end-systolic volume index
ESPS	European Stroke Prevention Study	ESWL	extracorporeal shockwave lithotripsy
ESR	Einstein-Stokes radius (of molecular size)	ESWS	end-systolic wall stress
		ESWT	end-systolic wall thickness
ESR	electron spin resonance ($=$ EPR, RPE)	ET	educational therapy
		ET *(card)*	ejection time ($=$ LVET)
ESR	erythrocyte sedimentation rate (or reaction)	ET	endotracheal tube
		ET	epicutaneous testing
		ET	ergotherapy
ESR	European Space Range	ET *(obst)*	estimated term

ET-3	erythrocyte triiodothyronine	ETT	exercise tolerance test
ETA	endotoxin, ectotoxin, anti-ectotoxin	ETU	Emergency and Trauma Unit
ETA	ethionamide (= ETH, ETHA)	ETU	Emergency Treatment Unit
ETA	European Thyroid Association	ETVG	European Tumour Virus Group (Copenhagen)
ETAl	endotoxin-ectotoxin in aluminum hydroxide	EU	entropy unit
et al.	et alii (L); and others, and co-workers	EU	enzyme unit
		EU	extrauterine (pregnancy)
ETC	effective thermal conductivity	EUA	examination under anesthesia
ETC	European Translation Centre (Delft/Holland)	EUL	expected upper limit
etc.	et cetera (L); and so forth	EULAR	European League against Rheumatism
ETCS	European Tissue Culture Society	EUP	erythrocyte uroporphyrin
ETD	erythemogenic threshold dose	EUPSYCA	European Working Group for Psychosomatic Cancer Research
ETDRS	Early Treatment Diabetic Retinopathy Study (cp. DRS)	EURATOM	European Atomic Agency
		EUREM	European Congress on Electron Microscopy
ETEC (bact)	enterotoxigenic Escherichia coli	EUROTOX	European Committee on Chronic Toxicity Hazards
ETF	electron-transferring flavoprotein	EUT	endoscopic ultrasound tomography
ETF	etilefrine	EUV	extreme ultraviolet laser
ETH	Eidgenössische Technische Hochschule (G); Swiss Technical University	EV	erythrocyte volume
		EV	evoked response (= ER)
ETH, ETHA	ethionamide (= ETA)	EV	extrasystole ventriculaire (F); ventricular ectopic beat
ETI	ejection time index	EV	extravascular
ETN	endotracheal narcosis, ... anesthesia (= ITN)	eV	electron volt
		EVA	ethylene vinyl acetate
ETN	erythrityl tetranitrate	EVA	ethyl violet azide
ETP	electron transport particle	EVA	extravehicular activity (in space aviation)
ETPhos	electron transport phosphorylation	EVE	ethyl vinyl ether
		EVG (card)	electroventriculogram
ETR	effective thyroxin ratio	EVG	epigastric vein graft
ETRO	European Thrombosis Research Organization	EVLW	extravascular lung water
		EVP	chemotherapy with endoxane, vincristin, and prednisolone (for non-Hodgkin lymphoma)
ETS	European Teratology Society		
ETT	epinephrine tolerance test	EVR	endocardial viability ratio
		EVR	extravascular resistance

EW	Emergency Ward	f.	female, feminine (=fem.)
EWGCF	European Working Group for Cystic Fibrosis	F_1, F_2	1st, 2nd filial generation
		FA *(chem)*	fatty acid
EWGCP	European Working Group on Cardiac Pacing	FA	febrile antigens
		FA	fetal antigens, fetoproteins
EWL	evaporative water loss	FA	fibrillation auriculaire (F); atrial fibrillation
EWPHE	European Working Party on Hypertension in the Elderly	FA *(mil)*	Field Ambulance
		FA	filterable agent
EXC	excitement, excited	FA	First Aid
exper.	experimental	FA	fluorescein-conjugated pertussis antiserum
EXREM	external radiation dose		
Ext.	extract	FA	fluorescent antibody
ext.	external	FA	folic acid
Ez	eczema	FA	formaldehyde
EZEE	Entectic Zone Electrical Evaluation	FA	formamide
		FA	Freund's adjuvant
		FA	functional activities
		FAA	folic acid activity
		FAA	folic acid antagonists
		FAA	formalin, acetic acid, alcohol (solution)

F

		F.A.A.N.	Fellow of the American Academy of Nursing
F *(phys)*	Fahrenheit		
F *(phys)*	farad, Faraday constant	F.A.A.P.	Fellow of the Amercian Academy of Pediatrics
F	female		
F *(phys)*	fick (unit of diffusion coefficient)	FAB, Fab	antigen-binding fragment
		F-AB	Forssman antibody, heterohemagglutinine
F	field of vision		
F	flow	FAB	French-American-British Working Group for Leukemia Classification
F	flush		
F	focus		
F	force	FAB	functional arm brace
F	formula(ry)	FABER	flexion, abduction and external rotation (test)
F	free		
F	French (catheter size)	FABP	folic acid binding protein
F *(card)*	friction	FAC	cytostatic combination therapy with 5-fluorouracil, adriamycin and cyclophosphamide
F *(phys)*	fusion point (=Fp.)		
f	femto (=10^{-15})		
f *(biol)*	forma (L); form		
f *(phys)*	frequency	FAC *(card)*	fractional area change
f	function	FAC	functional abdominal complaints
F.	Fellow		
F. *(ophth)*	field of vision	F.A.C.A.	Fellow of the American College of Anesthetists
f. *(pharm)*	fac, fiat, fiant (L); make, let it (them) be made		
		F.A.C.C.	Fellow of the American College of Cardiologists

F.A.C.D.	Fellow of the American College of Dentists	F.A.M.A.	Fellow of the American Medical Association
F.A.C.D.S.	Fellow of the Australian College of Dental Surgeons	FAMA test	fluorescent antibody against (varicella-zoster virus) membrane antigen test
F.A.C.F.S.	Fellow of the American College of Foot Surgeons	FAME	fumaric acid monoethylester
F.A.C.M.A.	Fellow of the Australian College of Medical Administrators	FAMMM	familial atypical multiple mole melanoma
F.A.C.O.G.	Fellow of the American College of Obstetricians and Gynecologists	fam.per.par.	familial periodic paralysis
		Fam.Phys.	family physician
		FAN	facteur anti-nucléaire (F); antinuclear factor ($=$ANF)
F.A.C.P.	Fellow of the American College of Physicians	F.A.N.S.	Fellow of the American Neurological Society
F.A.C.R.	Fellow of the American College of Radiologists	F antigen	fertilization antigen
FACS	fluorescence-activated cell sorter	F antigen	fimbriae antigen
		F antigen	Forssman antigen
F.A.C.S.	Fellow of the American College of Surgeons	FANY	First Aid Nursing Yeomanry
F.A.C.S.M.	Fellow of the American College of Sports Medicine	F.A.N.Z.C.P.	Fellow of the Australian and New Zealand College of Psychiatrists
FACT (psych)	Flanagan Aptitude Classification Test	FAO	Food and Agriculture Organization (of the UN) ($=$OAA)
FAD	familial form of Alzheimer's disease		
FAD	flavin adenine dinucleotide ($=$FADN)	F.A.O.T.A.	Fellow of the American Occupational Therapy Association
FADH$_2$	(reduced) flavin adenine dinucleotide	F.A.P.A.	Fellow of the American Psychiatric Association
FADN	flavin adenine dinucleotide ($=$FAD)	F.A.P.A.	Fellow of the American Psychoanalytical Association
FAD FMN	pyrophosphorylase adenylyl transferase	F.A.P.H.A.	Fellow of the American Public Health Association
FAF	fibroblast activating factor	FAR	flight aptitude rating
F-α_2	fast α_2 globulin (immunoelectrophoresis)	FAR	fluorescent antibody reaction
F.A.G.O.	Fellow of the Academy of Gynaecology and Obstetrics (UK)	FAS	Federation of American Scientists
		FAS	fetal alcohol syndrome
FAH	facteur anti-hémophilique (F); antihemophilic factor	Fasc.	fasciculus (L); small bundle
FAI	functional aerobic impairment	FASEB	Federation of American Societies for Experimental Biology
FAIDS	feline AIDS		
FAK	filtration artificial kidney		

F.A.S.H.N.S.	Fellow of the American Society of Head and Neck Surgery	FCC	flucloxacillin
FASST	Forum for the Advancement of Students in Science and Technology (USA)	FCCP	trifluoromethoxycarbonyl-cyanide-phenylhydrazone
		F.C.C.P.	Fellow of the American College of Chest Physicians
FAT	fluorescent antibody test (or technique)	FCD	focal cytoplasmic degradation
FATK	fatty acid thiokinase	FCF	fibroblast chemo-attractant factor
FAZ *(ophth)*	foveal avascular zone		
FB	factor B	FCF *(obst)*	fréquence cardiaque foetale (F); fetal heart rate
FB	finger breadth		
FB	foreign body	F.C.G.P.	Fellow of the College of General Practitioners
Fb	fibroblast		
FBA	fetal blood analysis	FCHL	familial combined hyperlipidemia
F.B.A.	Fellow of the British Academy		
		F-chromo-somes	parts of B-chromosomes formed by fragmentation
FBCOD	foreign body in cornea of right eye		
		F.Ch.S.	Fellow of the Society of Chiropodists
FBCOS	foreign body in cornea of left eye		
		FCM	flow cytometry
FBM	fat body mass	FCM *(obst)*	fréquence cardiaque maternelle (F); maternal heart rate
FBN	Federal Bureau of Narcotics USA)		
FBP	folate-binding protein	F.C.O.G. (S.A.)	Fellow of the College of Obstetricians and Gynaecologists (South Africa)
F.B.Ps.S.	Fellow of the British Psychological Society		
FBS	fasting blood sugar	FCP *(neur)*	final common pathway
FBS	feedback signal	F.C.Path.	Fellow of the College of Pathologists
FBS	feedback system		
FBS	fetal bovine serum	F.C.P.S.	Fellow of the College of Physicians and Surgeons
5-FC	5-fluorocytosine		
FC, F_c *(imm)*	fragment crystallizable	F.C.P.S.A.	Fellow of the College of Physicians and Surgeons of South Africa
FC	fréquence cardiaque (F); heart rate (=HR)		
		F.C.P.(SA)	Fellow of the College of Physicians (South Africa)
FC	frontal cortex		
FC	functional clearance	F.C.R.A.	Fellow of the College of Radiologists, Australasia
Fc	complement binding fraction		
		FCS	fetal calf serum
fc	foot candle (photometric unit, also: ft-c)	F.C.S.	Fellow of the Chemical Society
FCA	fluocinolone acetonide	FD	fatal dose
F.C.A.P.	Fellow of the College of American Pathologists	FD	field desorption
		FD	focal distance
FCC	Federal Communications Commission (USA)	FD	follicular dendritic cell
		FD	forceps delivery

FD	freeze-dried	F.D.S.R.C.-S.Eng.	Fellow in Dental Surgery of the Royal College of Surgeons of England
FD	frog dose (digitalis)		
FD_{50}	median fatal dose		
FDA	fluorescein diacetate	FDT *(obst)*	frontodextra-transversa (position of fetus)
FDA	Food and Drug Administration (Washington)		
		FDUMP	fluorodeoxyuridine monophosphate
FDA *(obst)*	frontodextra-anterior (position of fetus)		
		FDV	forced diffusion ventilation
Fd.Amb.Coy	Field Ambulance Company		
		FE	fetal erythroblastosis
FDC	Food, Drug, and Cosmetic Act (USA)	FE	fractional excretion (e.g. of electrolytes in the urine)
FDD	Food and Drug Directorate (Canada)	FE	fraction d'ejection (F); ejection fraction (= EF)
FDDC	ferric dimethyl dithiocarbonate	feb.dur.	febre durante (L); while the fever lasts
FDG	fluorodeoxyglucose	FEBS	Federation of European Biochemical Societies
FDH	focal dermal hypoplasia (Goltz-Gorlin syndrome)		
		FEC	final expiration capactiy
FDI	Fédération Dentaire Internationale (F); International Dental Federation	FECG	fetal electrocardiogram
		FECl	fractional excretion of chloride
		$FECO_2$	fractional excretion of CO_2
FDIU	fetal death in utero		
FDL	fluorescein dilaurate (test)		
FDMS	field desorption mass spectrometry	FECT	fibroelastic connective tissue
		Fed.Spec.	Federal Specifications
FDNB	1-fluoro-2,4-dinitrobenzene	FEEG	fetal electroencephalogram
F.D.O.	Fleet Dental Officer	FEF	forced expiratory flow
FDP	fibrin(ogen) degradation product	FEFANA	Fédération Européenne des Fabricants d'Adjuvants pour la Nutrition Animale (F); European Federation of Manufacturers of Substances for Animal Food (Bonn/Germany)
FDP	freeze-dried papain		
FDP *(obst)*	frontodextra-posterior (position)		
FDP *(biochem)*	fructose-1,6-diphosphate		
FDP-ALD	fructose diphosphate aldolase		
		FEH	fixed essential hypertension
FDPase	fructose-1,6-diphosphatase		
FDR	fluorogenic drug reagent	FEHBP	Federal Employees Health Benefits Program
FDS *(mil)*	Field Dressing Station (UK)		
		FEIM	Fédération Européenne d'Informatique Médicale (F); European Federation of Medical Information (= EFMI)
FDS *(card)*	fractional diameter shortening		
F.D.S.	Fellow in Dental Surgery		
F.D.S.R.C.-S.Ed.	Fellow in Dental Surgery of the Royal College of Surgeons of Edinburgh		
		FEK	fractional excretion of potassium

F-EKG	Funktions-Elektrokardio-gramm (G); functional electrocardiogram
FELASA	European Federation of Laboratory Animal Science
F electrode	functional electrode
FeLV	feline leukemia virus
FEM	field electron microscopy
FEM	force électromotrice (F); electromotive force (EMF)
fem.	female, feminine
fem.	femoral
FENa	fractional excretion of sodium
F enzyme	fluorokinase
FEP	Fédération Européenne de Pneumologie (F); European Society of Pneumology
FEP	free erythrocyte porphyrin
FEPO$_4$	fractional phosphate excretion
ferv.	fervens (L); boiling
FES	forced expiratory spirogram
FES	functional electrostimulation
FeSV	feline sarcoma virus
FET	feces excretion test
FET	field effect transistor
FEV	forced expiratory volume
FEV$_1$	forced expiratory volume in 1 second
FF	fat-free
FF *(rad)*	fine focus
FF *(card)*	filling fraction
FF	filtration fraction
FF	finger flexion
FF	fixing fluid
FF *(anat)*	Forel's field
FF	foster father
FF	fresh frozen
FFA	flufenamic acid
FFA	free fatty acids
F.F.A.	Fellow of the Faculty of Anaesthetists

F factor	antigen Duffy, Fy factor
F factor	fertility factor
F.F.A.R.C.S.	Fellow of the Faculty of Anaesthetists, Royal College of Surgeons
FFC	free from chlorine
FFD *(rad)*	focus-film distance
F.F.D.R.C.S.	Fellow of the Faculty of Dental Surgery, Royal College of Surgeons
FFDW	fat-free dry weight
F.F.Hom.	Fellow of the Faculty of Homoeopathy
FFI	free from infection
FFM	fat-free (body) mass
FFP	fresh frozen plasma
F.F.R.	Fellow of the Faculty of Radiologists
FFS	fat-free supper
FFT	fast Fourier transformation
FFT	flicker fusion threshold (or test)
FFU	focus-forming unit
FFWW	fat-free wet weight
FG *(dent)*	friction grip (drill)
FGAM, FGAR	formylglycinamide ribonucleotide
FGB	fully granulated basophil
FGF	fibroblast growth factor
FH	Faculty of Homoeopathy (UK)
FH	family history
FH	fetal heart
FH	follicle hormone
FH	Frankfurt horizontal (plane of the skull)
FH$_2$	dihydrofolic acid
FH$_4$	tetrahydrofolic acid
FHBL	familial hypo-ß-lipoproteinemia
FHCH	familial hypercholesterolemia
FHF	Fédération Hospitalière de France; French Hospital Federation
FhG	Fraunhofer-Gesellschaft (G); Fraunhofer Society

FHIP	Family Health Insurance Plan	FIFRA	Federal Insecticide, Fungicide, and Rodenticide Act (USA)
FHNH *(obst)*	fetal heart not heard	FIG	formiminoglycine
FHR	fetal heart rate	FIG	fosse iliaque gauche (F); left iliac fossa
FHRO	International Federation of Health Records Organizations	FIGIJ	Fédération Internationale de Gynécologie Infantile et Juvénile (F); International Federation of Gynaecology in Children and Adolescents
FHS	fetal heart sound		
FHT	fetal heart tone (= FHS)		
FI	fixed internal (reinforcement)		
FIA	fluorescent immunoassay	FIGLU	formiminoglutamic acid
FIA-ABS	fluorescence immune absorption test	FIGO	Fédération Internationale de Gynécology et Obstétrique (F); International Federation of Gynecology and Obstetrics
F.I.A.C.	Fellow of the International Academy of Cytology		
FIAT	Field Information Agency, Technical (USA)		
FIAT	free fatty acids incorporation in adipose tissue triglycerides	FIH	fat-induced hyperglycemia
		FIH	Fédération Internationale des Hôpitaux (F); Federación Internacional de Hospitales (S); International Hospital Federation
F.I.Biol.	Fellow of the Institute of Biology		
FIC	fluorescein isocyanate	fil.	filamentous
FIC	fractional inhibitory concentration (index)	FIM	field ion microscopy
		FIMF	Federación Internacional de Medicina Fisica (S); International Federation of Physical Medicine (= FIMP)
F.I.C.	Fellow of the Institute of Chemistry		
FICA	Federal Insurance Contribution Act (USA)		
F.I.C.A.	Fellow of the International College of Anesthetists	F.I.M.L.T.	Fellow of the Institute of Medical Laboratory Technology
F.I.C.D.	Fellow of the International College of Dentists	FIMP	Fédération Internationale de Médecine Physique (F); International Federation of Physical Medicine (= FIMF)
F.I.C.S.	Fellow of the International College of Surgeons		
FID	Fédération Internationale du Diabète (F); International Diabetes Federation		
		FIMS	Fédération Internationale de Médecine Sportive (F); International Federation of Sports Medicine
FID	flame ionization detector		
FID	fosse iliaque droite (F); right iliac fossa		
FID	free induction decay	FIN *(chir)*	fine intestinal needle
FIF	forced inspiratory flow	F-insulin	fibrous insulin
FIF	formaldehyde-induced fluorescence	F.Inst.S.P.	Fellow of the Institute of Sewage Purification

FiO$_2$	fraction of inspired oxygen	fl oz	fluid ounce
FIP	Fédération Internationale Pharmaceutique (F); International Pharmaceutical Federation (The Hague/The Netherlands)	FLP *(obst)*	frontolaeva-posterior (position of fetus)
		F.L.S.	Fellow of the Linnaean Society
		FLT *(obst)*	frontolaeva-transversa (position)
FIPM	Fédération Internationale de Psychothérapie Médicale (F); International Federation of Medical Psychotherapy	flu	influenza
		FLV	Friend leukemia virus (=FMuLV)
		FL cells	Fogh-Lund cells
FIS	forced inspiratory spirogram	FM	Faculté de Médecine (F); Faculty of Medicine
FISP	Fédération Internationale de la Sclérose en Plaques (F); International Federation for the Study of Atheromatous Plaques	FM *(obst)*	fetal movements
		FM	fibrin monomer
		FM	flavin mononucleotide
		FM	foster mother
		FM	frequency modulation
		FM	fusobacteria micro-organisms
FITC	fluorescein isothiocyanate	fm	femtomolar
FIV$_1$	forced inspiratory volume in 1 second	f.m. *(pharm)*	fiat mixtura (L); make a mixture (Rx)
FIVC	forced inspiratory vital capacity	FMAC	fetal movement acceleration (test)
FJRM	full joint range of movement	FMAU	2'-fluoro-2'-deoxy-5-methyl-ara-uridine
Fl. *(pharm)*	flos, flores (L); flowers, blossoms	FMB *(pharm)*	Formulae Magistrales Berolinenses (L); Berlin Magistral Formulas
fl.	fluid		
FLA	fibrinolysis activation		
FLA	flicker light activation, intermittent photostimulation	FMC	Foundation for Medical Care
		FM-card *(mil)*	field medical card
FLA *(obst)*	frontolaeva-anterior (position)	FMD	fibromuscular dysplasia
f.l.a.	fiat lege artis (L); let it be done according to the rule (Rx)	FMD	foot and mouth disease
		FME *(dent)*	full mouth extraction
		FMEF	forced mid-expiratory flow
FLAP	Federación Latinoamericana de Parasitologia (S); Latinamerican Federation of Parasitology	FMF	familial Mediterranean fever; Siegal-Cattan-Mamou disease
		FMF *(obst)*	fetal movement felt
fld.	fluid	FMFT	forced mid-expiratory flow time
fl dr	fluid dram		
FLEX	Federation Licensing Examination (USA)	FMG	Foreign Medical Graduate
FLI	fulminant liver insufficiency	FMH	fat-mobilizing hormone (=FMS)

FMH	Foederatio Medicorum Helveticorum (L); Federation of Swiss Physicians	FOB	fecal occult blood
		FOB *(clin)*	feet out of bed
		FOB	fiberoptic bronchoscopy
FML	flail mitral leaflet	FOC	fiberoptic catheter
FMLP	N-formyl-methionyl-leucyl-phenylalanine	FOD *(rad)*	focus-object distance
		Fol. *(pharm)*	folia (L); leaves
FMN	Fédération Mondiale de Neurologie (F); World Federation of Neurolgy	FOP	form of payment
		FOR	Faculty of Radiologists (also: FR)
FMN	flavin mononucleotide (cp. AMN)	For. *(anat)*	foramen (L); opening
		FORATOM	Forum Atomique Européen (F); European Atomic Forum
FMNH₂	(reduced) flavin mononucleotide		
fmol	femtomol	Fortran	formula translation (data processing language)
FMP	Family Nurse Practitioner		
FMP	first menstrual period	FP	facial paralysis
FMP	flumethasone pivalate	FP	Family Planning
FMP	fructose monophosphate	FP	family practitioner
FMR antigen	common antigen of Friend-, Moloney-, and Rauscher leukemia viruses	FP *(phys)*	fission product
		FP, Fp	flash point
		FP	flat plate
FM relation	female-male relation	FP	flavin phosphate, riboflavin-5'-phosphate (=FMN)
FMS	fat-mobilizing substance (=FMH)		
FMS	Fetal Monitoring System	FP	flavoproteins
FMS	fibromuscular stenosis	FP	foot pulse
FMS *(dent)*	full mouth series	FP *(phys)*	freezing point
FMuLV	Friend murine leukemia virus (=FLV)	FP	frozen plasma
		f.p. *(pharm)*	fiat potio (L); make a potion (Rx)
FMX *(dent)*	full mouth x-ray		
FN, fn	fibronectin	f.p. *(pharm)*	fiat pulvis (L); make a powder (Rx)
F-N *(neur)*	finger to nose (test)		
Fneg	false-negative	fp	foot-pound
Fn-FITC	fibronectin labelled with fluorescein isothiocyanate	fp *(phys)*	freezing point
		F-1-P	fructose-1-phosphate
FNH	focal nodular hyperplasia (liver tumor, benign)	F-6-P	fructose-6-phosphate
		F-1,6-P	fructose-1,6-diphosphate
FNP	fine-needle puncture	FPA	Family Planning Association
FNS	formule normale du sang (F); normal blood count		
		FPA	fibrinopeptide A
FNV	French neurotropic virus (yellow fever) vaccine	FPA	fluprednylidene acetate
		F1P-ALD	fructose-1-phosphate aldolase
FO	5-fluoro-orotic acid		
FO	fond d'oeil (F); fundus of the eye	FPB	fibrinopeptide B
		FPC	Family Planning Clinic
FO	foramen ovale	FPC	Family Practitioner Committee
FO	fronto-occipital		

FPC	febrile pharyngoconjunctivitis (cp. APC)
FPC	fish protein concentrate
FPE *(pharm)*	first-pass effect
FPF	fetal pulmonary fluid
FPG	fasting plasma glucose
FPH_2	(reduced) flavin phosphate
FPI *(psych)*	Freiburg Personality Inventory Test
FPIA	fluorescent polarization immunoassay
f.pil. *(pharm)*	fiant pilulae (L); make pills (Rx)
FPK	fructose-6-phosphate kinase
fpm	feet per minute
FPM test	filter paper microscopic test (for syphilis)
FPN	solution containing $FeCl_3$, perchloric acid, and nitrate
Fpos	false-positive
FPRNA	first pass radionuclide angiocardiography
fps	feet per second
fps	foot-pound-second
F.P.S.	Fellow of the Pharmaceutical Society
f.pulv.	fiat pulvis (L); make a powder, pulverize
FR	Faculty of Radiologists (also: FOR)
FR	failure rate (in contraception)
FR	feedback regulator
FR	fixed ratio
FR	flocculation reaction
FR *(anat)*	formatio reticularis
FR	fréquence respiratoire (F); respiratory rate
F + R	force and rhythm (of pulse)
Fr *(phys)*	Franklin (electrostatic unit)
Fr	frequency
fr *(phys)*	frigorie (caloric unit used in France)
FRA	flexor reflex afferentia

F.R.A.C.G.P.	Fellow of the Royal Australian College of General Practitioners
F.R.A.C.O.G.	Fellow of the Royal Australian College of Obstetricians and Gynaecologists
F.R.A.C.P.	Fellow of the Royal Australian College of Physicians
F.R.A.C.S.	Fellow of the Royal Australian College of Surgeons
F.R.A.I.	Fellow of the Royal Anthropological Institute
FRC	Federal Radiation Council (USA)
FRC	frozen red cells
FRC	functional residual capacity
FRCD	fixed-ratio combination drug
F.R.C.D.	Fellow of the Royal College of Dentists
F.R.C.G.P.	Fellow of the Royal College of General Practitioners
F.R.C.O.G.	Fellow of the Royal College of Obstetricians and Gynaecologists
F.R.C.P.	Fellow of the Royal College of Physicians
F.R.C.Path.	Fellow of the Royal College of Pathologists
F.R.C.P.(C)	Fellow of the Royal College of Physicians of Canada
F.R.C.P.Ed.	Fellow of the Royal College of Physicians of Edinburgh
F.R.C.P.(G)	Fellow of the Royal College of Physicians and Surgeons, Glasgow (= Physician, cp. F.R.C.S.(G)
F.R.C.P.I.	Fellow of the Royal College of Physicians of Ireland

F.R.C.P.S.	Fellow of the Royal College of Physicians and Surgeons (Glasgow)	F.R.I.P.H.H.	Fellow of the Royal Institute of Public Health and Hygiene
F.R.C.Psych.	Fellow of the Royal College of Psychiatrists	FRJM	full range joint movement
F.R.C.R.	Fellow of the Royal College of Radiologists	F.R.M.S.	Fellow of the Royal Microscopical Society
F.R.C.S.	Fellow of the Royal College of Surgeons	F.R.N.Z.C.-G.P.	Fellow of the Royal New Zealand College of General Practitioners
F.R.C.S.(C)	Fellow of the Royal College of Surgeons of Canada	FROM	full range of movement
F.R.C.S.Ed.	Fellow of the Royal College of Surgeons of Edinburgh	FRP *(card)*	functional refractory period (cp. ERP)
F.R.C.S.(G)	Fellow of the Royal College of Physicians and Surgeons of Glasgow (= Surgeon, cp. F.R.C.P.(G)	FRP-AVN	functional refractory period of the AV-node
		FRP-HPS	functional refractory period of the His-Purkinje system
F.R.C.S.I.	Fellow of the Royal College of Surgeons of Ireland	FRC-RA	functional refractory period of right atrium
FRC/TLC	ratio of functional residual capacity and total lung capacity	FRC-V	functional refractory period of the ventricle
F.R.C.V.S.	Fellow of the Royal College of Veterinary Surgeons	FRS	ferredoxin-reducing substance
		FRS	furosemide, frusemide
frem	fremitus vocalis (L); vocal fremitus	F.R.S.	Fellow of the Royal Society
F.R.E.S.	Fellow of the Royal Entomological Society	F.R.S.A.	Fellow of the Royal Society of Arts
FRF	follicle-stimulating hormone releasing factor (= FSH-RF, FSH-RH)	F.R.S.C.	Fellow of the Royal Society of Canada
		F.R.S.E.	Fellow of the Royal Society of Edinburgh
FRF	functional renal failure	F.R.S.H.	Fellow of the Royal Society for the Promotion of Health
F.R.F.P.S.	Fellow of the Royal Faculty of Physicians and Surgeons (Glasgow)	F.R.S.P.S.	Fellow of the Royal Society of Physicians and Surgeons (Glasgow)
FRG	Federal Republic of Germany	F.R.S.S.	Fellow of the Royal Statistical Society
FRH	follicle-stimulating hormone releasing hormone (= FRF, FSH-RF, FSH-RH)	FRT *(psych)*	figure-reasoning test
		FRT	full recovery time
		fru, fruc	fructose, levulose, fruit sugar
F.R.I.C.	Fellow of the Royal Institute of Chemistry	FRV	functional residual volume
		FS	factor of safety
frig.	frigidus (L); cold	FS	Fettsäure (G); fatty acid

FS *(card)*	fractional shortening
FS	frozen section
FSA	Federal Security Administration (USA)
FSA	fetal sulfoglycoprotein antigen
f.s.a. *(pharm)*	fiat secundum artem (L); to be done skilfully
FSC	Food Standards Committee (UK)
FSD *(rad)*	focus-skin distance
FSF	fibrin-stabilizing factor, factor XIII
FSG	functional scintigram
FSGS	focal segmental glomerulosclerosis
FSH	follicle-stimulating hormone
FSH-RF	FSH releasing factor (=FRF, FRH, FSH-RH)
FSH-RH	FSH releasing hormone (=FRF, FRH, FSH-RF)
FSK	frequency shift keying
FSMB	Federation of State Medical Boards (USA)
FSP	fibrinogen split product
f.sp.	forma specialis (L); special form (parasites)
F.S.R.	Fellow of the Society of Radiographers
FSS	fibrous subaortic stenosis
F.S.S.	Fellow of the Royal Society of Statistics
FST *(mil)*	Field Surgical Team (UK)
FSt	free sterol
FSU	Family Service Unit
FSU	follicle stimulating urine (=HMG)
FT	Fallot's tetralogy
FT	fluorescent antiglobulin test
FT	formol toxoid
FT	Fourier transformation
FT	free thyroxine
FT *(obst)*	full term
ft	foot
F_3T	5-trifluoromethyluracil

FTA-ABS	fluorescent treponemal antibody-absorption test (for syphilis) (also: FTA-ABT)
FTA test	fluorescent treponemal antibody test
FTBD *(obst)*	full term born dead
FTC	Federal Trade Commission
ft-c	foot candle
F_3TDR	trifluorothymidine deoxyriboside (also 3'F-TdR)
FTE	free thyroxine equivalent
F-test *(stat)*	Fisher's test (for assessment of homogeneity of median groups in analysis of variance)
F-II test	precipitin test using Cohn's fraction II
FTI	free thyroxine index
ftL, ft-la	foot-Lambert (photochemical unit)
FTLB *(obst)*	full-term living birth
FTLV	feline T-lymphotropic lentivirus
FTM	fractional test meal
FTND *(obst)*	full-term normal delivery
6-FTP	6-fluorotryptophane
FTT	failure to thrive
FTT *(mil)*	Field Transfusion Team
FTT	fluorescent talcum test (for porphyria)
FTT	fructose tolerance test
FT_4 test	determination of free thyroxine
FU	fecal urobilinogen
FU	Finsen unit
FU, 5-FU	5-fluorouracil
FU	follow-up
FU	fractional urinalysis
FUB	Free University of Berlin (Germany)
FUB	functional uterine bleeding
FUC	fucose
FUDR, 5-FUdR	5-fluorodeoxyuridine, floxuridine
FUM	fumarate hydratase, fumarase

FUO	fever of undetermined origin	G *(phys)*	gravitation constant (Newton)
FUR	fluoro-uridine	G *(chem)*	guanine
fur	furlong	G *(chem)*	guanosine (= Guo)
FV	fibrillation ventriculaire (F); ventricular fibrillation	g g *(phys)*	gram gravity force (on acceleration or deceleration)
FVC	forced vital capacity	G. *(anat)*	ganglion (= Ggl.)
FVG	femoral vein graft	GI, GII,	number of previous gravid-
FVR	force-velocity relation	GIII	ities
f.vs.	fiat venaesectio (L); let the patient be bled	GA	gastric analysis
		GA	general anesthesia
FW	forced whisper	GA	general appearance
fw	fresh water	GA, ga	gingivoaxial
FWA	Family Welfare Association	*(dent)*	
		GA	gluco-amylase
F-waves	flutter waves (in the ECG)	GA	glucuronic acid
FWB	full weight bearing	GA	glyceraldehyde
FWHM	full width at half maxi-	GA	Golgi apparatus
(rad)	mum	GA	guaiaretic acid
FWPCA	Federal Water Pollution Control Administration (USA)	GA	guessed average
		GA	gut-associated
		GABA	gamma-aminobutyric acid
FWTM *(rad)*	full width at tenth maximum	GABA-T	gamma-aminobutyrate alpha-ketoglutarate transaminase
Fx	fracture		
FY	full year	GABHS	group A beta-hemolytic streptococci
Fy-Faktor	Duffy factor, antigen Fy		
F.Z.S.	Fellow of the Zoological Society	GAC	glucose assimilation coefficient
		GAD	(general) acyl-CoA-dehydrogenase
		GAD	glutamic acid decarboxylase

G

		GADAM	Gesellschaft für Angewandte Datenverarbeitung und Automation in der Medizin (G); Society of Applied Data Processing and Automation in Medicine (Germany)
G *(chem)*	ganglioside
G	gastrin
G	gauge
G *(phys)*	Gauss
G	generation
G	gentamicin	GAG	glycosamine glycane
G	giga-	GAG	glyoxal-bis-guanylhydrazone
G, g *(dent)*	gingival		
G	globulin	gag *(gen)*	group-antigen
G	glucose	GAGPS	glycosamine-glycane polysulfate

GAH	globuline antihémophilique (F); antihemophilic globulin	GB	Guillain-Barré syndrome (=GBS)
Gal	galactose	Gb	Gilbert (unit of voltage in the electromagnetic CGS system)
gal	gallon		
GALCIT	Guggenheim Aeronautical Laboratory, California Institute of Technology	GBA	gastro-bioassay
		GBA, gba (dent)	gingivobuccoaxial
GalN	galactosamine	GBE	gingko biloba extract
GalNAc	N-acetylgalactosamine	GBH	gamma benzene hexachloride
Gal-1-P	D-galactose-1-phosphate		
Gal-1-PUT	galactose-1-phosphate uridyltransferase	GBM	glomerular basement membrane
GALT	gastrointestinal (or gut) associated lymphoid tissue	GBPS	gated blood-pool scanning
		GBS (rad)	gall bladder series
		GBS	glycerin buffered saline
GalTT	galactose tolerance test	GBS	group B streptococci
GALV, GaLV	gibbon-associated leukemia virus	GBS	Guillain-Barré syndrome (=GB)
Gal virus	gallus-adenolike virus	GC	ganglion cell
gamma-GT	gamma-glutamyl transpeptidase (=GGT, γ-GT)	GC	gas chromatography
		GC	glucocorticoid
gamma-M-FTA	gamma-M-fluorescent treponemal antibody test	GC	gonococci
		GC	guanine-cytosine
GAP	D-glyceraldehyde-3-phosphate	Gc	group-specific component
		gC	granulomatous colitis
GAP	growth-associated proteins	gcal	gram calorie
GAPDH	D-glyceraldehyde-3-phosphate dehydrogenase	GCFT	gonococcal complement fixation test
GAPS	General Adjustment and Planning Scale	GCIIS	glucose-controlled insulin infusion
GAR	glycinamide ribonucleotide	GC/MS	combination of gas chromatography and mass spectrometry
GARP	Global Atmospheric Research Program		
GAS	gastroenterology (=GE)	GCS	Glasgow Coma Score
GAS	general adaption syndrome	Gc/s	gigacycles per second, gigahertz, GHz
GAS	generalized arteriosclerosis		
GAS	global assessment scale	GCV	great cardiac veins
GAS	group A streptococci	GCVF	great cardiac vein flow
GASA (obst)	growth adjusted sonographic age	GCW	Gesellschaft der Chirurgen in Wien (G); Society of Surgeons in Vienna/Austria
GAT	glucose-arginine test		
GATB (psych)	General Aptitude Test Battery		
GAUS	German Activator Urokinase Study	GCWM	General Conference on Weights and Measures
GB	gallbladder	GD	gastroduodenostomy

GD	Gesamtdosis (G); total dose	GEMOI	Gesellschaft zur Erforschung der makromolekularen Organ- und Immuntherapie (G); Society for Research of Macromolecular Organotherapy and Immunotherapy
GDCh	Gesellschaft Deutscher Chemiker; German Society of Chemists		
GDH	glucose dehydrogenase		
GDH	glutamate dehydrogenase (=GLDH)	GEMT	German Eminase Multicenter Trial
GDH	glycine-3-phosphate dehydrogenase	GER	granular endoplasmic reticulum
GDH	growth and differentiation hormone	GET	gastric emptying time
GDMO	General Duties Medical Officer	GEU	grossesse extra-uterine (F); ectopic pregnancy
GDN	Gesellschaft Deutscher Neurologen; Society of German Neurologists	GeV	giga electron volt
		GF	germ-free
GDP	guanosine-5'-diphosphate	GF	glass factor (in tissue cultures)
GDPA	glycyldehydrophenylalanine	GF	glomerular filtrate
GDU	gastro-duodenal ulcer	GF	griseofulvin
GE	gastroenterology (=GAS)	G-F	globular-fibrous (proteins)
GE	gastroenteritis		
GE *(chir)*	gastroenterostomy	GFAP	glial fibrillary acidic protein
GE	Gesamteiweiß (G); total protein	G-forces	acceleration forces (gravity forces)
GE	gonadotrophic epithelium factor (=FSH)	G-form	gonidial form of culture medium colonies
GEC	galactose-eliminating capacity	GfK	Gesellschaft für Kinderheilkunde (G); (German) Society of Pediatrics
GECA	Groupe Européen de Chimiothérapie Anticancéreuse (F); European Working Group for Cancer Chemotherapy	GFP	gamma-fetoprotein
		GFR	glomerular filtration rate
		GG	gammaglobulin
GEF	gonadotrophin enhancing factor	GG	glycylglycine
		GGE	generalized glandular enlargement
Ge factor	Gerbich factor, antigen Ge		
GEFAP	Groupement Européen des Associations Nationales de Fabricants de Pesticides (F); European Union of National Associations of Pesticide Manufacturers	GGE	guaiacol glycerin ether
		GGG	glycine-rich gamma-glycoprotein
		GGG	gummi guttae gambiae (L); gamboge
		Ggl.	ganglion (=G.)
GEG	gamma encephalogram	GGT, -GT	gamma-glutamyl transpeptidase (=GGTP)
G-E index	granuloerythrocytic index	GG test	gammaglobulin test

GGTP	gamma-glutamyl trans-peptidase, D-glutamyl transferase (=GGT)	GIIP	Groupement International des Industries Pharmaceutiques des Pays de la CEE (F); International Association of Pharmaceutical Industries of Countries of the European Economic Community (Brussels/Belgium)
GH	General Hospital		
GH	gingival hyperplasia		
GH	growth hormone; somatotrophin (=STH)		
GHAA	Group Health Association of America		
GHC	Group Health Cooperative	GIK sol	glucose-insulin-potassium solution
GHIF, GHIH	growth hormone inhibiting factor, ... hormone	GIL	glabella-inion line
GHL	generalized hyperplastic lymphadenopathy	GIP	gastric inhibitory polypeptide
GHRF, GHRH	growth hormone releasing factor, ... hormone	GIP	giant-cell interstitial pneumonia
GHRIH	growth hormone release-inhibitory hormone	GIR	global improvement rating
		GIRP	Groupement International de la Repartition Pharmaceutique des Pays de la CEE (F); International Association of Pharmaceutical Wholesale Trade of Countries of the European Economic Community (Paris/France)
GHS	Gougerot-Houwer-Sjögren (syndrome), keratoconjunctivitis sicca		
GHz	gigahertz		
GI	gastrointestinal		
GI	globin insulin		
GI	gonadotrophic interstitial factor (=ICSH)	GIS (rad)	gastrointestinal series
GI	growth inhibition	GIS	gastrointestinal system
gi	gill	GIS	growth-initiating substance
GIAT	glucose incorporation in adipose tissue triglycerides	GISSI	Gruppo Italiano per lo Studio della Streptochinasi nell'Infarcto Miocardico (I); Italian Study Group on Streptokinase in Myocardial Infarction
GIES	Geriatric Interpersonal Evaluation Scale		
GIF	gonadotrophin inhibiting factor		
GIF	growth hormone inhibiting factor (=GHIF)	GIT	gastrointestinal tract
		GIT	glucose infusion test
		GIT	glutathione-insulin transhydrogenase
GIFT	gamete intrafallopian transfer	GITS	Gastrointestinal Therapeutic System
GIH	gastrointestinal hemorrhage	GITT	glucose insulin tolerance test (Himsworth)
GIH	gastrointestinal hormone	GK	glucokinase
GIH	growth hormone inhibiting hormone (=GHIH)	GK	glycerokinase
GII	gastrointestinal infection	GL	General Medical Laboratory (UK)

GL *(obst)*	greatest length (of embryo or fetus)	GMC	General Medical Council (UK)
Gl	glucinium (= beryllium)	GMC	grivet monkey cell (line)
Gl.	glandula (L); gland	GM-CSF	granulocyte-macrophage
Gl-I	glyoxylase I	*(imm)*	colony stimulating factor
GLA	gamma-linolenic acid	GMDS	Gesellschaft für Medizi-
GLA, gla *(dent)*	gingivolinguoaxial		nische Dokumentation und Statistik (G); Society
GLC	gas-liquid chromatography		for Medical Documentation and Statistics
Glc	glucose		(Germany)
glc	glaucoma	Gm-factors	gammaglobulin groups
Glc-N	D-glucosamine		Gm
Glc-6-P	glucose-6-phosphate (= G-6-P)	GMK	green monkey kidney (cells)
GLD	globoid leukodystrophy	GML	glabellomeatal line
GLDH	glutamate dehydrogenase (= GDH, GluDH)	gmol	gram-molecule, grammol
		GMP	glucose monophosphate
GLI	glucagon-like immunoreactivity	GMP *(pharm)*	"Good Manufacturing Practices"
GLL	glabella-lambda line	GMP	guanosine monophosphate
Gll.	glandulae (L); glands		(G-2-MP, G-3-MP,
Gln	glutamine		G-5-MP)
Glob. *(pharm)*	globuli	GMP *(pharm)*	Guidelines for Manufacturing Pharmaceuticals
GLP	generalized lymphadenopathy		(according to WHO)
		GMRI	gated magnetic resonance
GLP	glycolipoproteins		imaging
GLP	"good laboratory practice" (established procedures according to FDA rules in the USA)	GMS	General Medical Services
		GMS	glycerin monostearate
		GM + S	General Medicine and Surgery
Glu	glutamic acid	Gm system	gamma-marker system
GluDH	glutamate dehydrogenase (= GDH, GLDH)	GMT	Greenwich Mean Time
		GMV	gram-molecular volume
GLV	goat leukoencephalopathy virus	GMW	gram molecular weight
		GN	Graduate Nurse
Gly	glycocoll, glycine	GN	glomerulonephritis
GlyR	glyoxylate reductase	GN	gram-negative
GM	Geiger-Müller (counter)	G/N	glucose-nitrogen (ratio)
GM	General Medicine	GNA	alpha-glutamyl-beta-naphthylamide
GM	gentamicin		
GM	grand mal (F); epilepsy	GNA	glomérulo-néphrite post-
GM	granulocyte-macrophage		angineuse (F); postanginal
gm	gram (correct: g)		glomerulonephritis
GMA	glycol methacrylate	GNC	general nursing care
GMA	gross motor activities	GNC	General Nursing Council

GNRH,	gonadotrophin-releasing	GPC *(chem)*	glycerophosphorylcholine
GnRH	hormone	GPD	glyceraldehyde phosphate
GNT	ganglio-N-tetraose		dehydrogenase
GO, Go	gonorrhea		(=GAPDH)
G+O	gas and oxygen	GPD,	glucose-6-phosphate dehy-
Goᵃ-factor	Gonzales factor, antigen	G-6-PD	drogenase (=G-6-PDH)
	Goᵃ	-GPD	glycerophosphate dehy-
GOD	glucose oxidase		drogenase
GOD/POD	glucose oxidase peroxidase	GPDH,	glucose-6-phosphate dehy-
	(method)	G-6-PDH	drogenase (=G-6-PD)
GOE	gas, oxygen, ether	GPE	glycerophosphoryl etha-
	(anesthesia)		nolamine
GOK	"God only knows"	G.Ph.	Graduate in Pharmacy
GOL	glabella-opisthion line	G-phase	gap phase (in the cell
GOQ	glucose oxidation quotient		cycle)
GOR	gastro-oesophageal reflux	GPI	general paralysis of the
GOR	general operating room		insane; dementia paraly-
GOS *(neur)*	Glasgow Outcome Scale		tica
GOT	glutamic-oxaloacetic trans-	GPI	glucose phosphate iso-
	aminase, aspartate amino-		merase
	transferase (=AAT,	GPM	general preventive medi-
	SGOT)		cine
GOT-C	cytoplasmic GOT	GPM	glycerophosphate mutase
GOT-M	mitochondrial GOT	GPNA	N-glutaryl-L-phenylala-
GOX	gaseous oxygen		nine-p-nitranilide
GP	general paresis (or paraly-	GPO,	glycero-1-phosphate oxi-
	sis)	GPOX	dase
GP, G.P.	General Practitioner	GPP	generalized pustular pso-
GP	geometric progression		riasis
GP	glutamylphenylalanine	GPP	glucose-6-phosphate dehy-
GP	glycoprotein		drogenase (=G-6-PDH)
GP	gram-positive	GPRA	General Practice Reform
GP	guinea pig		Association
-GP	glycerin-1-phosphate	GPRT	guanosine phosphoribosyl
G-1-P	glucose-1-phosphate		transferase
G-6-P	glucose-6-phosphate	GPS	Goodpasture syndrome
G-1,6-P	glucose-1,6-diphosphate	GPS	guinea pig serum
gp *(imm)*	glycoprotein (e.g. gp41,	GPT	glutamic-pyruvic transami-
	gp120)		nase; alanine aminotrans-
GPA	glycophorin A		ferase (=ALAT, SGPT)
GPA(M)	glycophorin A (M-type)	GPU	guinea pig unit
GPA(N)	glycophorin A (N-type)	GR	gamma rays
G-6-pase	glucose-6-phosphatase	GR	gastric resection
GPB	glossopharyngeal breath-	GR	general research
	ing	GR	globule rouge (F); red
GPC *(lab)*	gel permeation chromatog-		blood cell, erythrocyte
	raphy	GR	glutathione reductase

GR	gymnastique respiratoire (F); respiratory therapy	GS	Goodpasture syndrome (=GPS)
gR, g-R	gram-roentgen (obsolete unit)	GS	glomerulosclerosis
gr	grain	gs	group-specific
GRA *(ophth)*	generalized relative aperture	GSA *(neur)*	general somatic afferent
		GSA	Genetics Society of America
grad.	gradient	GSC	gas-solid chromatography
GRAE	generally regarded as effective	GSC *(lab)*	gravity-setting culture
		GSD *(rad)*	genetically significant dose
gran.	granulated		
GRAS	generally recognized as safe	GSD	glutamic acid decarboxylase
grav.	gravid, pregnant	GSD	glycogen storage disease
GRD	β-glucuronidase	GSE *(neur)*	general somatic efferent
GRF	gonadotrophin releasing factor (=GRH)	GSE	glutene-sensitive enteropathy
GRF	growth hormone releasing factor (=GHRF, GHRH, GRH)	GSH	glutathione (reduced)
		GSP	gastro-secretagogue pancreatic peptide
Gr factor	Graydon factor, antigen Gr	GSR	galvanic skin response
GRG	Gastroenterologic Research Group (USA)	GSR	generalized Shwartzman reaction
GRH	gonadotrophin releasing hormone (=GRF)	GSSG	glutathione disulfide (oxidized glutathione)
GRH	growth hormone releasing hormone (=GHRF, GHRH, GRF)	GST *(dent)*	functional jaw impression method of Greene, Supplee und Tench
GRIA	gastrin radioimmunoassay	G-suit	anti-gravity protection suit
GRID	gay-related immunodeficiency	GSW	gunshot wound
		GT	galactosemia test
GRIF	growth hormone inhibiting factor (=GRIH)	GT	generation time
		GT *(biol)*	genetic therapy
GRIH	growth hormone inhibiting hormone (=GRIF)	GT	glucose tolerance
		GT	group therapy
gr.m.p. *(pharm)*	grosso modo pulverisatum (L); grossly pulverized	gt	granulation tissue
		gt.	gutta (L); drop
GRNV	gated radionuclide ventriculography	-GT	gamma-glutamyl transpeptidase (=GGT)
		GTF	glucose tolerance factor
GRS	Geriatric Rating Scale	GTH	glutathione
GRS	graphic rating scale	GTH	gonadotrophic hormone(s)
GS	ganglion spinale (L)	GTN	gestational trophoblastic neoplasia
GS	general surgery		
GS	Genetic Systems	GTN	glomerulo-tubulo-nephritis
GS	Gilbert syndrome, hyperbilirubinemia	GTN	glyceryl trinitrate; nitroglycerin

G-tolerance	tolerance of great accelation (G-forces)
GTP	guanosine-5'-triphosphate
GTPH	guanosine triphosphate cyclohydrolase
GTR	granulocyte turnover rate
GTS	glucose transport system
GTT	glucose tolerance test
gtt. *(pharm)*	guttae (L); drops
GU	gastric ulcer
GU	genito-urinary
GU	glucuronidase
GU	Goldblatt unit
GU	gonococcal urethritis
GU	gravitational ulcer
GU	Grundumsatz (G); basal metabolic rate
GV	gentian violet
GVA *(neur)*	general visceral afferent
GVE *(neur)*	general visceral efferent
GVHD	graft-versus-host defence (reaction)
GVHR	graft-versus-host reaction
GVHS	graft-versus-host syndrome
GWG	generalized Wegener granulomatosis
GX	glycine xylidide
Gy *(rad)*	Gray (unit of energy dose) ($=1$ J/kg $=100$ rd)
GYN	gynecology

H

H	enthalpy (Gibbs)
H *(phys)*	hefner (unit, now candela, cd)
H *(phys)*	henry (unit of electrical inductance)
H	heroin
H	histidine
H *(rad)*	Holzknecht unit
H *(rad)*	homogeneity
H	homosexual

H	hormone
H	Hounsfield unit
H	human
H	hyoscine (scopolamine)
H *(ophth)*	hypermetropia, hyperopia
H	magnetic field intensity (Oersted)
h	hecto- (prefix for 100)
h	hora (L); hour
h	quantum constant (Planck)
H_3	procaine hydrochloride
HA	headache
HA	hemadsorption (test)
HA	hemagglutination
HA	hemolytic anemia
HA	hemophilia A
HA	hepatitis A
HA	hepatitis associated (virus)
HA, Ha	human albumin
HA	hyaluronic acid
HA	11-hydroxyandrosterone
HA	hydroxy-apatite ($=$ HAP)
Ha *(ophth)*	absolute hyperopia
HA1, HA2	hemadsorption virus type 1, ... type 2
HAA	hemolytic anemia antigen
HAA	hepatitis-associated antigen, Australia antigen ($=HB_sAG$, SH-AG)
HAAb	hepatitis A antibody
HAAg	hepatitis A antigen
hab *(psych)*	habit
HAC	histamine transacetylase
HAC	hydroxy-apatite ceramics
HACC	hexachlorocyclohexane (also: HCC, HCCH, HCH)
HAd	hemadsorption
HAD	Hospital Administration, ... Administrator
HAD	3-hydroxyacyl-CoA dehydrogenase
HADES	histogram-adapted digital electric stimulation
HAE	hereditary angio-edema (cp. HAO)

HAGG	heat-aggregated gamma globulin	HAPPHY	Heart Attack Primary Prevention in Hypertension (clinical beta-blocker trial)
HAGG	hyperimmune antivariola gamma globulin	HAR	hemagglutination reaction (=HAT)
HAI	hemagglutination inhibition	Ha-RITC	human albumin labelled with rhodamine isothiocyanate
HAIns	Health and Accident Insurance	HAS *(psych)*	Hamilton Anxiety Scale (=HAMA)
HAIR	hemagglutination inhibition reaction (=HAI,HI)	HAS	highest asymptomatic (dose)
HAK	hemodialysis artificial kidney	HAS	hypertensive arteriosclerosis
HAL	hypo-alpha-lipoproteinemia	HASHD	hypertension and arteriosclerotic heart disease
HALP	homologous human anti-lymphocyte plasma	HASP	Hospital Admission and Surveillance Program
HaLV	hamster leukemia virus	HAT	hemagglutination test (=HAR)
HAM	human albumin microsphere	HAV	hemadsorption virus
HAMA *(psych)*	Hamilton Anxiety Scale (=HAS)	HAV	hepatitis A virus
HAMA	human anti-mouse antibody	HAW *(rad)*	high-active waste
HAMS	human albumin microspheres	HAWIE	Hamburg-Wechsler-Intelligenztest für Erwachsene (G); Hamburg-Wechsler Intelligence Test for Adults
HANE	hereditary angioneurotic edema		
HANES *(psych)*	Hamburg Neuroticism and Extraversion Scale (used for children and adolescents)	HAWIK	Hamburg-Wechsler-Intelligenztest für Kinder (G); Hamburg-Wechsler Intelligence Test for Children
HANP	human atrial natriuretic peptide (=ANF, ANP)	HAZ	hyperalgesic zone
H antigen	histocompatibility antigen	HB	hardness scale of Brinell
HAO	hereditary angio-oedema (=HAE)	HB	heart block
		HB	hepatitis B
HAP	heredopathia atactica polyneuritiformis (L); Refsum's syndrome	HB	His bundle
		Hb	hemoglobin (also: Hg, hgb)
HAP	heat-resistant alkaline phosphatase	Hb. *(pharm)*	herb
HAP	histamine azoprotein	3-HB	3-hydroxybutyric acid
HAP	hypertension-associated protein	HbA_1	glycosylated hemoglobin
		HBAg	hepatitis B antigen
HAP	hydroxy-apatite	HBB	His bundle block
HAPE	high altitude pulmonary edema	HBB	2-(alpha-hydroxybenzyl)-benzimidazole
		HbBC	hemoglobin-binding capacity

HBC	"hit by car"	HC	hydrocarbon
HBcAg	hepatitis B core antigen	HC	hydrocortisone
HbCO	carboxyhemoglobin	HC	hypertrophic cardiomyo-pathy (=HCM)
HBD, HBDH	3-hydroxybutyrate dehy-drogenase	h.c.	honoris causa (L); as a sign of honor (e.g. in titles)
HBE	His bundle electrogram	HC-3	hemicholinium 3
Hb$_E$	Hb content of the erythro-cyte (=MCH)	HCA	hepatocellular adenoma
HBeAg	hepatitis B envelope anti-gen	HCA	Hospital Corporation of America (Nashville)
HBF	hepatic blood flow	HCA	hydrocortisone acetate
Hb$_F$	fetal hemoglobin	HCAT	homocholic acid taurin
HBGM	home blood glucose moni-toring	HCB	hexachlorobenzene
Hb-Hp	hemoglobin-haptoglobin complex	HCC (vet)	hepatitis contagiosa canum (L); infectious canine hep-atitis
HBIG	hepatitis B immunoglobu-lin	HCC	hepatocellular carcinoma
HBL	hypo-beta-lipoproteinemia	HCC	hexachlorocyclohexane (=BHC, HACC, HCCH, HCH)
HBLV	human B-lymphotropic virus	25-HCC	25-hydroxycholecalciferol
HBM	Health Believe Model (to promote compliance)	HCCH	hexachlorocyclohexane (=BHC, HACC, HCC, HCH)
HbO$_2$	oxyhemoglobin	HCD	heavy chain disease
HBP	high blood pressure	HCD	homologous canine dis-temper antiserum
Hb$_P$	fetal ("primitive") hemo-globin	HCF	highest common factor
HbR	methemoglobin reductase, nicotinamide adenine di-nucleotide diaphorase	HCFA	Health Care Financing Administration (USA)
Hb$_s$:	sickle cell hemoglobin (also: Hb$_{sc}$)	HCG	human chorionic gonado-trophin
HBsAg	hepatitis B surface antigen	HCH	hexachlorocyclohexane (=BHC, HACC, HCC, HCCH)
HbSCD	hemoglobin sickle cell dis-ease		
HBT	6-hydroxy-1,3-benzoxa-thiol-2-one	H chain	heavy chain
HBSS	Hank's balanced salt solu-tion	HcImp (dent)	hydrocolloid impression
HBV	hepatitis B virus	HCL	hair cell leukemia
HC	handicapped	HCL test	heparin-calciumchloride-lipoprotein test
HC	hetacillin	HCM	hypertrophic cardiomyo-pathy (=HC)
HC	histocompatibilty		
HC	Hodgkin cells	HCMV	human cytomegalovirus (=CMV)
HC	Home Care	HCP	hereditary coproporphyria
HC	Hospital Corps	HCP	hexachlorophene
HC	house call		

HCR	hepatic clearance rate	HDC	hydroxyacetylene diureine carboxylic acid
HCS	hormone chorionique somatotrophique (F); chorionic somatotrophic hormone	HDCS	human diploid cell strain
		H.D.D.	Higher Dental Diploma (Glasgow)
HCS	Hospital Car Service	HDE	Hamburg Depression Scale (= HDS)
HCS	human chorionic somatomammotrophin (= HCSM, HPL)	H_4DE	1,2-bis-(2-di-(carboxymethyl)-aminoethoxyl)ethane (= EGTA)
HCSA	Hospital Consultants and Specialists Association	HDF	hemodiafiltration
HCSM	human chorionic somatomammotrophin (= HCS, HPL)	HDFP	Hypertension Detection and Follow-up Program
		HDHE	heparin-dihydroergotamine
HCSR	hypersensitive carotid sinus reflex	H-disease	Hartnup disease
		HDL	high density lipoproteins
HCSS	hypersensitive carotid sinus syndrome	HDLC	high-density lipoprotein cholesterol
HCT	hematocrit	HDLW	hearing distance left watch
HCT	human calcitonin	(otol)	(i.e. distance at which a
HCT	human chorionic thyrotrophin		watch is heard with the left ear)
HCT, HCTZ	hydrochlorothiazide	HDN	hemolytic disease of the newborn (= MHN, MNH)
HCV	human coronavirus	HDP	hexose diphosphate
HCVD	hypertensive cardiovascular disease	HDP	hypertensive disease in pregnancy
HCW	Health Care Worker	HDRW	hearing distance right
HCy	hemocyanin	(otol)	watch (cp. HDLW)
HD	Hansen's disease; leprosy	HDS (psych)	Hamburg Depression Scale (= HDE)
HD	hearing distance		
HD	heart disease	HDS	hemodynamic stroke
HD	hemodialysis	HDU	head drop unit (of curare)
HD	hemolysing dose	HDU	hemodialysis unit
HD (rad)	Herddosis (G); focal dose	HDV	hepatitis delta virus
		HD_{50} value	median value of reduction in optical density during hemagglutination
HD	herniated disc		
HD	hexadecane		
HD	high density	HE	hematoxylin-eosin (staining)
HD	hip disarticulation		
HD	Hodgkin's disease	HE	hepatic extraction
h.d.	hora decubitus (L); at bedtime	HE	heptachlorepoxide
		HE	highly explosive
HDA	hydroxydopamine	HE	human enteric
HDC	histidine decarboxylase	HE	hypophysectomy
HDC	human diploid cells	He	heparin
HDC	hydrocortisone (= HC)	H + E	hemorrhage and exudate

H + E *(psych)*	heredity and environment (= E + H)	HEP	human encephalitogenic protein
HEA	human erythrocyte antigen	HEP *(bact)*	human epitheloid cells
HEAO	High Energy Astronomical Observatory	HEPA *(hyg)*	high efficiency particulate air (filter)
HEAT	human erythrocyte agglutination test	HEPA	human extrinsic plasminogen activator
HEB	hemato-encephalic barrier (= BBB)	HEPES	N-2-hydroxyethylpiperazine-N'-2-ethanesulfonic
HED *(rad)*	Haut-Einheits-Dosis (G); unit skin dose		acid (buffer substance)
HEDP	hydroxyethane-diphosphonic acid	HEp-2	human epithelium-2 (cells from laryngeal epithelioma, e.g. for virus cul-
HEDTA	N'-(2-hydroxyethyl)-ethylene-diamine-N,N,N'-triacetic acid		tures)
		HES	hydroxyethyl starch
HEENT	head, ears, eyes, nose, throat	HET	hexaethyltetraphosphate (= HETP)
HEF	human embryonic fibroblasts	HETE	12(S)-hydroxy-5-cis-8-cis-10-trans-14-ciseicosatetra-
He factor	Henshaw factor, antigen He		enic acid
HEH	hyperkinetic essential hypertension	HETP	hexaethyltetraphosphate (= HET)
HEK	human embryonic kidney cells	HEW	Department of Health, Education, and Welfare (Washington) (now: U.S. Department of Health and Human Services)
HEL	hen's egg-white lysozyme	
HEL	human embryonic lung cells	HF	Hageman factor, factor XII
HeLa	Henrietta Lacks (sometimes: Helen Lake) tumor cell line	HF	hay fever
		HF	heart failure
HELLP	hemolysis, elevated liver enzymes, and low platelet counts syndrome (rare variant of pre-eclampsia)	HF	hemofiltration
		HF	hemorrhagic factor
		HF	hemorrhagic fever
		HF	high frequency
HELP	heparin-induced extracorporeal LDL precipitation	HFC	hard filled capsules
		HF factor	heredofamilial factor
HEMA	hydroxyethylmethacrylate	HFI	hereditary fructose intolerance
H$_2$-enta-H$_2$	ethylene diamine tetraacetate (= EDTA)	H fistula	horizontal esophago-tracheal fistula
H enzyme	adenylcarbonate pyrophosphorylase	HFJO	high frequency jet oscillation
HEP	high egg passage	HFJV	high frequency jet ventilation
HEP	high energy phosphate	
HEP	histamine equivalent in prick (test system)	HFM	hand-foot-and-mouth disease

HFME	hand-foot-mouth exanthem	H/H	Hunt/Hess (classification of subarachnoidal hemorrhage)
HFO	high frequency oscillation		
HFOV	high frequency oscillating ventilation	HHA	heterohemagglutinin
		HH cells	Hargraves-Haserick cells (= LE cells)
HFP	high frequency pulsation		
HFPPV	high frequency positive-pressure ventilation	HHD	hypertensive heart disease
		HHE	hemiconvulsion-hemiplegia-epilepsy syndrome (jacksonian epilepsy)
HFR, Hfr	high frequency of recombination		
Hfr cells	high frequency recombinant cells (F factor)	HHG	human hypophyseal gonadotrophin (= HPG)
HFRS	hemorrhagic fever with renal syndrome	HHHO	hypotonia, hypomentia, hypogonadism, obesity; Prader-Labhart-Willi-Fanconi syndrome
HFSH	human follicle-stimulating hormone		
HF surgery	high frequency surgery, electrosurgery	HHM	hemohydrometry
		HHM	humoral hypercalcemia with malignity
HFT	high frequency transduction	HHS	Helsinki Heart Study
HF titration	high frequency titration	HHS	hyperkinetic heart syndrome
HFV	high frequency ventilation	HHS	hypothalamic-hypophyseal system
HG	human gonadotrophin		
Hg	hemoglobin (= Hb, hgb)	HHT	hereditary hemorrhagic teleangiectasia; Osler's syndrome
HGA	homogentisic acid		
hgb	hemoglobin (= Hb, Hg)	HHT	hereditary hyperglycemic type
H gen	histocompatibility gen		
HGF	human growth factor	HHV	human herpes virus
HGF	hyperglycemic-glycogenolytic factor (glucagon)	HI	hemagglutination inhibition (= HAI)
Hg-F	fetal hemoglobin (usually: Hb_F)	HI	Herzindex (G); cardiac index (= CI)
HGG	human gamma globulin	HI	Hospital Insurance
HGH	human growth hormone; (= STH)	5-HIAA	5-hydroxyindole-acetic acid
HG insulin	human globulin insulin	HIB	haemophilus influenzae bacteria
HGO	hepatic glucose output		
HGP	hyperglycemic-glycogenolytic principle (= HGF)	HIC	Heart Information Center
		HID	headache, insomnia, depression (syndrome)
HGPRT	hypoxanthine guanidine phosphoribosyl transferase	HIF	histoplasma-inhibitory factor
HH	hard of hearing		
HH	Henderson-Haggard (inhaler)	HIFC	hog intrinsic factor concentrate
HH	Home Help	HIG, HIg	hyperimmunoglobulin
HH	hydroxyhexamide		

120

HIG test	hemolysis-in-gel test	HL	hypertrichosis lanuginosa, fetal hypertrichosis
HII	hemagglutination inhibition immunoassay	Hl *(ophth)*	latent hypermetropia
HIM	hexosephosphate isomerase (=HPI)	hl	hectoliter
		H/L	hydrophil/lipophil
HIMDA	N-hydroxy-ethyliminodiacetic acid	H+L	heart and lungs
		HLA	histocompatibility antigen (=H antigen)
HINT	Hinton's test (for syphilis)	HLA	homologous leukocytic antibodies
HINT	Holland Interuniversity Nifedipine/Metoprolol Trial	HLA	human leukocyte allo-antigen
HIOMT	hydroxyindole-O-methyl transferase	HLA	human lymphocytic antigen
HIP	Health Insurance Plan	HLAE	high left atrial electrogram
HIP	hydrostatic indifference point	HLB	hydrophil-lipophil balance factor
HIS	heat-inactivated serum	HLF	Heart and Lung Foundation (USA)
HIS	hyperimmune serum		
His	histidine	HLHS	hypoplastic left heart syndrome
HISG	human immune serum globulin	HLI	human leukocyte interferon
hist.	history		
histol.	histology, histological	HLM	heart-lung machine
HIT	hemagglutination inhibition test	Hlm *(phys)*	Hefner lumen
		H-locus *(gen)*	histocompatibility locus
HIT	histamine ion transfer		
HIU	hemaggregation inhibiting unit	HLP	heart-lung preparation
		HLP	human liver antigen preparation
HIV	human immunodeficiency virus (=HTLV, LAV)		
		HLP	human liver protein
HJ	Howell-Jolly bodies	HLP	hyperlipoproteinemia
HJR	hepatojugular reflux	HLQ	heart-lung quotient
HJV	Japanese hemagglutination virus (=HVJ)	HLR	heart-lung resuscitation
		HLS	Health Learning Systems
HK	hexokinase	HLS	von Hippel-Lindau syndrome (cerebroretinal angiomatosis)
H-K	hands to knee		
HK cells	human kidney cells		
HKH	hyperkinetic heart syndrome (=HHS)	HLSP	Heitler-London-Slater-Pauling (method)
HKS	hyperkinetic syndrome (e.g. in children)	HLT	heat-labile toxin
		HLT	hemolysis test
HL	half-life	HLV	herpes-like virus
HL *(rad)*	heart length	HM	hand movements
HL	Hodgkin's lymphoma (=OHL)	Hm *(ophth)*	manifest hypermetropia
		HMB	homatropine methylbromide
HL	Hygienic Laboratory		

5-HMC	5-hydroxymethyl cytosine	HNBB	2-hydroxy-5-nitrobenzyl bromide
HMCMP	hydroxymethyl cytidine monophosphate	HNC	hypothalamic-neurohypophyseal complex
HMD *(card)*	high mid dimension	HNCM	hypertrophic non-obstructive cardiomyopathy (=HNOCM)
HMD	hyaline membrane disease (=HMS)		
HME *(orth)*	heat, massage, exercise	HNKC	hyperosmolar nonketotic coma
HMF	hydroxymethyl-2-furaldehyde	HNOCM	hypertrophic non-obstructive cardiomyopathy (=HNCM)
HMG	human menopausal gonadotrophin		
HMG	3-hydroxy-3-methylglutaric acid	HNP	herniated nucleus pulposus
HMG-CoA	3-hydroxymethylglutaryl coenzyme A	HN-RNA	heterogenic nuclear RNA
		HNS	hypothalamic-neurohypophyseal system
HML	hypophyseal middle lobe	HNSHA	hereditary non-spherocytic hemolytic anemia
HMM	heavy meromyosin		
HMM	hexamethylmelamine	HO	House Officer
HMMA	4-hydroxy-3-methoxymandelic acid	H/o	history of
HMO	Health Maintenance Organization (USA)	HOADH	3-hydroxyacyl-CoA dehydrogenase
HMO	heart minute output (=CO)	HOCM	hypertrophic obstructive cardiomyopathy
HMP	hexose monophosphate	17-HOCS	17-hydroxycorticosteroid
HMPA	hexamethylphosphoramide	HOD	hyperbaric oxygen drenching (=HOT)
HMPG	4-hydroxy-3-methoxyphenylglycol	HofF	height of fundus
		HOG	Hermann-Oberth-Gesellschaft (G); Hermann Oberth Society (Germany)
HMS	Harvard Medical School (Cambridge/USA)		
HMS	heparin monosulfate	Homo-PAS	p-aminomethylsalicylic acid (=PAMSA)
HMS	hexose monophosphate shunt, pentose phosphate cycle	HON *(pharm)*	L-delta-hydroxy-gamma-oxonorvaline (antibiotic)
HMS	hyaline membrane syndrome (=HMD)	HOP	cytotoxic combination therapy with adriamycin, Oncovin (vincristin), and prednisone
HMT	hexamethylene tetramine		
HMT	histamin methyltransferase		
HMT	human molar thyrotrophin	HOP	heterogenic ovum penetration (test)
HMU	hydroxymethyluracil		
HMV	Herzminutenvolumen (G); cardiac output	HOP	high oxygen pressure
		HOP	hydroxyproline (=Hypro)
HN	Head Nurse	hor.decub.	hora decubitus (L); at bedtime (Rx)
h.n.	hoc nocte (L); tonight		
HNAB, HNANB	hepatitis type non-A non-B	hor.som.	hora somni (L); at bedtime (Rx)

122

hor.un.spat.	horae unius spatio (L); hourly, at the end of one hour (Rx)	HPCT	hereditary porphyria cutanea tarda
HOS	human osteosarcoma	HPCT *(psych)*	Hunter Pascal Concept Task
HOT	hematogenic oxidation therapy, "blood washing"	HPD *(card)*	Heimes portable drive (device)
HOT	human old tuberculin	HPD	home peritoneal dialysis
HOT	hyperbaric oxygen therapy	HPD	Hough-Powell digitizer
5-HOT	5-hydroxytryptamine, serotonin	HPD	hypothalamic-pituitary dysfunction
HP	handicapped person	H-6-PD	hexose-6-phosphate dehydrogenase
HP	hemoperfusion		
HP	heparin	HPE	heart valve prosthesis endocarditis
HP	hepatic porphyria		
HP	high pass (vd. HPF)	HPF	heparin precipitable fraction
HP	high potency		
HP	high pressure	HPF	high pass filter (=HP)
HP	highly purified	HPF, hpf	high-power field (of microscope)
HP, hp	horse power		
HP	hot pack (or pad)	HPF	hypothalamic-pituitary failure
HP	hot plate (test)		
HP	House Physician	HPG	human pituitary gonadotrophin (=HHG)
HP	human pharmacokinetics		
HP	hydrostatic pressure	HPG	human postmenopausal gonadotrophin (=HPMG)
HP	hydroxyproline (=HOP, Hypro)		
HP *(ophth)*	hyperphoria	HPI	hexose phosphate isomerase
HP	hypertension and proteinuria	HPI	history of present illness (=HPC)
Hp	haptoglobin	h.p.i.	hora(e) post injectionem (L); hour(s) after injection
H+P	history and physical (examination)	HPL	human parotid lysozyme
HPA	4-ethylsulfonyl-naphthalene-1-sulfonamide	HPL	human placental lactogen
		HPLC	high pressure liquid chromatography
HPA	heteropolyanion (antimony compound with antiviral and antiparasitic activity)	HPL-receptor	helix pomatia lecithin receptor
HPA	hypothalamic-pituitary-adrenal	HPMG	human postmenopausal gonadotrophin (=HPG)
HPC	hexadecyl phosphocholine	HPN	hypertension
HPC	history of present condition	HPO	hypothalamo-pituitary-ovarian (system)
HPC	hydroxyphenyl-cinchoninic acid	HPO, HPOA	hypertrophic pulmonary osteoarthropathy
h.p.c.	hora(e) post cenam (L); hour(s) after meal	HPP	hours post-prandial
HpCa	haptoglobin Carlberg	HPP	human pancreatic polypeptide

HPP	hydroxyphenylpyruvate	HREM	high resolution electron microscope
HPP	4-hydroxypyrazolopyrimidine, allopurinol	HRH	high renin hypertension
HPr	human prolactin	HRL	head rotated left
HPRSD	Hamilton Psychiatric Rating Scale for Depression	HRP	high risk pregnancy
		HRP	horseradish peroxidase
HPRT	hypoxanthine phosphoribosyl transferase (=HGPRT)	HRPP	heart rate pressure product
		HRP-WGA	horseradish peroxidase conjugated to wheat germ agglutinin (also: WGA-HRP)
HPS	high protein supplement		
HPS	His-Purkinje system		
HPT	histamine provocation test	HRR	head rotated right
HPT	human placenta thyrotrophin	HRS *(psych)*	Hamilton Rating Scale (=HPRSD)
HPT	hyperparathyroidism	HRS	Health Research Survey (USA)
HPT	hypothalamic-pituitary-thyroid (function)	HRS	hepatorenal syndrome
HP test	hydroxyproline test	HRS	high risk screening
HPTH	human parathyroid hormone	HRTR	Human Renal Transplant Registry
HPTCL	high pressure thin layer chromatography	HS	half strength
		HS *(dent)*	Hartman's solution
HPV	human papilloma virus	HS	head sling
HPV	hypoxic pulmonary vasoconstriction	HS	heart sounds
		HS	hemolytic system
HPV 77	high passage virus 77	HS	heparin sulfate
HPV 77 DK	high passage virus 77 dog kidney	HS	herpes simplex
		HS	homologous serum
HPVD	hypertensive pulmonary vascular disease	HS	homosexual
		HS	horse serum
HPX *(card)*	Hancock porcine xenograft	H.S.	House Surgeon
Hpx	hemopexin (=HX)	h.s.	hora somni (L); ad bedtime (=hor.som)
HQE	hereditary Quincke edema		
HR	heart rate	H/S *(imm)*	hyposensitization
HR	o-β-hydroxyethyl rutoside	H+S *(gyn)*	hysterotomy and sterilization
hr	hour		
HRA	Health Resources Administration	HSA	Health Services Administration
HRA, HRAE	high right atrial electrocardiogram	HSA	Hospital Savings Association
HRBC	horse red blood cells	HSA	human serum albumin
HRC-CSNS	heart rate controlled carotid sinus nerve stimulation	HSAP	heat-stable alkaline phosphatase
		HSCS	hypersensitive carotid sinus
HRE	high resolution electrocardiography	HSC syndrome	Hand-Schüller-Christian disease
H-reflex	Hoffmann reflex		

124

Hsb	Hefner stilb	5-HT	5-hydroxytryptamine, serotonin
HSD, HSDH	hydroxysteroid dehydrogenase	ht	height
HSE	herpes simplex encephalitis	H+T	hospitalization and treatment
HSF	histamine-sensitizing factor	HTA	histamine transmainase
HSG	herpes simplex genitalis	HTA	hypertension artérielle (F); arterial hypertension
HSG	hysterosalpingography	HTB	hot tub bath
HSGF	high-speed gel filtration	HTC	hepatoma cells, hepatoma tissue culture
HSGF	human skeletal growth factor	HTCVD	hypertensive cardiovascular disease
HSI	heart stress index	HTD	heart transversal diameter
HSI	hepatosomatic index	HTDV	human teratoma-derived virus
HSL	herpes simplex labialis		
HSLC	high-speed liquid chromatography	HTE	hip total endoprosthesis
		H-test	hemaggregation test
HSMHA	Health Services and Mental Health Administration (Washington)	H-tetanase	hemolytic component in tetanus toxin
		HTF	heterothyrotrophic factor
HSOR	hydroxysteroid oxidoreductase	HTF	humoral thymus factor
		HTG	human thyroglobulin
HSP	Henoch-Schönlein purpura	HTG	hypertriglyceridemia
		HTGL	hepatic triglyceride lipase
HSP	heterosexual partner	HTH	homeostatic thymus hormone
H-streptococci	hemolysing streptococci		
		HTO	tritiated water
H-stripe	Hensen's stripe	HTLV	human T-cell lymphotropic virus (=HIV, LAV)
h-strophanthin	hispidus strophanthin		
H-substance	heterogenetic substance	HTP	hyperimmune thrombocytopenia
H-substances	group of biologically active substances (histamine, 5-hydroxytryptamine, heparin) causing anaphylactic reactions	HTP	hypertension portale (F); portal hypertension
		HTP	hypertension pulmonaire (F); pulmonary hypertension
HSV	hamster sarcoma virus	5-HTP	5-hydroxytryptophan
HSV	herpes simplex virus	5-HTP-DC	5-hydroxytryptophan decarboxylase
HSV	highly selective vagotomy		
HT	hemolysin test	HTP test (psych)	house-tree-person test
HT	Herzton (G); heart sound		
HT	home treatment	HTQ	heart-thoracic quotient
HT	hydrotherapy	HTR	hemolytic transfusion reaction
HT	hyperthermia		
HT	hyperthyroidism	HTSH	human thyroid stimulating hormone
HT	hypothalamus		
Ht (ophth)	total hypermetropia		

HTSI	human thyroid stimulating immunoglobulin	HVJ	hemagglutinating virus of Japan (= HJV)
HTST	high temperature short time (pasteurization)	HVL *(rad)*	half value layer
HTT	heparin tolerance test	HVPE	high-voltage paper electro-phoresis
HTV	herpes-type virus	HVS	hyperventilation syndrome
HTVD	hypertensive vascular disease	HVT *(rad)*	half value thickness
		HVT	hepatic vein thrombosis
HU	Harvard University (Cambridge/USA)	HW	housewife
		HWS	hot water soluble
HU	Hounsfield unit	HWY	hundred woman years (statistical term in gynecology)
HU	human urine		
HU	hydroxyurea	HX	hemopexin
HU	hyperemia unit	HX	hypoxanthine, 6-hydroxy-purine
HuEPO	human erythropoietin		
Hu factor	Hunter factor, antigen Hu	Hx	history
		HXG	N,N-dihydroxyethyl glycine
HUS	hemolytic uremic syndrome		
		HXR	hypoxanthine riboside
HU-1 system	histocompatibility antigens (s. HLA)	Hy *(ophth)*	hypermetropia
		Hy *(psych)*	hysteria
HV	hardness value of Vickers	H-Y antigen	antigen causing histoincompatibility, coded by a gene of the Y chromosome
HV	heart volume		
HV	hepatitis virus		
HV	high vacuum	Hyl, Hylys	hydroxylysine
HV	hyperventilation	Hyp, Hypro	L-hydroxyproline
HVA	homovanillic acid	HYRAP	Hypertension Research Action Programm (of the WHO)
HV block	His-ventricular block		
HVC	hypertrophie ventriculaire combinée (F); combined ventricular hypertrophy		
		Hy-Sa *(gyn)*	hysterosalpingography (= HSG)
HVD	hypertensive vascular disease (= HTVD)	Hz	Hertz (unit of frequency)
		H-zone	Hensen zone (= H-stripe)
HVD	hypertrophie ventriculaire droite (F); right ventricular hypertrophy	HZV	herpes zoster virus
HVE	high-voltage electron microscopy		
HVG	host versus graft (reaction) (= HvGR)		
HVG	hypertrophie ventriculaire gauche (F); left ventricular hypertrophy		
HvGR	host versus graft reaction	I	inspired air
HVH	herpes virus hominis	I *(phys)*	impulse rate
HVI	human vaccinia immuno-globulin	I *(dent)*	incisor
		I	inclination
		I	increased
		I	index

I

I	indicator	IAATM	International Association of Accident and Traffic Medicine
I	induction		
I *(phys)*	inertia		
I	inhibitor, inhibition	IAB	Industrial Accident Board
I *(chem)*	inosine (= Ino)	IAB	insulin antibodies
I *(phys)*	intensity (light, sound, current)	IAB *(card)*	intra-atrial block
		IABC *(card)*	intra-aortic balloon counterpulsation
I	international		
I	intestinal	IABP	intra-aortic balloon pump
I	isotope		
i *(phys)*	(optically) inactive	IABS	International Association of Biological Standardization
i	insoluble		
i- *(chem)*	iso-		
IA	immunoadherence	IAC	International Academy of Cytology
IA	impedance angle		
IA	indole acetate	IACBC	International Advisory Committee on Biological Control
IA	infiltration anesthesia		
IA	inhibitory activity		
IA	insuffisance aortique (F); aortic insufficiency	IACD	implantable automatic cardioverter/defibrillator
IA	intelligence age	IAD	inactivating dose
IA	intrinsic activity	IAD	inhibitory antibiotic dose
IA	irradiation area	IADR	International Association of Dental Research
Ia	anodal current		
ia	infra-audible	IADS	International Association of Dental Students
i.a.	intra-arterial		
i.a.	intra-articular	IADSA	intra-arterial digital subtraction angiography
i.a.	intra-atrial		
IÅ	International Ångström Unit	IAEA	International Atomic Energy Agency (Vienna) (= AIEA)
IAA	indole-3-acetic acid		
IAA	insulin auto-antibodies (= IAAB)	IAEA	International Atomic Energy Authority
IAA	International Antituberculosis Association	IAEO	International Atomic Energy Organization
IAA	International Association of Allergology	IAF	International Astronautical Federation
IAA	interrupted aortic arch	IAFB	incomplete anterior fascicular block
IAA	iodo-acetic acid		
IAAA	International Agranulocytosis and Aplastic Anemia (Study)	IAFI	infantile amaurotic familial idiocy
		IAFS	International Association of Forensic Science
IAAB	insulin auto-antibodies (= IAA)	IAG	inosine, adenine, guanosine
IAAP	International Association of Applied Psychology		
		IAG	International Association of Gerontology

127

IAGP	International Association of Geographic Pathology	IAP	International Academy of Pathology
IAGT	indirect antiglobulin test	IAP	International Association of Psychotechnics
IAGUS	International Association of Genito-Urinary Surgeons	IAPB	International Association for Prevention of Blindness
IAHA	immunoadherence-hemagglutination	IAPP	International Association for Preventative Pediatrics
IAHA	Inter-American Hospital Association	IAPP	islet amyloid polypeptide
IAHT	immunoadherence hemagglutination technique	IAPT	inhalant antigen pneumatometry test
IAI *(gyn)*	induction-abortion interval	IARC	International Agency for Research on Cancer (Lyon/France)
IALP	International Association of Logopaedics and Phoniatrics	IARS	International Anaesthesia Research Society
IAM	impulse amplitude modification	IART	intra-arterial re-entry tachycardia
IAMANEH	International Association for Maternal and Neonatal Health	IAS	Institute of the Aerospace Sciences
		IAS	interatrial septum
IAMAT	International Association for Medical Assistance to Travellers (Toronto)	IAS	intra-amniotic saline
		IASD	interatrial septal defect (=ASD)
IAMB	International Association of Microbiologists	IASL	International Association for the Study of the Liver
IAMC	Indian Army Medical Corps	IASP	International Association for Suicide Prevention
IAMLT	International Association of Medical Laboratory Technologists	IASP	International Association for the Study of Pain
IAMM	International Association of Medical Museums	IAT	inhalant allergen test
		IAT	intraoperative autotransfusion
IAMS	International Association of Microbiolocigal Societies	IAT	iodine azide test
		IATA	International Air Transport Association
IAN	International Anatomical Nomenclature	IAV	intermittent assisted ventilation
IANC	International Anatomical Nomenclature Committee	IB	immune body
		IB	inclusion bodies
IAO *(clin)*	immediately after onset	IB	index of body build
IAO	intermittent aortic occlusion	IB	infectious bronchitis
		ib.	ibidem (L); in the same place
IAP	instable angina pectoris	IBA	indolyl-3-butyric acid
IAP	intracisternal A-particle	I-band	isotropic band (of a muscle fiber
IAP	Institute of Animal Physiology (UK)		

IBBBB	incomplete bilateral bundle branch block	i.c. *(pharm)*	inter cibos (L); between meals (Rx)
IBC	insulin-binding capacity	i.c.	intracardial
IBC	iron-binding capacity	i.c.	intracerebral
IBD	inflammatory bowel disease	i.c.	intracranial
IBF	immunoglobulin binding factor	i.c.	intracutaneous
		ICA	immune complex assay
IBI	intermittent bladder irrigation;	ICA	insuffisance du coeur aigue (F); acute heart failure
IBI	Istituto Biochimico Italiano; Italian Biochemical Institute	ICA	internal carotid artery
		ICA	International Chiropractors Association
IBP, ibp	initial boiling point	ICA	islet-cell antibodies (=ICAB)
IBP	International Biological Program		
		ICAA	International Council on Alcohol and Addiction
IBP	iron-binding protein		
IBR *(vet)*	inclusion body rhinitis (in pigs)	ICAA	Invalid Children's Aid Association
IBR *(vet)*	infectious bovine rhinotracheitis	ICAAC	Interscience Conference on Antimicrobial Agents and Chemotherapy
IBRO	International Brain Research Organization (Paris)		
		ICAB	islet-cell antibodies (=ICA)
IBS	irritable bowel syndrome; colon irritabile	ICAO	International Civil Aviation Organization (Montreal/Canada)
IBT	isatin-β-thiosemicarbazone		
IBU	international benzoate unit	ICASSI	International Committee for Adlerian Summer Schools and Institutes
IBV	infectious bronchitis vaccine		
		ICBL	International Conference on the Biochemistry of Lipids
IBV	infectious bronchitis virus		
IBW	ideal body weight		
IBWM	International Bureau for Weights and Measures (Sèvres/France)	ICBN	International Commitee on Bacteriological Nomenclature
		ICBP	intercellular binding proteins
IC	index cardiaque (F); cardiac index		
		ICC	Information Center Complex
IC	initial condition		
IC	inspiratory capacity	ICC	insuffisance circulatoire cérébrale (F); cerebral circulatory failure
IC	integrated circuit		
IC	intensive care		
IC	intercellular	ICC *(rad)*	internal conversion coefficient
IC	intercostal		
IC	interstitial cells	ICC	International Congress Center (Berlin)
IC	intracellular		
IC	intrapleural catheter		

ICCM	idiopathic congestive cardiomyopathy	ICF(M)A	International Cystic Fibrosis (Mucoviscidosis) Association
ICCR	International Committee for Contraceptive Research	ICFV	intracellular fluid volume
ICD	impulse conduction defect	ICG	indocyanine green
ICD	Institute for Crippled and Disabled	ICG	International Congress of Genetics
ICD *(card)*	intercapillary distance	ICH *(vet)*	infectious canine hepatitis
ICD *(ophth)*	intercorneal distance	ICH	intracranial (or intracerebral) hematoma
ICD	intermittent claudication distance	ICHD	Inter-Society Commission for Heart Diseases Resources (USA)
ICD	International Classification of Diseases, Injuries and Causes of Death	ICHT	International Committee on Haemostasis and Thrombosis
ICD	International Congress on Dietetics	ICI	Imperial Chemical Industries
ICD *(gyn)*	intrauterine contraceptive device (= IUCD, IUP)	ICLA	International Committee on Laboratory Animals
ICD	isocitric dehydrogenase (= ICDH, IDH)	ICM	infiltrative cardiomyopathy
ICD	isoconcentration dosage	ICM	intercostal margin
ICDA	International Classification of Diseases, Adapted	ICM	Intergovernmental Committee for Migration
ICD-CM	International Classification of Diseases, Clinical Modification	ICM	International Confederation of Midwives
ICDH	isocitric dehydrogenase (= ICD, IDH)	ICMMP	International Committee of Military Medicine and Pharmacy
ICDRG	International Contact Dermatitis Research Group	ICMP	International College of Medical Practice
ICDS	International Cardiac Doppler Society	ICN	International Council of Nurses
ICECN	International Congress on Encephalography and Clinical Neurology	ICNBV	International Code of Nomenclature of Bacteria and Viruses (London/ Delft)
ICF	indirect centrifugal flotation	ICNT	International Committee for Natural Therapeutics
ICF	intensive care facility	ICO	International Commission for Optics
ICF	intermediate care facility	ICO	International Congress of Otolaryngology
ICF	intracellular fluid		
ICF	intravascular coagulation and fibrinolysis	ICOPA	International Congress of Parasitology
ICFA	induced complement-fixing antigen	ICP	impulse cytophotometry
		ICP	infantile cerebral palsy

ICP	International Candle Power
ICP	intracranial pressure
ICPA	International Commission for the Prevention of Alcoholism
I-C-PM-M (dent)	incisors, canines, premolars, molars
ICPP	International Committee of Planned Parenthood
ICPPC	International Classification of Process in Primary Care
ICR	(distance between) iliac crests
ICR	International Congress of Radiology
ICR	intracutaneous reaction
ICRC	Indian Cancer Research Centre
ICRC	International Committee of the Red Cross
ICRE	International Commission on Radiological Education
ICRO	International Cell Research Organization (Paris)
ICRP	International Commission on Radiation Protection
ICRS	Index Chemicus Registry System
ICRS	International Commission on Radium Standards
ICRU, ICRUM	International Commission on Radiological Units and Measurements (Washington)
ICS	impulse-conducting system
ICS	Intensive Care, Surgical
ICS	intercostal space
ICS	intermediate coronary syndrome
ICS	International College of Surgeons
ICS	International Continence Society
ICS	intracranial stimulation
ICSA	islet-cell surface antibodies
ICSF	International Council on Social Welfare
ICSG	International Center of Social Gerontology (Paris)
ICSH	International Committee for Standardization in Haematology (Utrecht/ The Netherlands)
ICSH	interstitial cell stimulating hormone
ICSHB	International Committee for Standardization in Human Biology
ICSO (card)	intermittent coronary sinus occlusion
ICSSPE	International Council of Sports and Physical Education
IC-STK	intracoronary streptokinase
ICSU	International Council of Scientific Unions (Rome/ Italy)
ICSW	International Congress on Social Welfare
ICT	inflammation of connective tissue
ICT	insulin coma therapy (=IST)
ICT	intracranial tumor
ICT	isovolumic contraction time
ICTMM	International Congress on Tropical Medicine and Malaria
ICU	Intensive Care Unit
ICUMSA	International Commission for Uniform Methods of Sugar Analysis
ICV	intracellular volume
i.c.v.	intracerebroventriculary (=i.vt.)
ICW	intracellular water
ID	immunodeficiency
ID	immunodiffusion
ID	immunological difference
ID	inclusion disease

ID *(stat)*	index of discrimination	IDMMC	interdigestive migrating motor complex
ID	infectious disease	IDN	incipient diabetic nephro-pathy
ID	infective dose		
ID	inhibitory dose	IDO	International Dental Orga-nization
ID	initial dose		
ID	inside diameter	IDP	immunodiffusion proce-dures
ID *(obst)*	intrauterine dystrophy		
ID	intrinsic deflection (in the ECG)	IDP	inosine-5'-diphosphate
		IDP	integrated data processing
ID	isotope dilution	IDPN	β,β'-imino-dipropionitrile bisulfate
id.	idem (L); the same		
i.d.	in dies (L); daily (Rx)	IDS	inhibitor of DNA synthesis
i.d.	intradermal	IDS	Investigative Dermatologi-cal Society
I + D	incision and drainage		
ID_{50}	median infective dose (= DIM)	IDT	immunodepressive therapy
		IDT	immunodiffusion test
IDA	imino-diacetic acid	IDT	indicator dilution tech-nique
IDAV	immunodeficiency-asso-ciated virus (= HIV, HTLV, LAV)		
		IDT	intradermal test
		IDU	idoxuridine, 5-iodo--2'-deoxyuridine (= 5-IUDR)
IDC	idiopathic dilated cardio-myopathy		
IDC	International Documenta-tion Society for Chemistry (Frankfurt/Germany)	IDU	International Digitalis Unit
		IDV	intermittent demand venti-lation
IDCN	Infectious Disease Control Nurse	IE	Immunisierungseinheit (G); immunizing unit
IDD	immunodeficiency disease		
IDDM	insulin-dependent diabetes mellitus	IE	immunoelectrophoresis
		IE	intermittent exophthalmos
IDF	International Dental Fed-eration	IE	Internationale Einheit (G); International Unit (IU)
IDF	International Diabetes Federation	i.e.	id est (L); that is
		IEA	immunoelectrophoretic analysis
IDH	isocitric dehydrogenase (= ICD, ICDH)		
		IEA	International Epidemio-logical Association
IDI	immunologically detect-able insulin (= IMI, IRI)		
		IEA	intravascular erythrocyte aggregation
IDI	inspiratory distribution volume		
		IEC	International Electrotech-nical Commission
IDL	intermediate density lipo-proteins		
		IEC	intraepithelial carcinoma
IDM	idiopathic disease of the myocardium	IEC	ion exchange chromatogra-phy
IDM *(obst)*	infant of a diabetic mother	IEE	inner enamel epithelium
IDM	infarctus du myocarde (F); myocardial infarction	IEF	isoelectric focussing
		I-effect	induction effect

IEG	immunological evolution groups	IFGO	International Federation of Gynaecology and Obstetrics (= FIGO)
IEM	immune electron microscopy	IFIP	International Federation for Information Processing
IEM	inborn error of metabolism	IFL-rA	recombinant leukocyte-A-interferon (international nomenclature: IFN-alpha$_2$)
IEP	immune electrophoresis (= IE)		
IEP	isoelectric point	IFM	impulse frequency modulation
IER	Institute of Educational Research		
IET	immunoenzyme technique	IFMBE	International Federation for Medical and Biological Engineering
IET *(obst)*	intrauterine exchange transfusion		
IF	immunofluorescence	IFME	International Federation of Medical Electronics
IF	inflammatory factor		
IF	inhibiting factor	IFMP	International Federation of Medical Psychotherapy
IF	interferon (also: IF, INF)		
IF	intermediate frequency	IFMSA	International Federation of Medical Students Associations
IF	interstitial fluid		
IF	intrinsic factor		
IFA	idiopathic fibrosing alveolitis	IFMSS	Inernational Federation of Multiple Sclerosis Societies
IFA	immunofluorescence assay	IFN	interferon (also: IF, INF)
IFA	inspiratory flow assistance	IFN-alpha$_2$	recombinant leukocyte-A-interferon (= IFL-rA)
IFAPP	International Federation of Associations of Pharmaceutical Physicians	I-form	indeterminate form of leprosy
IFAR	indirect immunofluorescence antibody reaction	IFORS	International Federation of Operational Research Societies
IFA test	indirect fluorescence antibody test	IFOS	International Federation of Oral Surgeons
IFB *(card)*	inferior fascicular block	IFOS	International Federation of Otorhinolaryngological Societies
IFC	International Federation of Chromatography		
IFCC	International Federation of Clinical Chemistry	IFPM	International Federation of Physical Medicine
IFCPC	International Federation of Cervical Pathology and Colposcopy	IFPMA	International Federation of Pharmaceutical Manufacturers Associations
IFECG	indirect fetal electrocardiogram	IFRP	International Fertility Research Program
IFEES	International Federation of Electro-Encephalographical Societies	IFSECN	International Federation of Societies for Electroencephalography and Clinical Neurophysiology (Boston)
IFFS	International Federation of Fertility Societies		

IFSEM	International Federation of Societies for Electron Microscopy	IGY	International Geophysical Year
IFT	immunofluorescence test	IH	idiopathic (cardiac) hypertrophy
IFT	International Frequency Tables	IH	immediate-type hypersensitivity
IFV	interstitial fluid volume	IH	infectious hepatitis
IG, Ig	immunoglobulin	IH	inguinal hernia
IgA	immunoglobulin A	IH	inhibitory hormone
IGAM	Internationale Gesellschaft für Allgemeinmedizin (G); International Society of General Medicine	IH	inpatient hospital
		IH	intracerebral (or intracranial) hematoma
		IH	iron hematoxylin
IGCI	Internationale Gesellschaft für Chemo- und Immuntherapie (G); International Society of Chemotherapy and Immunotherapy	I.H.	Institute of Hygiene
		IHA	indirect hemagglutination
		IHA	International Hospital Association
		IHAR, IHAT	indirect hemagglutination reaction, ... test
IgD	immunoglobulin D	IHB (card)	infra-His block
IgE	immunoglobulin E	IHC	idiopathic hypercalciuria
IGF	insulin-like growth factor	IHC	International Health Conference
IGFM	Internationale Gesellschaft für Menschenrechte (G); International Society for Human Rights (= ISHR, SIDH)	IHC	isolation hemodialysis center
		IHCT	International Histological Classification of Tumors
IgG	immunoglobulin G		
IGH	immunoreactive growth hormone	IHD	ischemic heart disease
IgM	immunoglobulin M	IHDR	Ischemic Heart Disease Register (WHO/Geneva)
IGO	integrated gastrin output		
IGPM	Internationale Gesellschaft für Prospektive Medizin (G); International Society for Prospective Medicine	IHEMI	International Health Economics and Management Institute (USA)
		IHF	International Health Foundation
IGR	Internationale Gesellschaft für Radiobiologie (G); International Society of Radiobiology	IHF	International Hospital Federation
		IHFJV	intermittent high frequency jet ventilation
IGSAS	Interactive Graphics Survival Analysis System	IHG	isometric hand grip
IGT	impaired glucose tolerance	IHGT	insulin hypoglycemia test (= IHT)
IGTT	intravenous glucose tolerance test	IHO	International Health Organization
IGV	intrathoracic gas volume (= ITGV)	IHP	inositol hexaphosphate
		IHR (card)	intra-His re-entry

IHS	International Haemophilia Society	IKAR	Internationale Kommission für alpines Rettungswesen (G); International Commission for Alpine Rescue
IHSA	iodinated human serum albumin (=RIHSA)		
IHSS	idiopathic hypertrophic sub-aortic stenosis	IKS	Interkantonale Kontrollstelle für Heilmittel (G); Intercantonal Supervision Agency for Drugs (Bern/ Switzerland)
IHT	insulin hypoglycemia test (=IHGT)		
IH virus	infectious hepatitis virus, hepatitis A virus		
II	icterus index	IK unit	infusoria killing unit
IIA	International Institute of Anthropology	IL	interleukin
		IL, il (dent)	incisolingual
IIASA	International Institute for Applied System Analysis	i.l.	intralumbar
		ILA	insulin-like activity
IIBEM	Indian Institute of Biochemistry and Experimental Medicine	ILA	International Leprosy Association
		ILa, ila (dent)	incisolabial
IIE	International Institute of Embryology	ILAE	International League against Epilepsy
IIF	indirect immunofluorescence	ILAR	International League against Rheumatism
IIFT	indirect immunofluorescence test	ILBBB	incomplete left bundle branch block
IIH	insulin-induced hyperglycemia	Ile, Ileu	isoleucine
IIHDS	Israel Ischaemic Heart Disease Study	ILEP	International Association of Leprosy Charity Organizations
IIMEBE	International Institute of Medical Electronics and Biological Engineering	ILF	idiopathic lung fibrosis
		ILM	Institute of Laser Technology in Medicine (Ulm/ Germany)
IIN	inhibitory interneuron		
IIS	International Institute of Sociology	ILMAC	International Exhibition of Laboratory Technique, Measuring, and Automation in Chemistry
IIT	integrated isometric tension		
IITB	(German) Institute of Information Processing in Technology and Biology		
		ILN	intermediolateral nucleus
		ILO	International Labor Organization (Geneva) (=OIT)
IITS	isatin-β-isothiosemicarbazone		
IJD	inflammatory joint disease	ILo	iodine lotion
IJP	inhibitory junction potential	ILS	idiopathic lymphadenopathy syndrome
IK	Immunkörper (G); immune bodies	ILST	iterative least square technique (in computerized tomography)
IK (ophth)	interstitial keratitis		

ILV	independent lung ventilation	IMI	indirect membrane-immunofluorescence
IM	impulse modulation	IMI	inferior myocardial infarction
IM	Index Medicus		
IM	indomethacin (= IMC)	^{131}I-MIBG	radioactive labelled metaiodobenzyl guanidine
IM	infectious mononucleosis		
IM	insuffisance mitrale (F); mitral insufficiency	IMIS	integrated mean inhibition score
IM	Internal Medicine	IMLC	incomplete mitral leaflet closure
i.m.	intramuscular		
IMA	Indian Medical Association	IMLT	Institute of Medical Laboratory Technology (UK)
IMA	Industrial Medical Association		
IMA	internal mammary artery	IMLT	intermittent multiple load test
IMA	Irish Medical Association		
IMAO	inhibiteur de monoaminoxidase (F); monoaminooxidase inhibitor (= MAOI)	IMP	inosine-5'-monophosphate
		IMP	Institute of Medical Psychology (UK)
		IMP	Institute of Molecular Pathology (Vienna/Austria)
IMB	Institute of Microbiology		
IMBC	indirect maximum breathing capacity	IMP	intramyocardial pressure
		IMPA *(dent)*	incisal mandibular plane angle (Margolis)
IMBI	Institute of Medical and Biological Illustrators		
		IMPS	Inpatient Multidimensional Psychiatric Scale
IMC	indomethacin (= IM)		
IMC	International Medical Corporation	IMRaD	introduction, material, results, and discussion (structure of a scientific paper)
IMCD	inner medullary collecting duct		
IMD	Institute for Muscle Diseases (USA)	IMS	Indian Medical Service (USA)
IMD	Institut für Medizinische Datenverarbeitung (G); Institute of Medical Data Processing (Germany)	IMS	Information Management System
		IMS	Institutes for Medical Science (San Francisco)
IME	inborn metabolic error (= IEM)	IMS	Institut für Medizinische Statistik; Institute of Medical Statistics (Frankfurt/Germany)
IMED	idiopathic mural endomyocardial disease		
IMF	internal magnetic focus tube	IMS	Intercontinental Medical Statistics
IMI	immunologically measurable insulin (= IDI, IRI)	IMS	International Menopause Society (Brussels)
		IMV	intermittent mandatory ventilation

IMVC test	differentiation of entero-bacteria by: indole assay, methyl red reaction, Voges-Proskauer reaction, and citrate test
IMVI	Institute of Medical Virology and Immunology (Essen/Germany)
IN	icterus neonatorum (L); jaundice of the newborn
IN	interstitial nephritis
In	inulin
in.	inch
i.n.	intranasal
INA	immunologic-nephelometric assay
INA	infectious nucleic acid
INA	International Normal Atmosphere
INA	International Neurological Association
INA	Jena Nomina Anatomica (=JNA)
INAH	isonicotinic acid hydrazide (=INH)
INB *(card)*	intranodal block
INC	insulin neutralizing capacity
IncB	inclusion body
IND *(pharm)*	Investigational New Drug
Ind.	indication
IN-EX ratio	ratio of inspiration and expiration time
INF	interferon (also: IF, IFN)
Inf.	infirmary
Inf.	infusion
Inf.	infection
inf.	inferior
INFAS	Institut für Angewandte Sozialwissenschaften; Institute for Applied Social Sciences (Bonn/ Germany)
INFIT	intracranial fluid infusion tamponade
ING	isotope nephrography (=RIN)

ing.	inguinal
INGP	indolglycerophosphate
INH	isonicotinic acid hydrazide, isoniazid
Inh.	inhalation
INHS	1-isonicotinoyl-2-salicylidene hydrazine
INI	intranuclear inclusion
Inj.	injection
inj.	injury
INN *(pharm)*	International Non-Proprietary Name
Ino	inosine (=I)
INPEA	N-isopropyl-p-nitrophenyl ethanolamine
INPH	iproniazid phosphate
INPRONS	information processing in the central nervous system
INPV	intermittent negative pressure ventilation
INR	international normalized ratio
INREM	internal radiation dose
INRIA	Institut National de Recherche en Informatique et en Automatique (F); National Institute of Research on Information and Automation
INS	idiopathic nephrotic syndrome
INSERM	Institut National pour la Santé et la Recherche Médicale (F); National Institute of Health and Medical Research
INSTAND	Institut für Standardisierung und Dokumentation im medizinischen Laboratorium (G); Institute of Standardization and Documentation in the Medical Laboratory
INT	intranasal test
INT	iodo-nitrotetrazolium
int *(gen)*	integrase
int.	internus (L); internal

INTACT	International Nifedipine Trial of Antiatherosclerotic Therapy	IPA, IPAA	International Psychoanalytical Association
int.cib.	inter cibos (L); between meals	IPAP	inspiratory positive airway pressure
InV	inhibiting factor Virm	IPAT	Institute for Personality and Ability Testing
IO	intestinal obstruction	IPC	International Poliomyelitis Congress
IO	intraocular		
I+O	intake and output	IPC	International Psychological Congress
IOA	6-methylheptanic acid		
IOAT	International Organization against Trachoma	IPC	isopropylchloride
		IPC	isopropyl-N-phenylcarbamate (= IPPC)
IOFB	intraocular foreign body		
IOGT	International Order of Good Templars	IPCG	intracardial phonocardiography
IOM	Institute of Medicine (of the National Academy of Sciences/USA)	IPCS	International Program on Chemical Safety
IOMP	International Organization for Medical Physics	IPCS	intrauterine progesterone contraceptive system
IOP	intraocular pressure	IPD	intermittent peritoneal dialysis
IOPAB	International Organization for Pure and Applied Biophysics (Boston)	IPF	International Pharmaceutical Federation
IOS	International Organization of Standardization (Geneva/Switzerland)	IPFB *(card)*	incomplete posterior fascicular block
		IPG	impedance pneumography
IOTA	information overload testing aid	IPG	infusion pyelography (= IUG)
IP	icterus praecox	IPH	idiopathic pulmonary hypertension
IP	immunoperoxidase (test)	i.pl.	intrapleural
IP *(dent)*	incisoproximal	IPM	impulsif-petit-mal (F); impulsive epilepsy
IP	incubation period		
IP	infection prevention	ipm	impulses per minute
IP	inpatient	IPMR	Institute of Physical Medicine and Rehabilitation
IP	instantaneous pressure		
IP, I.P.	International Pharmacopeia	IPNA	International Pediatric Nephrology Association
IP	interphalangeal		
IP	isoelectric point (= IEP)	IPNA	isopropyl noradrenaline; isoprenaline
IP$_3$	inositol triphosphate		
i.p.	intraperitoneal	IPNPV	intermittent positive-negative pressure ventilation
IPA	immunoperoxidase antibody (test)		
		IPP	Institute of Plasma Physics (Munich/Germany)
IPA	International Paediatric Association		
IPA	isopentyl adenosine	IPP	interstitial plasma cell pneumonia, pneumocystis pneumonia
IPA	isopropyl alcohol		

IPP	isopotential point ($=$IEP)	IPTH	immunoreactive parathyroid hormone
IPPA *(clin)*	inspection, palpation, percussion, auscultation	IPU	Inpatient Unit
		IPUP	intrapulmonary percussion
IPPB	intermittent positive pressure breathing	IPV	inactivated poliomyelitis vaccine (Salk)
IPPC	isopropyl-N-phenylcarbamate ($=$IPC)	IPV *(vet)*	infectious pustular vulvovaginitis
IPPD	isopropyl-phenyl-p-phenylene diamine	IPV	insufficient perforating veins
IPPDB	intermittent positive pressure dead space breathing	IPZ	insulin-protamine-zinc
		IQ	intelligence quotient
IPPF	International Planned Parenthood Federation	IQS elixir	iron-quinine-strychnine elixir
IPPNW	International Physicians for Prevention of Nuclear Warfare	IR *(psych)*	ideational recall
		IR	immediate reaction
		IR	immunoreactivity
IPPPSH	International Prospective Primary Prevention Study in Hypertension	IR	infection rate
		IR	infra-red
		IR	insoluble residue
IPPR	intermittent positive pressure respiration ($=$IPPB, IPPV)	IR	insulin resistance
		IR	internal resistance
		IR	ischemic region
IPPV	intermittent positive pressure ventilation ($=$IPPB, IPPR)	IR *(card)*	isovolumetric relaxation phase
		IRA	immunoregulatory alphaglobulin
IPQ *(psych)*	intimacy potential quotient		
IPR	Institut für sozialmedizinische Präventions- und Rehabilitationsforschung (G); Institute of Sociomedical Prevention and Rehabilitation Research	IRA	insuffisance respiratoire aigue (F); acute respiratory insufficiency
		IRB	Institutional Review Board (USA)
		IRBBB	incomplete right bundle branch block
IPR	isoproterenol, isoprenalin	IRBF	intrarenal blood flow
IPS	International Confederation for Plastic Surgery	IRC	inspiratory reserve capacity
		IRC	insuffisance respiratoire chronique (F); chronic respiratory insufficiency
ips	impulses per second		
ips	inches per second		
IPSC	Interagency Primate Steering Committee	IRC	International Red Cross
		IRCC	International Red Cross Committee ($=$ICRC)
IPSF	International Pharmaceutical Students Federation	IRCP	International Commission on Radiological Protection
IPSP	inhibitory postsynaptic potential		
IPTD	2-isopropyl-5-sulfanilamido-1,3,4-thiadiazole	IRCS	International Research Communication System
IPTG	isopropyl thiogalactoside		

IRDS	idiopathic respiratory distress syndrome	IRT	inversion recovery technique
I-retina	inhibitory retina	IRT	isovolumic relaxation time (= IRP)
IRG, IRGl	immunoreactive glucagon		
IRGCP	International Research Group for Carcinoembryonic Proteins	IRU	Industrial Rehabilitation Unit
		IRU	International Radium Unit
IRHGH	immunoreactive human growth hormone	IRV	inspiratory reserve volume
IRI	immunoreactive insulin (= IDI, IMI)	IS	immune serum
		IS	immunosuppressive (agent)
IRINS	irreversible ischemic neurological symptoms	IS	infarct size
IRIS	infarction risk screening	IS	intercostal space
IRIS	International Research Information Service	IS	International Standard
		IS	intraspinal
IRM	innate releasing mechanism	IS	ischemic score (in the ECG)
IRM	Institute of Rehabilitation Medicine	ISA	Instrument Society of America
IRM	insulin reactivity measure	ISA	International Sociological Association
IRMA	immunoradiometric assay		
IRMP	Intermountain Regional Medical Program	ISA	intravenous subtraction angiography
IRO	International Refugee Organization	ISA (pharm)	intrinsic sympathomimetic activity
IROS	ipsilateral routing of signal	ISA	iodinated serum albumin
IRP	immunoreactive proinsulin	ISADH	inappropriate secretion of antidiuretic hormone
IRP (pharm)	International Reference Preparation	ISAM	International Society of Aerosols in Medicine
IRP	intestinal insulin releasing polypeptide	ISAM	Intravenous Streptokinase in Acute Myocardial Infarction (Study)
IRP	isovolumic relaxation period (= IRT)		
IRPA	International Radiation Protection Association	ISAO	International Society for Artificial Organs
IRPTC	International Register of Potentially Toxic Chemicals	ISB	Institute of Medical Information Processing, Statistics, and Biomathematics (Germany)
IRR (lab)	International Reference Reagent	ISB	International Society of Biometry
irr.	irreversible		
IRS	immunologically reacting somatostatin	ISBB	International Society of Bioclimatology and Biometeorology
IRS	immunoreactivity score		
IRS	induced rat sarcoma	ISBN	International Standard Book Number
IRT	immunoreactive trypsin		

ISBT	International Society of Blood Transfusion	ISGE	International Society of Gastroenterology
ISC	International Society of Cardiology	ISGIID	International Study Group on Diabetes Treatment with Implantable Insulin Delivery
ISC	International Statistical Classification		
ISC	interstitial cells	ISGP	International Society of Geographical Pathology
ISCA	Indian Science Congress Association (Calcutta)	ISH	immature sinus histiocytes
ISCB	International Society of Cell Biology	ISH	International Society of Haematology
ISCEH	International Society of Clinical and Experimental Hypnosis	ISH	International Society of Hypertension
		ISHAM	International Society of Human and Animal Mycology
ISCERG	International Society for Clinical Electroretinography		
		ISHR	International Society for Heart Research
ISCLT	International Society for Clinical Laboratory Technology	ISI	initial slope index
		ISI	Institute for Scientific Information (USA)
ISCOM, Iscom	immunostimulating complex		
		ISI	interstimulus interval
ISCP	International Society of Clinical Pathologists	ISI	International Sensitivity Index
ISCP	International Society of Comparative Pathology	ISIM	International Society of Internal Medicine
ISD	isosorbide dinitrate (= ISDN, ISN)	ISIMV	inspiration-synchronized intermittent mandatory ventilation
ISDB	International Society of Developmental Biologists		
		ISIS	International Study of Infarct Survival
ISDN	Integrated Services Digital Network	ISKDC	International Study of Kidney Diseases in Children
ISDN	isosorbide dinitrate (= ISD, ISN)		
		ISM	International Society of Microbiologists
ISE	ion-selective electrode		
ISEH	International Society for Experimental Haematology	ISMH	International Society of Medical Hydrology
		IS-5-MN	isosorbide-5-mononitrate
ISF	immunoglobulin San Francisco	ISN	inosine (= I, Ino)
		ISN	International Society of Neurochemistry
ISF	International Society for Fat Research		
		ISN	isosorbide dinitrate (= ISD, ISDN)
ISF	interstitial fluid (= IF)		
ISFET	ion-sensitive field effect transistor	ISO	International Standardization Organization (Geneva) (= IOS)
ISG	immune serum globulin		

ISOM	International Standard Orthopedic Measurements	ISU	International Society of Urology
ISP	(distance between) iliac spines	I-substance	inhibitor substance
		ISW	interstitial water
ISP	insulin-specific protease	i.sy.	intrasynovial
ISP	intracellular serine proteinase	IT	immunological tolerance
		IT	immunotoxin
ISP	isoproterenol, isoprenaline	IT	inhalation therapy
ISPN	International Society of Paediatric Neurosurgery	IT	injection time
		IT	intrathoracic
ISPO	International Society of Paediatric Oncology	I/T	ratio of immature and total neutrophils
ISPO	International Society for Preventive Oncology	I/T	intensity/time (vd. i/t curve)
ISPO	International Society for Prosthetics and Orthotics	ITA	induced thrombocyte aggregation
ISPOG	International Society of Psychosomatic Obstetrics and Gynecology	ITA	International Tuberculosis Association
		ITA	itaconic acid
ISPP	International Study Group of Prenatal Psychology	ITAA	International Transactional Analysis Association
i.s.q.	in statu quo (L); unchanged	ITCVD	ischemic thrombotic cerebrovascular disease
ISR (psych)	individual specific reaction	ITEC	intraglomerular tubule epithelium cells
ISR	International Society of Radiology (Copenhagen)	ITF	interferon (= IF, IFN, INF)
ISRRT	International Society of Radiographers and Radiological Technicians	ITF	intratesticular tissue fluid
		ITGV	intrathoracic gas volume (= IGV)
ISS	isoxsuprine	i/t curve	electrodiagnostic curve derived from intensity (strength of impulse) and time (duration)
ISSHP	International Society for the Study of Hypertension in Pregnancy		
ISSN	International Standard Serial Number	ITh	intensive therapy
		i.th.	intrathecal
IS-spike	initial segment spike	ITLC	instant thin-layer chromatography
IST	insulin shock therapy		
IST	Intelligence Structure Test	ITM (psych)	inborn trigger mechanism
IST	isometric systolic tension	ITN	Illustrated Tumor Nomenclature
ISTD	International Society of Tropical Dermatology	ITN	intratracheal (intubation) anesthesia (= ETN)
I-stripe	isotropic segment of the myofibril	ITP	idiopathic thrombocytopenia, idiopathic thrombocytopenic purpura
ISU	"Integrated Spinal Unit" (of a neurosurgical department)		
		ITP	inosine-5'-triphosphate

ITP	intratubar pessary	IUP	International Union of Pharmacy
ITr	intratracheal	IUP *(obst)*	intrauterine pregnancy
ITS	Interactive Training System	IUP	intrauterine pessary (=IUCD, IUD)
ITT	insulin tolerance test	IUPAC	International Union of Pure and Applied Chemistry (Basel/ Switzerland)
IU	immunizing unit		
IU	international unit		
IU	intrauterine		
IUA	intrauterine adhesions		
IUAC	International Union against Cancer	IUPAP	International Union of Pure and Applied Physics (London)
IUADM	International Union of Associations of Doctor-Motorists		
		IUPHAR	International Union of Pharmacology
IUAES	International Union of Anthropological and Ethnological Sciences	IUPS	International Union of Physiological Sciences
		IUS	International Union of Students
IUAT	International Union against Tuberculosis	IUT	intrauterine transfusion
IUB	International Union of Biochemistry	IUTM	International Union against Tuberculosis (Mycobacterium) (=IUAT)
IUBS	International Union of Biological Sciences		
IUC	International Union of Chemistry	IUTCT	International Union for Thermal Medicine and Climatothalassotherapy
IUCD	intrauterine contraceptive device (=IUD)		
		IUVDT	International Union against Venereal Diseases and Treponematoses
IUCr	International Union of Crystallography		
IUD	intrauterine death	IV	interventricular, intraventricular
IUD	intrauterine device (=IUCD)		
		IV	intervertebral
5-IUDR	5-iodouracil-2'-deoxyriboside, idoxuridinum (=IDU)	IV	iodine value
		i.v.	intravenous
		IVC	inferior vena cava
IUFB	intrauterine foreign body	IVC	inspiratory vital capacity
IUG	infusion urography (=IPG)	IVC	intravenous cholangiogram
IUGR *(obst)*	intrauterine growth retardation	IVC	intraventricular cells
		IVC	isovolumic contraction
IUGS	International Union of Geological Sciences	IVCD	intraventricular conduction defect (or delay)
IUIS	International Union of Immunological Societies	IVCT	isovolumic contraction time
IUNS	International Union of Nutritional Sciences	IVD	insuffisance ventriculaire droite (F); right ventricular failure

IVD	intervertebral disc
IVDA	intravenous drug abuser
IVDSA	intravenous digital subtraction angiography
IVF	intravascular fluid
IVF *(gyn)*	in vitro fertilization
IVG	insuffisance ventriculaire gauche (F); left ventricular failure
IVGTT	intravenous glucose tolerance test
IVI	isovolumic index
IVJC	intervertebral joint complex
IVP	intravenous pyelogram (=IVU)
IVPFC	isovolume pressure flow curve
IVRP, IVRT	isovolumic relaxation period, ... time
IVS	interventricular septum
IVSD	interventricular septal defect (=VSD)
IVSDM	interventricular septal diastolic motion
IVSG	International Virus Study Group
IVSSM	interventricular septal systolic motion
IVT	idiopathic ventricular tachycardia
IVT	intravenous transfusion
i.vt.	intraventricular (=i.c.v., IV)
IVU	intravenous urogram (=IVP)
i.w., i.wt.	isotopic weight
IWIT	initial warm ischemia time (for renal transplants)
IZS	insulin zinc suspension

J

J *(rad)*	ion dose
J	joint
J	joule
J.	journal
JAAD	Journal of the American Academy of Dermatology (official abbreviation: J. Amer. Acad. Derm.)
JACC	Journal of the American College of Cardiology (official abbreviation: J. Amer. Coll. Card.)
JAI	juvenile amaurotic idiocy, cerebromacular dystrophy, Stock-Spielmeyer-Vogt syndrome, Batten-Mayou syndrome
JAMA	Journal of the American Medical Association (official abbreviation: J. Amer. med. Ass.)
JBE	Japanese B encephalitis (=JE)
JBJS	Journal of Bone and Joint Surgery (official abbreviation: J. Bone Jt Surg.)
JCA	juvenile chronic arthritis
JCAE	Joint Committee on Atomic Energy (USA)
JCAH	Joint Commission on Accreditation of Hospitals
JCE	Journal of Continuing Education (American publication series, e.g. JCE Ob/Gyn, JCE ORL etc.)
J-chain	joining chain (of polypeptides)
JCP	juvenile chronic polyarthritis
jct.	junction
JE	Japanese B encephalitis (=JBE)
JEB *(card)*	junctional ectopic beat

JEE	Japanese equine encephalitis	JRA	juvenile rheumatoid arthritis
JESSI	Joint European Silicon Submicron Institute	JSB stain	staining solution of J. Singh und Bhattacharij
JET *(card)*	junctional ectopic tachycardia	JSRT	Japanese Society of Radiological Technology
JFCR	Japanese Foundation of Cancer Research	JSU	Junkmann-Schoeller unit (of thyrotrophin)
JFS	Jewish Family Service	Jt, jt	joint
JGA	juxtaglomerular apparatus	juv.	juvenile
JGC	juxtaglomerular cell	JV	jugular vein
JGCC	juxtaglomerular cell count	JVP	jugular vein pulse
JGI	juxtaglomerular index		
JH	juvenile hormone (of insects)		
JHMO	Junior Hospital Medical Officer		

K

JHR	Jarisch-Herxheimer reaction		
JHPIEGO	Johns Hopkins Program for International Education in Gynecology and Obstetrics	K	Boltzmann constant
		K	coefficient of coupling
		K	electrostatic capacity
		K	ionization constant
JHU	Johns Hopkins University (Baltimore)	K	Kelvin
		17-K	17-ketosteroids
JJ	jaw jerk	KA	ketoacidosis
JM	Jendrassik manoeuver	KA	ketoandrosterone
JNA	Jena Nomina Anatomica (1935); Jena Anatomical Nomenclature (=INA)	KA	King-Armstrong (unit of alkaline phosphatase) (=KAU)
JNCI	Journal of the National Cancer Institute (USA) (official abbreviation: J. Natl Cancer Inst.)	kA	kiloampère
		KAAD	kerosene, alcohol, acetic acid, dioxane (mixture)
JND	just noticeable difference	KAF	kinase activating factor
JOD	juvenile onset diabetes (mellitus)	KAP	knowledge, aptitude, and practices (in reproduction)
JODA	juvenile onset diabetes of the adult	kat	Katal (unit of enzyme activity)
JP	Justice of Peace	KAU	King-Armstrong unit
J-P, J point	junction point (in the ECG)	KB	ketone bodies
JPSA	Joint Program for the Study of Abortion	KBR	Komplementbindungsreaktion (G); complement fixation reaction (=CFR, CFT)
^{131}J-PVP test	Gordon's test (using ^{131}J-labelled polyvinylpyrrolidone	KC	kathodal closing
		kc	kilocycle
		kcal	kilocalorie

KCC	kathodal closing contraction ($=$CCC)	KID	keratitis-ichthyosis-deafness syndrome
KCE	keratoconjunctivitis epidemica	K^+i/K^+e	potassium quotient, ratio between intracellular and extracellular potassium
K cell	killer cell		
kCi	kilocurie	KIT *(psych)*	Kahn Intelligence Test
kcps, kc/s	kilocycles per second ($=$kHz)	KIU	kallikrein inactivator unit
		KIVA	ketoisovaleric acid
KCT	kathodal closing tetanus ($=$CCTe)	KJ	knee jerk ($=$KK)
		KK	knee kick ($=$KJ)
KD	kathodal duration	KKS	kallikrein-kinin system
kD	kilodalton (unit of molecular weight)	KL bac.	Klebs-Loeffler bacilli, diphtheria bacilli
KE	Kendall's Compound E ($=$cortisone)	KLS	kidney, liver, spleen
		KM	kanamycin
KE	kinetic energy	Km	Michaelis constant
Kerma *(rad)*	kinetic energy released in material	kMc	kilomegacycle
		KMEF	keratin, myosin, epidermin, fibrin (class of proteins)
KES	Klebsiella-Enterobacter-Serratia (group of microorganisms)	km/h	kilometers per hour
		kmol	kilomol
		kN	kilonewton
keV	kiloelectron volts	KNL	substitution therapy with potassium (kalium), sodium (natrium), and lactate (Darrow's solution)
K-factor	Kell-(Cellano-) factor, antigen K		
KFD	Kyasanur forest disease; hemorrhagic fever occurring in India (Kyasanur)		
		KO, k.o.	knockout
K-8 fever	Kobe-8 fever	KOC	kathodal opening contraction ($=$COC)
KFZ	Krebsforschungszentrum (G); Cancer Research Center (Heidelberg/Germany)	KP *(ophth)*	keratic precipitate
		KP *(ophth)*	keratitis punctata
α-KG	alpha-ketoglutaric acid	K-P	Kaiser-Permanente (diet)
kgR	kilogram-roentgen	kp	kilopond
kgrd	kilogram-rad	kPa	kilopascal
KGS, 17-KGS	17-ketogenic steroids	Kp^a factor	Penney factor, antigen Kp^a (Kell system)
		KPF	ketoprofen
KH	Kohlenhydrate (G); carbohydrates	KPI	karyopyknotic index
		kpm	kilopond-meter
KHF	Korean hemorrhagic fever	KR *(lab)*	Kahn (turbidity) reaction
KHK	koronare Herzkrankheit (G); coronary heart disease ($=$CAD, CHD)	KRAG method	erythrocyte staining using kitone red and almond green
kHz	kilohertz		
KI	Krönig isthmus	KRB	Krebs-Ringer bicarbonate buffer
KIA *(mil)*	killed in action		
KIA	Kligler iron agar (medium)	KRP	Kolmer test with Reiter protein antigen
K_{ic}	intracellular potassium		

KRP	Krebs-Ringer phosphate solution
KS	Kaposi's sarcoma
KS	keratane sulfate
17-KS	17-ketosteroids
KSS	Russian acronym for: AIDS related complex
KTSA *(psych)*	Kahn Test of Symbol Arrangement
KUB	kidney, ureter, bladder
KUL	Catholic University of Leuven (Belgium)
kV	kilovolt
kVA	kilovolt-ampère
kVCP	kilovolt constant potential
kVp	kilovoltage peak
KW *(phys)*	Kurzwelle (G); short wave
kW	kilowatt
KWB	Keith-Wagener-Barker (classification of retinopathy)
kWh	kilowatt-hour
KWIC	keyword in context (USA)
KWS	Kimmelstiel-Wilson syndrome

L

L	inductivity (Avogadro's constant)
L	lambert (unit of light)
L	left
L	light
L	limes
L	lingual
L	Linné
L	liquor
L	Loschmidt's number
L	lues; syphilis
L *(anat)*	lumbar
L.	Lactobacillus

L. *(anat)*	ligamentum (= Lig.)
L- *(chem)*	stereoisomer (levorotatory)
L1, L2	first, second lumbar vertebra, etc.
L_o	limes zero
L_+	limes death
L/3	lower third
LA	latex agglutination
LA	leucine aminopeptidase (= LAP)
LA	left atrium, left atrial
LA *(dent)*	linguoaxial
LA	local anesthesia
LA	long-acting
LA	lupus anticoagulant
LA	lymphovenous anastomosis
La, la	lambert (= L)
l.a.	lege artis (L); according to the art
L + A *(ophth)*	light and accommodation
LAAO	L-amino acid oxidase
LAAS	laser-assisted aneurysm shrinkage
LAB *(anat)*	left atrial branch (of the coronary vessels)
LAB *(card)*	left anterior fascicular block (= LAFB)
Lab	laboratory
LABS	Laboratory Admission Baseline Studies
LAC	left atrial contraction
LAC *(dent)*	linguo-axiocervical
LaC *(dent)*	labiocervical
lac.	laceration
LAD	lactic acid dehydrogenase (= LDH, MDH)
LAD *(card)*	left anterior descending (artery)
LAD	left atrial diameter
LAD *(card)*	left axis deviation (= LAXD)
LAD	linoleic acid depression
LADA *(obst)*	left acromio-dorso-anterior (position of fetus)
LADI	left atrial dimension index

LADME *(pharm)*	liberation, absorption, distribution, metabolism, excretion	LaL *(dent)*	labiolingual
LAD-method	leuco-agglutinins using defibrinated blood, Dausset's method	LAMMA	laser microprobe mass analyzer
		LAMP	left atrial mean pressure
LADP *(obst)*	left acromio-dorso-posterior (position)	LANA	laser-assisted nerve anastomosis
LAE	left atrial enlargement	LANSI	Laser Association of Neurological Surgeons International
LAE	lysergic acid ethylamide		
LAEDV	left atrial end-diastolic volume	LAO *(rad)*	left anterior oblique (projection)
LAEF	left atrial ejection fraction	L.A.O.	Licentiate in the Art of Obstetrics
LAESV	left atrial end-sysolic volume	LAOD	L-amino acid oxidase
LAEV	left atrial emptying volume	LAP	left atrial pressure
LAF	laminar air flow	LAP	leucine aminopeptidase (=LA)
LAF	left anterior fascicle		
LAF	lymphocyte augmenting factor	LAP	leukocyte alkaline phosphatase
LAFB	left anterior fascicular block (=LAB)	LAP	lyophilized anterior pituitary (tissue)
LAG *(dent)*	linguo-axiogingival	Lap.	laparotomy, laparoscopy
LaG *(dent)*	labiogingival	LAR	latex agglutination reaction
L-aggl.	streptococci-L-agglutination	LAR	left atrial rhythm
LAH *(card)*	left anterior hemiblock (=LAHB)	l.a.r.	left arm recumbent
		LARC	leucocyte automatic recognition computer
LAH	left atrial hypertrophy		
LAH	leucylanilide hydrolase	LAS	linear alkyl sulfonate
LAH	lithium-aluminum hydride	LAS	local adaptation syndrome
L.A.H.	Licentiate of Apothecaries Hall (Dublin)	LAS	lung alveolar surfactant (=AAF)
LAHB	left anterior hemiblock (=LAH)	LAS	lymphadenopathy syndrome (=AIDS)
LaI *(dent)*	labioincisal	LASA	Laboratory Animal Science Association
LAIDS	"lesser AIDS"		
LAIS	Leiter Adult Intelligence Scale	LASER	light amplification by stimulated emission of radiation
LAIT	latex agglutination inhibition test		
		LAT	left anterior triangle
LAI test	leukocyte adherence inhibition test	lat, latm	liter atmosphere
		lat.	lateral
LAK cells	lymphokine-activated killer cells	LATS	long-acting thyroid stimulator
		lats *(mil)*	latrines
LAL	limulus amebocyte lysate (test)	LATS-P	long-acting thyroid stimulator protector

LAV	lymphadenopathy-associated virus (=HIV, HTLV)	LCD	liquid crystal data (or display)
LAVA	laser-assisted vascular anastomosis	LCF	left circumflex (=LCC, LCCA, LCX)
LAXD	left axis deviation (=LAD)	LCF	leuconostoc citrovorum factor
LB	liver biopsy	LCFA	long-chain fatty acid
LB	lower back	LCGU	local cerebral glucose utilization
lb	libra (L); pound		
LBBB	left bundle branch block	L.Ch.	Licentiate in Surgery
LBCD, LBD	left border of cardiac dullness	L-chains	light chains
		LCI	lung clearance index
LBF	Lactobacillus bulgaricus factor	LCIA	luminescence cofactor immunoassay
LBF	liver blood flow	LCL	Levinthal-Coles-Lillie (bodies)
LBH	length, breadth, height		
LBI	length-breadth index (of skull)	LCM	Laboratoire pour le Contrôle des Médicaments (F); Laboratory for Drug Control (Switzerland)
LBL	lymphoblastic leukemia		
LBM	lean body mass		
LBP	liver blind puncture	LCM	latent cardiomyopathy ("small vessel disease")
LBP	low back pain		
LBP	low blood pressure, hypotension	LCM	left costal margin
		LCM	lowest common multiple
LBPP	lower body positive pressure	LCM	lymphocytic choriomeningitis
LBT	loose-body test	LCME	Liaison Committee on Medical Education (USA)
LBV	lung blood volume		
LBW	low birth weight	LCP	long-chain polysaturated (fatty acid)
LC (pharm)	lethal concentration (=LD)		
		L.C.P.S.	Licentiate of the College of Physicians and Surgeons
LC (dent)	linguocervical		
LC	liver cirrhosis	LCR	liquide céphalo-rachidien (F); cerebrospinal fluid (=CSF, LCS)
LC	loop carpal (of finger prints)		
LCA	left coronary artery	LCS	liquor cerebrospinalis (L); cerebrospinal fluid (=CSF)
LCA	leukocyte common antigen		
LCA	liver cytoplasma antibodies		
LCAT	lecithin-cholesterol acyltransferase	LCT	larva cutanea tarda
		LCT	long-chain triglycerides
LCBF	local cerebral blood flow	LCT	lung capillary time
LCC	left circumflex coronary (=LCX)	LCTA	lymphocytotoxic antibody
		LCU	life change unit (score)
LCCA	left circumflex coronary artery (=LCC, LCX)	LCX	left circumflex branch (of coronary artery)
LCCS	low cervical cesarean section	LD	lactic dehydrogenase (=LDH)

LD	lethal dose	LED	lupus erythematodes disseminatus (=SLE)
LD	light-dark		
LD	light differentiating ability	LEDP	left ventricular enddiastolic pressure
LD *(dent)*	linguodistal		
LD	lipodystrophy	LEF	leukocyte migration enhancing factor
LD	liver diease		
LD	living donor	LE factor	lupus erythematosus factor
LD	longitudinal diameter		
LD	loop distal (of finger prints)	Le factor	Lewis factor, antigen Le
		LEIA	luminiscence enzyme immunoassay
LD	low density		
LD	lymphocytic determinant	LEM	Leibovitz-Emory medium
LD$_{50}$	median lethal dose (=DL$_{50}$)	LEMIT	luminiscence enzyme-multiplied immunotechnique
LDA *(obst)*	left dorso-anterior (position of fetus)	LEOPARD	syndrome consisting of lentiginosis, ECG abnormality, ocular malformation, pulmonary stenosis, abnormalities of the genitalia, retarded growth, and deafness; so-called cardiocutaneous syndrome
LDE	lauric diethamide		
LDEF	Long Duration Exposure Facility		
LDF	lymphocyte depressing factor		
LDH	lactate dehydrogenase (=LAD, LD, MDH)		
		LEP	low egg passage
LDL	low density lipoproteins	LES	local excitatory state
LDL-C	low density lipoprotein cholesterol	LES	Locke's egg serum (medium)
LDP *(obst)*	left dorso-posterior (position of fetus)	LES	lower esophageal sphincter
		LESP	lower esophageal sphincter pressure
LD-proteins	low density proteins (=LDL)		
LDS	laser Doppler spectroscopy	LESVI	left ventricular end-systolic volume index
L.D.S.	Licentiate in Dental Surgery		
		LET	linear energy transfer
L.D.Sc.	Licentiate in Dental Science	let.	letalis (L); lethal
		LE-test	lupus erythematodes test
LDUB	long double upright brace	Leu	leucine
LE	lactate extraction	Leuc.	leukocytes
LE	left eye (=OS)	Leurose	Leube-Rosenthal meat extract
LE	liver extract		
LE	lower extremity	LEV	lupus erythematodes visceralis
LE	lung embolism (=PE)		
LE	lupus erythematodes	LF	low frequency
LEA *(card)*	latest epicardial activation	LF, Lf	limes flocculation
LEC	lupus erythematodes chronicus	LF	lung fibroblasts
		LF	lung fibrosis
LE cells	lupus erythematosus cells	LF	lymph flow
LED	light-emitting diode	LFA *(obst)*	left fronto-anterior (position of fetus)

LFAB *(card)*	left fasciculate anterior block	LGT	limulus gelation test
L-factor	Lewis factor (= Le factor)	LGV	lymphogranuloma venereum
LFD	least fatal dose	LH	lateral hypothalamic
LFD	low-fat diet	LH	left handed
LFD	lymphocyte depressing factor	LH *(ophth)*	left hyperphoria
LFH	left femoral hernia	LH	lower half
L-form	form of bacterial growth observed in the Lister Institute	LH	lues hereditaria (L); congenital syphilis
LFP *(obst)*	left fronto-posterior (position of fetus)	LH	lung hemosiderosis
LFPPV	low-frequency positive-pressure ventilation	LH	luteinizing hormone
L.F.P.S.	Licentiate of the Faculty of Physicians and Surgeons	LHA	left hypothalamic area
L-fraction	labile fraction	LHC *(anat)*	left hypochondrium
LFS	liver function scan	LHD	lipoprotein of high density (= HDL)
LFT	latex fixation test	LHPO	lipid hydroxyperoxide
LFT *(obst)*	left fronto-transverse (position of fetus)	LHRF,	LH-releasing factor, LH-releasing hormone
LFT	liver function tests	LHRH	
LFT	low frequency transduction	LHS	lymphoid hyperplasia syndrome
L_f value	flocculation value (limes flocculation)	LHT *(ophth)*	left hypertropia
LG	leucyl glycine	LHT	Lwoff-Horne-Tournier system (of viruses)
LG *(dent)*	linguogingival	LI	labelling index
LG	lipophagic granuloma (Whipple)	LI	lateral infarction
LG	lymphogram, lymphangiogram	LI *(dent)*	linguo-incisal
LG	lymphogranulomatosis	LI	looping ill; meningo-encephalitis
LGA	large-for-gestational-age	L.i.	Lamblia intestinalis
LGC	liquid gas chromatography	LIA	luminiscence immunoassay
LGG	leucyl glycyl glycine	lib.	libra (L); pound (usually: lb)
LGH	lactogenic hormone (= LMTH, LTH, PH)	LIBC	latent iron-binding capacity
LGH	leucyl glycine hydrolase	LICA	left internal carotid artery
LGL	large granular lymphocyte	LICM	left intercostal margin
Lgl.	lymphoglandula (L); lymph node	Lic.Med.	Licentiate in Medicine (= L.M.)
LGL syndrome	Lown-Ganong-Levine syndrome	LID	lobe inférieur droit (F); right lower lobe
LGP	laser goniopuncture	LIDAR	Light Detecting and Ranging
LGS	liver-gallbladder scintigram	LIF	left iliac fossa
		LIF	leukocyte inhibitory factor
		LIF	leukocytosis-inducing factor
		LIG	lobe inférieur gauche (F); left lower lobe

Lig., Ligg.	ligament(s)	LLE	left lower extremity
LIH	left inguinal hernia	LL-factor	Laki-Lorand factor, factor XIII
LIHD	limited isovolemic hemodilution	LLL	La Lèche League (organization to promote breast-feeding)
LIMA	left internal mammary artery		
Lin. *(pharm)*	liniment	LLL *(ophth)*	left lower lid
LIO *(rad)*	left inferior oblique	LLL	left lower lobe
LIP	lymphatic/lymphocytic interstitial pneumonia	LLM	localized leukocyte mobilization
LIP	lymphoid interstitial pneumonia	LL.M.	Master of Laws
		LLPV	left lower pulmonary veins
Liq.	liquor	LLQ	left lower quadrant
liq.	liquid	LLSB	lower left sternal border
LIRBM	liver, iron, red bone marrow	LLRA	low lateral right atrium
		LM	legal medicine
LIS	Laboratory Information System	LM	light microscope
		LM	lincomycin
LIS	lobular in situ (carcinoma)	LM *(dent)*	linguomesial
LISL	laser intracorporeal shock wave lithotripsy	LM	Listeria monocytogenes
		LM	lunar month
LIT	liver incorporation test	L.M.	Licentiate in Midwifery
LIV	law of initial value (of J. Wilder)	L.m.	Listeria monocytogenes
		lm	lumen
LIVC	left inferior vena cava	LMA	laser micro-spectral analysis
LIVCD *(card)*	left intraventricular conduction delay		
		LMA *(obst)*	left mento-anterior (position)
LIVT	left idiopathic ventricular tachycardia	LMA	limbic mid-brain area
Lixiscope *(rad)*	low intensity x-ray imaging scope	LMA	liver membrane auto-antibodies
L.K.Q.C.P.I.	Licentiate of the King and Queen's College of Physicians in Ireland	LMAF	lymphocyte migration activating factor
		LMAT	leukocyte migration in agarose test
LL	lateral left		
LL	liver lipase	LMB syndrome	Laurence-Moon-Biedl syndrome
LL *(ophth)*	lower lid	LMC	left main coronary (artery)
LL	lymphatic leukosis	LMC	lymphocyte mediated cytolysis (or cytotoxicity)
LL.B.	Bachelor of Laws		
LLBCD	left lower border of cardiac dullness	LMCA	left middle cerebral artery
LLC	liquid-liquid chromatography	LMCAD	left main coronary artery disease (= LMCD)
L.L.C.O.	Licentiate of the London College of Osteopathy	L.M.C.C.	Licentiate of the Medical Council of Canada
LLD	Lactobacillus lactis Dorner	LMCD	left main coronary (artery) disease
LL.D.	Doctor of Laws		

LMD	local medical doctor	LMS	level measuring set
LMD	low molecular dextran (=LMWD)	LMS	London Medical Society
		LMS	London Microscopical Society
LME	lysine methylester		
L.Med.Ch.	Licentiate in Medicine and Surgery (=L.M.S.)	L.M.S.	Licentiate in Medicine and Surgery (=L.Med.Ch.)
LMF	cytotoxic combination therapy with Leukeran (chlorambucil), methotrexate and 5-fluorouracil	L.M.S.S.A.	Licentiate in Medicine and Surgery of the Society of Apothecaries (London)
		LMSV	left maximum spatial vector
LMF	leukocyte mobilizing factor		
LMF	lipid mobilizing factor	LMT *(phys)*	length, mass, time (system of electrical units)
LMFP	cytotoxic combination therapy with Leukeran (chlorambucil), methotrexate, 5-fluorouracil and prednisone	LMT *(obst)*	left mento-transverse (position of fetus)
		LMT	leukocyte migration test
		LMTH	luteomammotrophic hormone (=LGH, LTH, PH)
LMFS	linear muscle fiber stretch		
LMG	leuko-malachite green	LMV	left margin vein
LMGA	levo-malposition of the great arteries	LMW	low molecular weight
		LMWD	low molecular weight dextran (=LMD)
LMH	lipid mobilizing hormone		
LM-hormones	larval and metamorphosis hormones (in insects)	LMWH	low molecular weight heparin
LMIF	leukocyte migration inhibitory factor	LN	lymph node
		LNA	L-leucine-ß-naphthylamide
LMIT	leukocyte migration inhibition test	LNC	lymph node cells
		LNCM	Laboratoire National de Contrôle des Médicaments (F); National Laboratory of Drug Control (France)
LML *(gyn)*	left mediolateral (episiotomy)		
LML	left midline		
LMM *(card)*	left ventricular muscle mass		
LMM	lentigo-malignant melanoma	LNH	leucylnaphthylamide hydrolase
		LNMP	last normal menstrual period
LMM	light meromyosin		
LMMI	left ventricular muscle mass index	LNPF	lymph node permeability factor
LMN	lower motor neuron	LNS	Lesch-Nyhan syndrome
LMP	last menstrual period	LN-type	lepromatosa/nervosa (mixed form of leprosy)
LMP *(obst)*	left mento-posterior (position of fetus)		
		LO *(dent)*	linguo-occlusal
LMP	lumbar puncture	LOA	leave of absence
LMR	linguomandibular reflex	LOA *(obst)*	left occipito-anterior (position of fetus)
L.M.R.C.P.	Licentiate in Midwifery of the Royal College of Physicians		
		loc.dol.	loco dolenti (L); to the painful spot

log	logarithm	LPAT	lysophosphatidyl acyl transferase
LOL *(obst)*	left occipito-lateral (position of fetus)	LPB *(card)*	left posterior (fascicular) block (=LPFB)
LOM	limitation of movement	Lp-B	lipoprotein B
LOMSA	left otitis media suppurativa acuta	Lp-C	lipoprotein C
LOMSCh	left otitis media suppurativa chronica	LPC, LPCh	lysophosphatidyl choline
long.	longitudinal	LPEP	left ventricular pre-ejection period
LOP	leave on pass	LPEPC	lysopolyenyl phosphatidyl choline
LOP	left oblique position (coronary angiography)	LPF	left posterior fascicle
LOP *(obst)*	left occipito-posterior (position of fetus)	LPF	leukocytosis-promoting factor
LOPS	length of patient stay	LPF	leukopenia factor
LORAN	long range navigation	LPF	low pass filter
LORCS	League of Red Cross Societies (=LRCS)	LPF, lpf	low-power field (of microscope)
LOS	length of stay	LPF	lymphocytosis promoting factor
LOS *(card)*	low output syndrome	LPFB *(card)*	left posterior fascicular block (=LPF)
L.O.S.	Licentiate in Obstetrical Science	LPG	liver, pancreas, gallbladder
LOT *(obst)*	left occipito-transverse (position)	LPH	lipotrophic pituitary hormone
lot.	lotion	LPh	leukocyte phosphatase
LOX	liquid oxygen (cp. GOX)	LPHB *(card)*	left posterior hemiblock
LP	laboratory procedure	LPL	lipoprotein lipase
LP *(gyn)*	last period	LPLA	lipoprotein lipase activity
LP	latent period	LPMF	liquid-protein-modified fast (diet)
LP	light perception	LPN	Licensed Practical Nurse
LP *(dent)*	linguopulpal	LPP	liver phosphorylase phosphatase
LP	lipide phosphorus		
LP	lipoprotein	LPP	lipothiamide pyrophosphate
LP	loop proximal		
LP	low pass (=LPF)	L/P ratio	lymphocyte/polymorph ratio
LP	low power (microscopy)		
LP	low pressure	LPS	lipopolysaccharide
LP	lumbar puncture (=LMP)	lps	liters per second
		LPV	left pulmonary vein
LP	lympho(cyto)poiesis	LPV	lymphopathia venerea, lymphogranuloma venereum (=LGV)
L/P	lactate/pyruvate ratio		
LPA	left pulmonary artery		
Lp-A	lipoprotein A		
LPAM	L-phenylalanine mustard, melphalan	LPVCS	left persistent vena cava superior
LPAR	local passive Arthus reaction		

Lp-X	(abnormal) lipoprotein X	LRH	luteinizing hormone releasing hormone (=LHRF, LHRH, LRF)
LQ *(stat)*	likelihood quotient		
LQ	lowest quadrant		
LQTS *(card)*	long QT syndrome	LRI	lower rate interval
LR	laboratory report	LRL	Leptospirosis Reference Laboratory
LR	latency relaxation		
LR	lateral right	LRL	Lunar Receiving Laboratory
LR	level recorder		
LR	light reaction (of pupils)	LRQ	lower right quadrant
LR	limes reaction	LRR	labyrinthine righting reflex
LR	loop radial	LRR	light reflection rheography
LR	low resistor	LRS, LRSh	left-right shunt
L$_R$	rating sound level	LS	laparoscopy
LRA	lower right atrium	LS	lateral suspensor
LRC	Lipid Research Clinic	LS *(anat)*	limbic system
LRC-CPPT	Lipid Research Clinic Coronary Primary Prevention Trial	LS	liminal sensitivity
		LS	lumbosacral
		LS	luteal steroids
		LS	lymphoscintigram
L.R.C.P.	Licentiate of the Royal College of Physicians	L.S.	Licentiate in Surgery
L.R.C.P.S.I.	Licentiate of the Royal College of Physicians and Surgeons of Ireland	L/S	lecithin/sphingomyelin ratio
		LSA *(obst)*	left sacro-anterior (position of fetus)
LRCS	League of Red Cross Societies (=LORCS)	LSA	left subclavian artery
		L.S.A.	Licentiate of the Society of Apothecaries (London)
L.R.C.S.	Licentiate of the Royal College of Surgeons	LS antigen	antigen complex specific for variola-vaccine viruses containing thermolabile and thermostable components
L.R.C.S.E.	Licentiate of the Royal College of Surgeons, Edinburgh		
L.R.C.S.I.	Licentiate of the Royal College of Surgeons of Ireland		
		LSB *(card)*	left septal block
LRF	latex and resorcinol formaldehyde	LSB	left sternal border
		LSC	liquid scintillation counter
LRF	liver residue factor	LScA *(obst)*	left scapulo-anterior (position of fetus)
LRF	luteinizing hormone releasing factor (=LHRF, LHRH, LRH)		
		LScP *(obst)*	left scapulo-posterior (position of fetus)
L.R.F.P.S.	Licentiate of the Royal Faculty of Physicians and Surgeons	LSCR	Ligue des Sociétés de la Croix Rouge (F); League of Red Cross Societies (=LORCS, LRCS)
LRF test	latex rheumatoid factor test (=LFT, LTT)		
		LSCS	lower segment cesarean section
LRG	longitudinal rheogram		
LRH	low renin hypertension	LSD	League for Spiritual Discovery

LSD	least significant differ- ence	LSU	Louisiana State University (Baton Rouge)
LSD *(rad)*	leukemia-significant dose	LSVC	left superior vena cava
LSD	lobe supérieur droit (F); right upper lobe	LSWI	left ventricular stroke work index
LSD	lung standard diagnostics	LT	labyrinthine reflex
LSD	lysergic acid diethylamide	LT *(imm)*	leukotriene
LSF *(card)*	left septal fascicle	LT	low temperature
LSF	line spread function	LT	lues test
LSF	lymphocytosis-stimulating factor	LT	lymphotoxin
		lt	low tension
LSFB *(card)*	left septal fascicular block	LT$_3$	levo-triiodothyronine
LSG	lobe supérieur gauche (F); left upper lobe	LT$_4$	levo-tetraiodothyronine
		LTAS	lead tetra-acetate Schiff
LSH	lymphocyte-stimulating hormone	LTB	laryngotracheobronchitis
		LTC	lanatoside C
LSI	large-scale integration	LTC	long-term care
LSK	liver, spleen, kidneys	L-test *(psych)*	Laszlo's test
LSL *(obst)*	left sacro-lateral (position of fetus)	LTF	lipotropic factor (=LTH)
		LTF	lymphocyte transformation factor (=LST)
LSLP	liver-specific lipoprotein		
LSM	lysergic acid morpholide	l-TGA	transposition of the great
LSP *(obst)*	left sacro-posterior (posi- tion of fetus)		arteries, left type (=cor- rected form)
LSP	life span	LTH	lipotrophic hormone
LSP	liver-specific protein		(=LPH, LTF)
LSPA	least square phase analysis	LTH	low temperature holding
LSR	lecithin/sphingomyelin ratio	LTH	luteotrophic (lactotrophic) hormone (=LGH, LMTH, PH)
LSR	lues seroreaction		
LSRA	low septal right atrium	LTHRF	LTH-releasing factor
L/S ratio	lecithin/sphingomyelin ratio (=LSR)	LTP	long-term potentiation
		LTPP	lipothiamide pyrophos- phate (=LPP)
LSRSS *(psych)*	Lipman Self-Rating Symp- tom Scale	LTR *(gen)*	long terminal repetitive (redundancy)
LSS	Life Supporting System	LTT	lymphocyte transformation
LST *(anat)*	lateral spinothalamic tract		test (=LST)
LST *(obst)*	left sacro-transverse (posi- tion of fetus)	LTT	lipoprotein turbidity test
		LUE	left upper extremity
LST	lymphocyte stimulation test (=LTT)	Lu-factor	Lutheran factor, antigen Lu
LST *(lab)*	lysine decarboxylase sulf- hydrase test	LUIMO	Libera Università Interna- zionale di Medicina Ome-
L-strepto- cocci	lactis streptococci		opatica (Napels/Italy)
		LUL *(ophth)*	left upper lid
LSU	lactose-saccharose-urea (medium)	LUL	left upper lobe

LUO	left ureteral orifice	LVESP	left ventricular end-systolic pressure
LUOQ	left upper outer quadrant		
LUPV	left upper pulmonary vein	LVESS	left ventricular end-systolic (wall) stress
LUQ	left upper quadrant (abdomen)		
		LVESV	left ventricular end-systolic volume
LUTI	lower urinary tract infection		
		LVET	left ventricular ejection time
LV	live vaccine		
LV	liver volume	LVETI	left ventricular ejection time index
LV *(card)*	left ventricle, left ventricular		
		LVFI	left ventricular function index
LV	lumbar vertebra		
LVA	lymphovenous anastomosis	LVFP	left ventricular filling pressure
LVAD	left ventricular assist device	LVFS	left ventricular fractional shortening
LVAW	left ventricular anterior wall	LVFV	left ventricular filling volume
LVC	left ventricular cavity	LVH	left ventricular hypertrophy
LVC	left ventricular contraction		
LVD	left ventricular diameter	LVICT	left ventricular isovolumic contraction time
LVD	low viscous dextran (=LMD, LMWD)		
		LVIDd(s)	left ventricular internal dimension (diameter) in diastole (systole)
LVDD	left ventricular diastolic diameter		
LVDV	left ventricular diastolic volume	LVMBF	left ventricular myocardial blood flow
LVE	left ventricular enlargement	LVM, LVMM	left ventricular muscle mass
LVEDD	left ventricular end-diastolic diameter	LVMWI	left ventricular minute work index
LVEDI	left ventricular end-diastolic index	LVN	Licensed Visiting Nurse
		LVN	Licensed Vocational Nurse
LVEDL	left ventricular end-diastolic (fiber) length	LVOO	left ventricular outflow obstruction
LVEDP	left ventricular end-diastolic pressure	LVOT	left ventricular outflow tract
LVEDV	left ventricular end-diastolic volume	LVP	left ventricular pressure
		LVPSP	left ventricular peak systolic pressure
LVEF	left ventricular ejection fraction		
		LVP test	lysine-vasopressin test
LVER	left ventricular ejection rate	LVPW*(T)*	left ventricular posterior wall (thickness)
LVESD	left ventricular end-systolic diameter	LVROI	left ventricular regions of interest
LVESL	left ventricular end-systolic (fiber) length	LVSD	left ventricular systolic diameter

LVSF	left ventricular shortening fraction
LVSO	left ventricular systolic output
LVSP	left ventricular systolic pressure
LVSR	left ventricular segmental relaxation
LVSTI	left ventricular systolic time intervals
LVSV	left ventricular systolic (or stroke) volume
LVSW(I)	left ventricular stroke work (index)
LVT	lysine vasotonin
LVTD	left ventricular total diameter
LVTV	left ventricular total volume
LVV	left ventricular volume
LVWI	left ventricular work index
LVWS	left ventricular wall stress
LVWT	left ventricular wall thickness
LVWV	left ventricular wall volume
LW	long wave (= LF)
LW *(card)*	période de Luciani-Wenckebach (F); Wenckebach's period
L + W	living and well
LWCT	Lee-White coagulation time
LWPES	Lawson Wilkins Pediatric Endocrine Society
LW substance	blood cell substance (named after Landsteiner and Wiener)
LX *(card)*	long axis
lx	lux
LY *(bact)*	lactalbumin-yeast
Ly, lymphos	lymphocytes
Ly, Lys	lysine
LZM	lysozyme

M

M	male
M	malignant
M	mass
M	mega (10^6)
M	memory
M	mesial
M	metabolite
M *(gen)*	metaphase
M *(gen)*	minutes
M	mitochondria
M	mitosis
M *(chem)*	mol, molarity
M *(dent)*	molar
M	morphin
M	murmur
M	mutual inductance
M *(ophth)*	myopia
M	myosin
m	milli- (10^{-3})
m	minim
m	molar
M.	Micrococcus
M.	mixture
M.	morbus (L); disease
M.	morphium
M.*(anat)*	musculus (L), muscle
M'	effective mass
m.	masculine
m. *(pharm)*	misce (L); mix (Rx)
m- *(chem)*	meta-
M/3	middle third (e.g. of a bone)
MA	Medical Academy
MA	membrane antigens
MA	menstrual age
MA	mental age
MA	meta-adrenaline
MA	micro-aggregation
MA	mitral area
MA	muramidase activity
mA	milliampère
M.A.	Magister Artium (L); Master of Arts

MAA	macroaggregated albumin	MAFP	maternal alpha-fetoprotein
MAA	Medical Assistance to the Aged	mafr	mass fraction
		Mag	magnesium
MAA	mercapto-alkylamine	Mag.	Magister
MAA	mitochondria-associated antigen	M-Ag	matrix antigen
		MAGE	mean amplitude of gly-cemic excursion
MAACL *(psych)*	Multiple Affect Adjective Check List	magn.	magnification
MAAGB	Medical Artists Associa-tion of Great Britain	magn.	magnetic
		MAGIC	microprobe analysis gener-alized intensity correc-tions
MAB, MAb	monoclonal antibodies (=MCAB, MoAB)		
M-Ab	antibody occurring in infectious mononucleosis (heterohemagglutinin)	MAI	Mycobacterium avium intracellulare
		MAIS	group of mycobacteria (Mycobacterium avium, M. intercellulare, M. scrofula-ceum)
MABP	mean arterial blood pres-sure		
MAC	malignancy-associated changes	maj.	major
		MAL	malabsorption syndrome (=MAS)
MAC	maximal allowable con-centration		
MAC *(pharm)*	maximum allowable cost	MAL	mid-axillary line
		Mal.	malate
MAC *(mil)*	Medical Administration Corps (USA)	MALIMET	Master List of Medical Indexing Terms
MAC	minimal alveolar concen-tration	MALT	Munich Alcoholism Test
		MAM	methylazoxymethanol
MAC *(mil)*	Motor Ambulance Com-pany	mAm, MAM	milliampère-minute
Mac.	maceration	M+Am *(ophth)*	myopic astigmatism
mac	mass concentration		
M.A.C.D.	Member of the Australian College of Dermatology	MAME	maleic acid monoethylester
		MAN, Man	mannose
M.A.C.G.P.	Member of the Australian College of General Practi-tioners	MaN	macronucleus
		MANOVA	multivariate analysis of variance
MACS	Multicenter AIDS Cohort Study	man.pr.	mane primo (L); early in the morning (Rx)
MAD	malonyl aldehyde	M-antigen	mucosus antigen
MAD	methylandrostenediol	MAO	maximum acid output (of the stomach)
MAD	mind-altering drug		
MAD	minimum average dose	MAO	monoamine oxidase
MAE	Medical Association of Eire	M.A.O.	Magister Artis Obstetriciae (L); Master of the Art of Obstetrics
MAF	macrophage activating fac-tor		
		MAOI	monoamine oxidase inhib-itor
MAF	minimum audible field		

MAOS	microsomal alcohol oxidation system	MASU *(mil)*	Mobile Army Surgical Unit
MAP	macro-albumin particle	MAT	malignant anaplastic teratoma
MAP	M-associated protein		
MAP	mean action potential	MAT	manual arts therapist
MAP	mean airway pressure	MAT	multifocal atrial tachycardia
MAP	mean aortic pressure		
MAP	mean arterial pressure	MAT	myocardial appearance time
MAP	Medical Aid Post		
MAP	Medical Audit Program	MATA	membrane-associated tumor antigens
MAP	membrane action potential		
MAP	6-methyl-17-acetoxyprogesterone	MAVIS	mobile artery and vein imaging system
MAP	minimum audible pressure	MAWM *(card)*	mean anterior wall motion
MAP	monophasic action potential		
		max.	maximal, maximum
MAP	muscle action potential	MB	buccal margin
MAP	muscle adenosine phosphoric acid	MB	Marsh-Bendall (factor)
		MB *(dent)*	mesiobuccal
MAPHY	Metoprolol Atherosclerosis Prevention in Hypertensives (Study)	MB	métabolisme basal (F); basal metabolic rate (= BMR)
MAPP	maintained airway positive pressure	MB	methylbromide
		MB	methylene blue
MAP test	murine antibody production test	MB	myeloblast (= Mbl)
		Mb	melanoblast
MAR *(rad)*	maximum acceptable risk	Mb	myoglobin
MAR	minimal angle resolution	mb	millibar
MAS	malabsorption syndrome (= MAL)	M.B.	Medicinae Baccalaureus (L); Bachelor of Medicine
MAS	malassimilation syndrome	m.b. *(pharm)*	misce bene (L); mix well (Rx)
MAS *(obst)*	meconium aspiration syndrome		
MAS *(obst)*	movements alarm signal	MBA	mean value of biological age
mAs, MAS	milliampère-second	MBA	methylbenzyl alcohol
MASA	Morgagni-Adams-Stokes attack	MBA	methyl-bis-(2-chloroethyl)-amine, chlormethine (= DEMA)
masc.	masculinum (L); male		
MASER	microwave amplification by stimulated emission of radiation	M.B.A.C.	Member of the British Association of Chemists
		M-band	middle segment of a myofibril
MASH	Mobile Army Surgical Hospital	MBAO	methyl-bis-aminoxide; chlormethinoxide
MAS syndrome	Morgagni-Adams-Stokes syndrome	MBAO	morning basal acid output
MASTIF	Multiple Axes Space Test Inertia Facility	MBAP	mean brachial artery pressure

MBBA	methoxybenzoyl bromo-acrylate	MBT	2-mercaptobenzthiazole
MBC	maximum binding capacity	MBTH	3-methyl-2-benzthiazolone-hydrazone
MBC	maximum breathing capacity	MBTS	modified Blalock-Taussig shunt
MBC	methylbenzyl chloride	MC	Medical Corps
MBC	minimal bactericidal concentration	MC	mesangial cell proliferation
MBCK	muscle-brain creatinine phosphokinase	MC	mesiocervical
MbCO	carbon monoxide myoglobin	MC	metacarpal
MBD	minimal brain dysfunction	MC	methicillin
MBF	myocardial blood flow	MC	Minnesota Code
MB factor	Marsh-Bendall factor	MC	minocycline (6-demethyl-6-deoxy7-dimethylamino-tetracycline)
MBH	methylene blue, reduced	MC	mitomycin
MBL	Marine Biological Laboratory (USA)	MC	monkey cells
MBL	menstrual blood loss	MC	motor cortex
MBL	myeloblastic leukemia	MC	Multiple Choice (Examination System)
Mbl	myeloblast	MC	myocarditis
MBLA	mouse-specific B-lymphocyte antigen	M.C.	Magister Chirurgiae (L); Master of Surgery (=M.Ch., M.Chir.)
MBN	malignant blue nevus	M-C	mineralocorticoid
MBO *(dent)*	mesiobucco-occlusal	M+C	morphin/cocaine
MbO$_2$	oxymyoglobin	MCA	Manufacturing Chemists Association
MBP	mean blood pressure	MCA	median cerebral artery
MBP	"melitensis, bovine, porcine" (serum for brucellosis)	MCA	mesocaval (mesenteriocaval) anastomosis
MBP *(dent)*	mesiobuccopulpal	MCAB	monoclonal antibodies (=MAB, MoAB)
MBP	Munich Blood Pressure Program	MCADA	2-mercapto-cyclohexyl-amine diacetate
MBP	myelin basic protein	MCAR	mixed cell agglutination reaction
MBQ *(psych)*	Mini-Biography Questionnaire	MCAT	Medical College Admission Test
MBRT	methylene blue reduction time	MCAT	myocardial contrast appearance time
MBSA	methylated bovine serum albumin	MCB	membranous cytoplasmic bodies
MBSR	micro-blood cell sedimentation rate	McB	McBurney's point
MB syndrome	Marie-Bamberger syndrome; osteoperiostitis ossificans toxica	MCC	mean cell concentration
		MCC	marked cocontraction
		McC *(urol)*	McCarthy device, electrotome

MCCU	Mobile Coronary Care Unit	mCi	millicurie
MCD	mean corpuscular diameter	mCid *(rad)*	millicurie destroyed
MCD	minimal cerebral dysfunction (= MBD)	mCih	millicurie/hour
MCD *(bact)*	minimal curative dose	MCIM	methylcholanthrene-induced muscle sarcoma (in mice)
MCD cells	mastcell-depleted cells	MC insulin	monocomponent insulin
MCE	massage cardiaque externe (F); external cardiac massage	MCL	midclavicular line
		MCL	modified chest lead
MCF	macrophage chemotactic factor	MCLS	mucocutaneous lymph node syndrome, Kawasaki's disease (= MLNS)
MCF	medium corpuscular fragility	MCMP	5-methylcytidine monophosphate
MCFP	mean circulatory filling pressure	MCNS	minimal change nephrotic syndrome
MCFT	micro-complement fixation test	M-component	macroglobulin Waldenström (= M-protein)
MCG	magnetocardiography	MCP	Medical Congress Preview
MCG	mechanocardiography	MCP	metacarpophalangeal
mcg	microgram, 10^{-6} g (more correct: μg)	MCP	metoclopramide
		MCP	minimal cerebral palsy
MCH	Maternal and Child Health	MCP	mitotic control protein
		MCPA	2-methyl-4-chlorophenoxy-acetic acid
MCH	mean corpuscular hemoglobin	M.C.P.A.	Member of the College of Pathologists of Australia
mch	millicurie/hour (= mCih)	M.C.Path.	Member of the College of Pathologists
M.Ch.	Magister Chirurgiae (L); Master of Surgery	MCPH	metacarpophalangeal
MCHC	mean corpuscular hemoglobin concentration	M.C.P.S.	Member of the College of Physicians and Surgeons
M.Ch.D.	Magister Chirugiae Dentalis (L); Master of Dental Surgery	MCP test	mucin clot prevention test
		MCR	Medical Corps Reserve
M.Chir.	Magister Chirurgiae (L); Master of Surgery	MCR	metabolic clearance rate
		M.C.R.A.	Member of the College of Radiologists of Australia
M.Ch.Orth.	Master of Orthopedic Surgery	MCS	Medico-Chirurgical Society (UK)
M.Ch.Otol.	Master of Otologic Surgery	MCS	Modular Computer and Software Systems (lab computers)
MCHR	Medical Committee for Human Rights		
M-chromosome	chromosome with median centromere	MC shunt	mesocaval shunt (= MCA)
M.Ch.S.	Member of the Society of Chiropodists	M.C.S.P.	Member of the Chartered Society of Physiotherapy
MCI	methylcholanthrene-induced sarcoma (in mice)	MCT	mean (red) cell thickness
		MCT	mean circulation time

MCT	medium-chain triglycer-ides	MDA	Muscular Dystrophy Association
MCT	medullary carcinoma of the thyroid	MDAP	mean diastolic arterial pressure
MCT (pharm)	multiple compressed tablet	MDCC	mean daily capsule count (method to check the patient's compliance)
MCTD	mixed connective tissue disease	MDCK	Madin-Darby-canine kidney (cell line)
MC tumors	tumors induced by 3-methylcholanthrene	M.D.D.	Medicinae Dentalis Doctor (L); Doctor of Dental Medicine
MCU, MCUG	micturition cysto-urethrogram	M.Dent.Sc.	Master of Dental Science
MCV	mean corpuscular volume	MDF	myocardial depressant factor
MCZ	Museum of Comparative Zoology (Harvard)	MDGF	macrophage-derived growth factor (= MGF)
MD	macula densa	MDH	malate dehydrogenase
MD	maintenance hemodialysis	MDHR	Middlebrook-Dubos hemagglutination reaction
MD	malic dehydrogenase (= MDH)	MDL	Medical Data Ltd.
MD	manic-depressive	MDLVP	mean diastolic left ventricular pressure
MD (pharm)	maximum dose (occasionally also "median dose")	MDM (imm)	minor determinant mixture
MD (stat)	mean deviation	MDNB	m-dinitrobenzene
MD (anat)	Meckel's diverticulum	MDP	maximum diastolic potential
MD	Medical Department	MDP (obst)	mento-dextra posterior (position of fetus) (also: mento-dorso posterior)
MD	mentally deficient		
MD (dent)	mesiodistal		
MD	mitral disease	MDP (chem)	methyldiphosphonate
MD	muscular dystrophy	MDPLP	mean diastolic pleural pressure
MD	myocardial disease		
Md	mutation difference	MDQ	minimum detectable quantity
M.D.	Medicinae Doctor (L); Doctor of Medicine	MDR	minimum daily requirement
m.d.	more dicto (L); as ordered (Rx)	MDR (pharm)	multiple drug resistance
MDA	malone dialdehyde	MDS (mil)	main dressing station
MDA (obst)	mento-dextra anterior (position of fetus) (also: mento-dorso-anterior)	MDS	microliter dosing syringe
		MDS	myelodysplastic syndrome
MDA	methylene dioxy-amphetamine	M.D.S.	Master of Dental Surgery
MDA	monodehydro-ascorbic acid	m.d.s. (pharm)	misce, da, signa! (L); mix, pack and label (Rx)
MDA	motor discriminative acuity		

MDT *(obst)*	mento-dextra transvera (position of fetus) (also: mento-dorso-transversa)	MEFR	maximal expiratory flow rate
MDWS	malignant dopa withdrawal syndrome	MEFT	maximal expiratory flow time
ME	maximum effort	MEFV	maximal expiratory flow-volume curve
ME	Medical Examiner	MEG	monoethylene glycol
ME	metabolizable energy	MEGX	monoethylglycine xylidide
ME	methylephedrine	MEH	melanophore expanding
ME	middle ear		hormone; melanotrophin,
ME	minute excretion		intermedin (= MSH)
M_e	electron mass	MEH	mean erythrocyte hemoglobin concentration
MEA	mercapto-ethylamine		
MEA	mono-ethanolamine	MEHA	multiple endocrine hereditary adenomatosis
MEA	multiple endocrine adenomatosis	MEIDA	2-mercapto-ethylimino-diacetate
MEB	methylene blue (= MB)	MEK	methylethylketone
MEB	muscle-eye-brain disease	MEM	minimal essential medium
MEC	maximum emission concentration	MEMS	Medication Event Monitoring System
MEC	minimum effective concentration	MEM test	macrophage electrophoretic mobility test
MED	minimal effective dose (of antibiotics)	MEN	multiple endocrine neoplasia
MED *(rad)*	minimum erythema dose	MEND	Medical Education for National Defense
MED	mean erythrocyte diameter	MeOH	methyl alcohol
med.	medialis	MEOS	microsomal ethanol oxidation system (= MAOS)
med.	medical	MEP	maximal expiratory pressure
Medcol	medical computer language		
MEDICO	Medical International Cooperation	MEP	mean effective pressure
		MEP	motor end-plate
MEDLARS	Medical Literature Analysis and Retrieval System	MEP	motor evoked potential
		MEP	multiple exposure photography
MEDLINE	MEDLARS on line	MEPA	cytotoxic combination therapy with methotrexate, Endoxan, Purinethol, and arabinoside C
MEDSAC	Medical Data System for Analysis of Clinical Information		
Med.Sc.D.	Medicae Scientiae Doctor (L); Doctor of Medical Science	MEPO	cytotoxic combination therapy with methotrexate, Endoxan, Purinethol, and Oncovin
MEE	methylethyl ether		
MEE	middle ear effusion	MEPP	motor end-plate potential
MEF	maximal expiratory flow	MEQ	methaqualone

mEq	milli-equivalent (= mval)	mF, mfd	millifarad
MER	mean ejection rate	Mf.	microfilaria
MER	methanol extractable residue	m.f. *(pharm)*	misce, fiat ... (L); mix to prepare ... (Rx)
MES	maintenance electrolyte solution	M/F *(stat)*	male/female
MES	microsomal enzyme system	MFA	Medizinische Forschungsanstalt (G); Medical Research Establishment (of the Max Planck Society)
MESA	mean epithelial surface area		
Mesc	mescaline	MFA	methylfluoroacetate
MESH	Medical Subject Headings (of MEDLARS)	MFD	mean fertilizing dose
		MFD	minimum fatal dose
MET *(derm)*	mean epidermal thickness	MFD	muscle fiber diameter
		MFF	macrophage fusion factor
MET	metabolic equivalent	MFG	modified heat degraded gelatin
Met	methionine		
Meta	metaldehyde	M.F.Hom.	Member of the Faculty of Homoeopathy
metab.	metabolism, metabolic		
Met-Hb	methemoglobin	MFKP	maladie fibro-kystique du pancréas (F); fibrocystic disease of the pancreas
MeThCh	methylthiocholine		
m. et n.	mane et nocte (L); in the morning and evening		
		M.flac.	membrana flaccida, Shrapnell's membrane
m. et sig.	misce et signa (L); mix and label (Rx)		
		MF method *(bact)*	membrane (or millipore) filter method
MeV	mega electron volts		
ME-virus	mouse-Elberfeld virus	M-form	mucosus growth form of microorganisms
MEVR	modified endocardial viability ratio		
		MFP	mean filling pressure
MEX	maximal expiratory pressure	MFP	monofluorophosphate
		m.f.pil.	misce, fiant pilulae (L); mix to prepare pills
MF *(pharm)*	Magistral Formulae		
MF	maximum flow (rate)	m.f.plv.	misce, fiat pulvis (L); mix to prepare powder
MF	medium frequency		
MF *(phys)*	megafarad	MFR	myocardial blood flow reserve
MF *(chem)*	melamine-formaldehyde		
MF	microscopic factor	MF rate	maximum flow rate
MF	mitochondrial fragments	MFS	muscle fiber stretch
MF	mitotic factor	MF sol.	merthiolate-formaldehyde solution
MF *(rad)*	median field		
MF	multiplying factor	MFT	muscle function test
MF	mycosis fungoides	m.ft. *(pharm)*	mistura fiat (L); prepare a mixture (Rx)
MF	myelinized nerve fiber		
MF	myelofibrosis	MFVEB	multifocal ventricular ectopic beats
MF	myocardial fibrosis		
MF	myofilament	MG	menopausal gonadotrophin
Mf	microfibril		

MG *(dent)*	mesiogingival	MH	molecular hematology
MG	methylglyoxal	MHA	Mental Health Administration
MG	Molekulargewicht (G); molecular weight	MHA	micro-angiopathic hemolytic anemia
MG	monoglyceride	MHb	myohemoglobin
MG	myasthenia gravis	MHC	major histocompatibility complex
MGA	malposition of the great arteries	MHD	minimal hemolytic dose
MGA	melengestrol acetate	MHF	morbus haemolyticus fetalis (L); hemolytic disease of the fetus
MG aggl.	McGinnis agglutination reaction		
MGD	mixed gonadal dysgenesis	MHH	Medizinische Hochschule Hannover; Medical Academy of Hanover/Germany
mg/dl	milligram/deciliter (formerly: mg%)		
MGE	methylglycol ether		
mgeh *(rad)*	milligram element x hour	MHK *(bact)*	minimale Hemmkonzentration (G); minimal inhibitory concentration (=MIC)
MGF	macrophage-derived growth factor (=MDGF)		
MGG	molecular and general genetics	MHL	Medizinische Hochschule Lübeck; Medical Academy of Lübeck/Germany
MGH	Massachusetts General Hospital (Boston/USA)		
MGH	monoglyceride hydrolase	MHMA	3-methoxy-4-hydroxy-mandelic acid
mgh *(rad)*	milligram x hour	MHN, Mhn	morbus haemolyticus neonatorum (L); hemolytic disease of the newborn (=HDN, MNH)
MGI	macrophage and granulocyte inducer		
MGL	milder grade of lymphadenopathy		
MGN	membranous glomerulonephritis	MHO	microsomal heme oxygenase
MGO	methylglucamine orotate	mho	"reciprocal" ohm, siemens
MGP	marginal granulocyte pool	MHP	"mini" heparin prophylaxis
M-gradient	myeloma gradient (in paraproteinoses)		
MG strept.	McGinnis streptococci	MHPG	3-methoxy-4-hydroxy-phenylglycol
MGTD	metastatic gestational trophoblastic disease	MHR	maximal heart rate
MGW	magnesium sulfate, glycerol, water (for enema)	MHRI	Mental Health Research Institute (USA)
MH	malignant hyperthermia	MHS	major histocompatibility system (=MHC)
MH	mammotrophic hormone (=prolactin)	MHV	murine hepatitis virus
MH	marital history	M.Hyg.	Master of Hygiene
MH	medical history	MHz	megahertz
MH	melanophore hormone	MI	malignancy index
MH	menstrual history	MI *(dent)*	mesio-incisal
MH	mental health	MI	metabolic index

MI	migration inhibition	MIFC	merthiolate-iodo-formalde-hyde centrifugation
MI	mitral insufficiency		
MI	myocardial infarction	MIFR	maximal inspiratory flow rate
MI	myocardial ischemia		
MIA	mono-iodoacetate	MIFVC	maximal inspiratory flow-volume curve
M.I.A.C.	Member of the International Academy of Cytology		
		MIH	melanotrophin inhibiting hormone
Mi^a-factor	Miltenberger factor, antigen Mi$_a$	MII	multiple insulin injections (as opposed to CSII)
MIAMI	Metoprolol in Acute Myocardial Infarction (Study in Sweden)	MILIS	Multicenter Investigation of Limitation of Infarct Size (Study)
MIBG	meta-iodobenzyl guanidine (vd. ^{131}I-MIBG)	MIMS	Monthly Index of Medical Specialities
MIBK	methylisobutylketone	min	minute
MIBT	methylisatine-beta-thio-semicarbazone	min.	minimal, minor
		MINA	mono-isonitroso-acetone
MIC	maternity and infant care	MINIA	monkey intranuclear infectious agent
MIC	maximum immission concentration		
		MInstSP	Member of the Institution of Sewage Purification
MIC (bact)	minimal inhibitory concentration	MIO	minimal identifiable odor
MIC	minimal isorrheic concentration	MIP	maximal inspiratory pressure
MICP	mean intracranial pressure	MIRD	Medical Internal Radiation Dose
MICR	Myocardial Infarction Community Register	MIRU	Myocardial Infarction Research Unit
MICU	Mobile Intensive Care Unit	MISC	mean inhibitory scores per concentration
MID (dent)	mesio-incisodistal	MISREP	Multiple Item System for Rheumatic Patients
MID	minimum infective dose		
MID	minimum inhibiting dose	MIST	Medical Infomation Service by Telephone
MID	multi-infarction dementia		
MIDT	micro-immune diffusion test	mist.	mistura (L); mixture
		MIT	Massachusetts Institute of Technology
MIF	macrophage (migration) inhibitory factor	MIT	(macrophage) migration inhibition test
MIF	melanocyte inhibiting factor		
		MIT	metabolic inhibition test
MIF	membrane immunofluorescence	MIT	miracidial immobilization test
MIF	merthiolate-iodo-formalde-hyde (technique of fecal examination)	MIT	3-mono-iodotyrosine
		MITC	minocycline-tetracycline
MIF	migration inhibition factor	MIVP (card)	mean intraventricular pressure

167

MIW *(card)*	middle inferior wall	MLI *(dent)*	mesiolinguo-incisal
MIX	methylisobutyl xanthine	MLNS	mucocutaneous lymph node syndrome, Kawasaki's disease (= MCLS)
MJ	marijuana		
MK	myokinase		
MK-cells	monkey kidney cells	MLO *(dent)*	mesiolinguo-occlusal
MKSA system	meter-kilogram-second-ampère system of measures	MLP *(obst)*	mento-laeva posterior (position of fetus)
		MLP *(dent)*	mesiolinguopulpal
MKS system	meter-kilogram-second system of measures (cp. CGS system)	MLR	micro-liquor reaction
		MLR	mixed lymphocyte reaction
		MLS	median life span
ML	lingual margin	MLS	median longitudinal section
ML	macrophage lysine		
ML	malignant lymphoma	MLS	monocytic-lymphocytogenic system
ML	mammary leukemia		
ML	Medical Laboratory	MLS	myatrophic lateral sclerosis (= ALS)
ML *(dent)*	mesiolingual		
ML	midline	MLT *(rad)*	median lethal time
ML	middle lobe	MLT	Medical Laboratory Technician
ML	myeloic leukemia		
M.L.	Licentiate in Medicine (= L.M., Lic.Med.)	MLT *(obst)*	mento-laeva transversa (position of fetus)
Ml	meter lens	MLTC	mixed lymphocyte tumor cell culture
ml	milliliter		
MLA	Medical Library Association	MLU	MacLagan unit
		MLV	murine leukemia virus
MLA *(obst)*	mento-laeva anterior (position of fetus)	MM	malignant melanoma
		MM	morphium muriaticum
MLa *(dent)*	mesiolabial	MM	mucous membranes
MLAD *(card)*	marked left axis deviation	MM	mumps meningitis
		MM	myeloic metaplasia
MLal *(dent)*	mesiolabio-incisal	Mm.	musculi (L); muscles
MLAO	modified left anterior oblique (position)	mm	millimeter
		mM, mmol	millimol
MLAP	mean left atrial pressure	MMA	methyl malonic acid
MLaP *(dent)*	mesiolabiopulpal	MMAD	mass median aerodynamic diameter
MLC	mixed lymphocyte culture		
MLC	murine lymphocytic choriomeningitis	MMb	metmyoglobin
		MMC	metamyelocyte
MLC	myosin light chain	MMC	methylmercury chloride
MLCA	main left coronary artery	MMC	migration myoelectric complex
MLD	metachromatic leukodystrophy		
		MMDA	methoxymethylene dioxyamphetamine
MLD	minimum lethal dose		
MLD$_{50}$ *(rad)*	median lethal dose	M.Med.	Master of Medicine
MLF	mitochondria lysis factor	MMEF, MMF	maximal mid-expiratory flow
MLG	modified liquid gelatine		

M.M.F.	Member of the Medical Faculty	MMWR	Morbidity Mortality Weekly Report (USA)
MMFR	maximal mid-expiratory flow rate	MMZ	metamizole
		MN	(alpha-)methylnoradrena-
mm Hg	millimeter mercury		line
MMI	macrophage migration inhibition	MN	metanephrine
		MN	mononuclear, mononucle-
MMI	methyl-mercapto-imida- zole, thiamazole		osis
		MN	motor neuron
MMIS	Medicaid Management and Information System	MN	multinodular
		MN	myoneural
MMK operation	surgical correction of uri- nary incontinence accord- ing to Marshall-Marchetti- Krantz	M_n	neutron mass
		mN	millinormal
		M.N.	Master of Nursing
		MNA	metanoradrenaline
MML	myelo-monocytic leukemia	MNA	metronidazole
mmm	millimicron (= m0)	MNCV	motor nerve conduction velocity
MMN syndrome	multiple mucosal neuro- mas (or neurofibromas)		
		MND	minimal necrotizing dose
MMPI (psych)	Maudsley Multiphasic Per- sonality Inventory	MNG	N-methyl-N-nitroso-N- nitroguanidine
MMPI (psych)	Minnesota Multiphasic Personality Inventory	MNH	morbus neonatorum haem- olyticus (L); hemolytic dis- ease of the newborn (= HDN, MHN)
mmpp	millimeters partial pressure		
6-MMPR	6-methyl-mercaptopurine riboside		
		MNH lymphoma	malignant non-Hodgkin lymphoma
MMQ (psych)	Maudsley Medical Ques- tionnaire	MNJ	myoneural junction
MMR	Mass Miniature Radiogra- phy	MNNG	N-methyl-N-nitro-N-nitro- soguanidine
		MNP	meningopneumonitis
MMR	maternal mortality rate	MNS	MNS blood group system
MMR	monomethylrutin	MNSER (card)	mean normalized systolic ejection rate
MMR	monosynaptic mass reflex		
MMS	Manufacturing Monitoring System	MNU	N-methyl-N-nitroso-urea
		MNYC medium	modified New York City medium (for the diagnosis of gonorrhea)
MMS	methylmethane sulfonate		
M.M.S.	Master of Medical Science		
MMT	manual muscle test	MNZ	miconazole
MMTV	murine mammary tumor virus	MO	manually operated
		MO	Medical Officer
MMU	mercapto-methyluracil	MO (dent)	mesio-occlusal
MMuLV	Moloney murine leukemia virus (= MoMLV)	MO	mineral oil
		MO (card)	minute output (= CO)
MMV	mandatory minute volume	Mo	morphin (= M.)
MM virus	encephalomyocarditis virus (= EMC virus)	mo.	month(s)
		M.O.	Master of Obstetrics
mmW	millimeter wave (= EHF)		

MOA	(+)-6-methyloctanic acid	MOPS	3-(N-morpholino)-pro-
MoAB	monoclonal antibodies		panesulfonic acid
	(= MAB, MCAB)	MOPV	monovalent oral polio vac-
MOC	maximum organ concen-		cine
	tration	MOR	magneto-optic rotation
MOD	maturity onset diabetes		spectroscopy
MOD *(dent)*	mesio-occlusodistal	MORD	magneto-optic rotation
mod.praesc.	modo praescripto (L); as		dispersion
	prescribed (Rx)	MORC	Medical Officers Reserve
MODS	Medically-Oriented Data		Corps
	System	MORD	magneto-optic rotation
MODY	maturity onset diabetes in		dispersion
	young people	mor.sol.	more solito (L); as usual
MOF	marine oxygenation/fer-		(Rx)
	mentation (medium)	MOS	metal-oxide semiconductor
MOF	multiple-organ failure	MOS	mitral opening sound
M.O.G.	Master of Obstetrics and	mOsm,	milliosmol
	Gynaecology	mosm	
M.O.H.	Medical Officer of Health	MOTT	mycobacteria other than
mol.	molecule, molecular		tubercle
mol.	molar (= m, M)	MOV	Manned Orbital Vehicle
mol.wt.	molecular weight	MOV	minimal occlusal volume
MOM,	milk of magnesia (antacid)	MP	mandibular plane
MoM		MP	maximal pulse
MOMA	3-methoxy-4-hydroxy-	MP	menstrual period
	mandelic acid	6-MP	6-mercaptopurine
	(= MHMA)	MP *(dent)*	mesiopulpal
MoMLV	Moloney murine leukemia	MP	metacarpophalangeal
	virus (= MMuLV)	MP	metatarsophalangeal
MONA	multiple of normal activity	MP	methylprednisolone
MONICA	Monitoring of Trends and	MP	methylpyrazole
	Determinants in Cardio-	MP	microperoxidase
	vascular Diseases (WHO	MP	mucopeptide
	study)	MP	mucopolysaccharide
Mono	monocytes, mononucleosis		(usually: MPS)
MOP	5-methoxypsoralene	MP *(gyn)*	multipara, multiparous
MOP	myositis ossificans progres-	MP *(neur)*	myelopathy
	siva	M_P	proton mass
MOPA	morpholinopropane-sul-	mP	mobile phase
	fonic acid	mp	melting point
MOPEG	3-methoxy-4-hydroxyphen-	MPA	main pulmonary artery
	ylglycol	MPA	6-alpha-methyl-17-alpha-
MOPP	cytotoxic combination		hydroxyprogesterone ace-
	therapy with mustine (mus-		tate
	targen), vincristin	MPA	microprecipitation in agar
	(Oncovin), procarbazine	MPAP	mean pulmonary artery
	and prednisone		pressure

MPB	male pattern baldness
MPB	meprobamate
MPC	maximum permissible concentration
MPC	mean plasma concentration
MPC	methylpyrazole-3-carboxylic acid
MPCA	mouse-specific plasma cell antigen
MPCP	mean pulmonary capillary pressure
MPCU	maximum permissible concentration of unidentified radionuclides
MPCWP	mean pulmonary capillary wedge pressure
MPD *(rad)*	maximum permissible dose
MPD	minimum phototoxic dose
MPD	minimal pyrogenic dose
MPD	myofacial pain dysfunction
MPDE *(rad)*	maximum permissible dose equivalent
M-period	mitotic period
MPG	Max-Planck-Gesellschaft; Max Planck Society (Germany)
MPG	mean pressure gradient
MPGA *(obst)*	mean projected gestational age
MPGN	membrane-proliferative glomerulonephritis
Mph	melanophore
M.P.H.	Master of Public Health
mph	miles per hour
M.Pharm.	Master of Pharmacy
M-phase	mitotic phase (of the cell cycle)
MPI *(psych)*	Maudsley Personality Inventory (vd. MMQ)
MPI	maximum point of impulse
MPI	Max-Planck-Institut (multiple scientific institutes in the Federal Republic of Germany)
MPI	myocardial perfusion imaging
MPIP	Multicenter Post Infarction Program (USA)
MPI-test	multiphasic personality inventory test
MPL	maximum permissible level
MPL *(dent)*	mesiopulpolabial
MPL	methylprednisolone
MPMP	N-(1-methylpiperidyl-3-methyl)-phenothiazine
MPMV	Mason-Pfizer monkey virus
MPN	most probable number (of bacteria)
MPO	myeloperoxidase
MPP	mean pulmonary (artery) pressure (=MPAP)
MPR	marrow production rate
M-protein	macroglobulin Waldenström (=M-component)
MPS *(ophth)*	Macular Photocoagulation Study
MPS	membrane plasma separation
MPS	mitral valve prolapse syndrome
MPS	mononuclear phagocytic system
MPS	movement produced stimuli
MPS	mucopolysaccharides
MPS	multiphasic screening
MPS	myeloproliferative syndrome
M.P.S.	Member of the Pharmaceutical Society
MPSI *(psych)*	Male Procreative Superiority Index
MPT	maximal phonation time
MPT	(alpha-)methyl-p-tyrosine
MPT	mucoprotein tyrosine
MPTP	1-methyl-4-phenyl-1,2,3,6-tetrahydropyridine
MPTT	mean pulmonary transit time
MPU	Medical Practitioners Union (UK)

MQ *(card)*	muscle quotient	M.R.C.P.G.	Member of the Royal College of Physicians and Surgeons of Glasgow
MR *(gen)*	multiple reactivation		
MR	mentally retarded		
MR	metabolic rate	M.R.C.P.I.	Member of the Royal College of Physicians of Ireland
MR, M.R.	methylred reaction		
mR	milliroentgen		
MRA	mean right atrial (pressure) (=MRAP)	M.R.C.Psych.	Member of the Royal College of Psychiatrists
MRA	Medical Record Administrator	M.R.C.S.	Member of the Royal College of Surgeons
M.R.A.C.P.	Member of the Royal Australian College of Physicians	M.R.C.S.E.	Member of the Royal College of Surgeons of Edinburgh
M.R.A.C.S.	Member of the Royal Australian College of Surgeons	M.R.C.S.I.	Member of the Royal College of Surgeons of Ireland
M.Rad.	Master of Radiology		
mrad	millirad	M.R.C.V.S.	Member of the Royal College of Veterinary Surgeons
MRAP	mean right atrial pressure (=MRA)		
MRBC	monkey red blood cells	MRD	minimum reacting dose
MRC	Medical Registration Council	MRE	maximal respiratory effectiveness
MRC	Medical Research Committee	mrem	millirem (milliroentgen equivalent man)
MRC	Medical Research Council (UK)	M-receptor	morphin receptor
MRC	Medical Reserve Corps (=MORC)	MRF	mesencephalic reticular formation
MRC	methylrosaniline chloride, gentian violet	MRF	MSH-releasing factor (=MRH)
M.R.C.G.P.	Member of the Royal College of General Practitioners	MRFIT	Multiple Risk Factor Intervention Trial
MRCI	Medical Registration Council of Ireland	MRGM *(bact)*	multi-resistant gram-negative (organisms)
MRCI	Medical Research Council of Ireland	MRH	MSH-releasing hormone (=MRF)
M.R.C.O.G.	Member of the Royal College of Obstetricians and Gynaecologists	MRHA	mannose resistant hemagglutination
M.R.C.P.	Member of the Royal College of Physicians	MRI	magnetic resonance imaging
M.R.C.Path.	Member of the Royal College of Pathologists	M.R.I.	Member of the Royal Institution
M.R.C.P.E.	Member of the Royal College of Physicians of Edinburgh	MRIH	melanocyte stimulating hormone release inhibiting hormone
		MRK syndrome	Mayer-Rokitansky-Küster syndrome
		MRL	Medical Record Librarian

MRL	Medical Research Laboratory	M.S.	Magister Scientiae (L); Master of Science (=M.Sc.)
mRNA	messenger ribonucleid acid	M.S.	Master of Surgery (=M.Ch., M.Surg.)
MRO	muscular receptor organ	ms	millisecond
MRQ	mitral regurgitation quotient	m/s	meters per second
MRP	membrane resting potential	MSA	mannitol salt agar
M.R.O.	Member of the Register of Osteopaths	MSA	Medical Services Administration
MRQ *(bact)*	mean resistance quote	MSA	membrane stabilizing activity
MRR	marrow release rate		
MRS	magnetic resonance spectrum	MSA	mine safety appliance
MRS *(mil)*	medical reception station	MSAP	mean systolic arterial pressure
MRS	Medical Research Society (UK)	MSC	Medical Service Corps
M.R.S.H.	Member of the Royal Society of Health	MSC	monkey stable cells
		M.Sc.	Magister Scientiae (L); Master of Science (=M.S.)
MRT	magnetic resonance tomography	MSCAV	mid-systolic closure of the aortic valve
MRT *(psych)*	Metropolitan Readiness Test	mscp	mean square candle power
MRT	motor reaction time	MSD	mechanical systole duration
MRU *(bact)*	minimal reproductive units		
MRV	mitral regurgitation volume	MSD	Merck, Sharp, and Dohme
		M.S.D.	Magister Scientiae Dentalis (L); Master of Dental Science
MRV	mixed respiratory vaccine		
MRVP	methylred Voges-Proskauer medium	MSDC	Mass Spectrometry Data Centre (UK)
MS	manuscript		
MS	mass screening	MS-DOS	Microsoft Disk Operating System
MS	mass spectroscope; mass spectrometry	msec	millisecond (=ms)
MS	mechanical systole	MSER	mean systolic ejection rate
MS	mediastinal shift	MSER *(psych)*	Mental Status Examination Record
MS	methionine synthetase		
MS	mitral stenosis	MSERI	mean systolic ejection rate index
MS	modal sensitivity		
MS	molar solution	MSF	macrophage slowing factor
MS	morphin sulfate	MSF	melanocyte stimulating factor (=MEH, MSH)
MS	multiple sclerosis		
MS	muscle shortening	MSG	mean systolic gradient
MS	muscle spindle	MSG	monosodium glutamate
MS	muscle strength	MSG	myeloscintigraphy
MS	musculoskeletal	MSH	melanocyte-stimulating hormone (=MEH, MSF)
MS	myocardial scintigraphy (=SMS)		
		MSH-IF	MSH-inhibiting factor

MSH-RF	MSH-releasing factor	MSS	Medical Superintendents' Society
MSH-RH	MSH-releasing hormone		
MSH-RIF	MSH-release inhibiting factor	MSS	mental status schedule
		MSS	musculoskeletal system
MSI	methionine sulfoximine	MSS	muscular subaortic stenosis
MSI	mitral valve separation index (ratio between mitral valve-septum distance and left ventricular diameter)	M.S.S.E.	Master of Science in Sanitary Engineering
		MSST	Meeting Street School Screening Test
MSI	multiple subcutaneous injections	MSSVD	Medical Society for the Study of Venereal Diseases
MSK Center	Memorial Sloan Kettering Cancer Center (New York)	MST	macrophage stimulation test
MSL	Medical Society of London (UK)	MST	maladies sexuelles transmissibles (F); sexually transmitted diseases (= STD)
MSL	midsternal line		
MSLA	mouse-specific lymphocyte antigen		
		MST	mean survival time
M.S.N.	Master of Science in Nursing	MST	microtome section thickness
MSP	maximum systolic peak	MST, MSt	mitral stenosis (= MS)
MSP	mefloquine/sulphadoxine/pyrimethamine (anti-malaria drug combination)	MSTFA	N-methyl-N-trimethylsilyl-trifluoro-acetamide
		MsTh	mesothorium
		M-strains	monkey strains of rhinoviruses
MSPG	mean systolic pressure gradient		
		MSUD	maple syrup urine disease
M.S.P.H.	Master of Science in Public Health	M.Surg.	Master of Surgery (= M.Ch., M.S.)
M-spike	medullated spike		
MSQ	Mental Status Questionnaire	MSV	murine sarcoma virus
		MSW	Medical Social Worker
MSR	maximum secretory response	M.S.W.	Master of Social Welfare
		M.S.W.	Master of Social Work
M.S.R.	Member of the Society of Radiographers	3-M syndrome	Miller-McKusick-Malvaux syndrome
M-S-R change	change of appearance of micro-organisms (M = mucoid; S = smooth; R = rough)	MS cells	monkey stable cells
		MT	mammary tumor
		MT	Medical Technologist
		MT	Medical Tribune
MSRCL	maximal sinus rhythm cycle length	MT	médecine du travail (F); occupational medicine
M.S.R.G.	Member of the Society for Remedial Gymnastics	MT	membrana tympani
		MT	metatarsal
MSRPP	multidimensional scale for rating psychiatric patients	MT	methoxytyramine
		MT (psych)	mosaic test
		MT	music therapy
MSS	mean severity score	MT	muscular training

MTA	Medical Technical Assistant	MTT	minimal transit time (sometimes also: mean ...)
MTA	methenamine		
MT*(ASCP)*	Medical Technologist (registered by the American Society of Clinical Pathology)	MTTI	myocardial tension time index
		MTU	methylthio-uracil
		MTV	mammary tumor virus
MTB	Meinicke's turbidity reaction (=MTR)	MTV	murine tumor virus, Bittner virus
MTBE	methyl-tert-butyl ether	MTX	methotrexate
MTbR	Meinicke's tuberculosis reaction	MU	Mache unit
		MU	mouse unit
MTC	maximum tolerated concentration	mU, MU	milli-unit (of enzymes)
		MUC	maximum urinary concentration
MTC	methacycline (6-methyl-6-deoxy-5-hydroxy-6-methylene-tetracycline)	Muc. *(pharm)*	mucilage
MTCL *(pharm)*	metoclopramide	MUDr.	Medicinae Universalis Doctor (L); Doctor of General Medicine
MTD	maximal tolerated dose		
M.T.D.	Midwife Teacher's Diploma	m.u.f. *(pharm)*	misce ut fiat ... (L); mix to prepare ... (Rx)
m.t.d. *(pharm)*	mitte tales doses (L); divide in equal doses	MUGA	multiple gate acquisition
		MuLV	murine leukemia virus (=MLV)
mtDNA	mitochondrium deoxyribonucleic acid	MUO	myocardiopathy of unknown origin
MTF	modulation transfer function	MurNAc	N-acetylmuramate
MTGP	mammary tumor glycoprotein	MUSC	Medical University of South Carolina (Charleston)
MTHF	5-methyltetrahydrofolic acid		
MTI	malignant intermediate teratoma	MUWU	mouse uterine weight unit
		MV	mechanical ventilation
MTOC	microtubular organizing complex	MV	megavolt
		MV	microvibration
MTP	metatarsophalangeal	MV	microvilli
MTP	metioprime	MV	minute volume
MTR	Meinicke's turbidity reaction (=MTB)	MV	mitral valve
		MV	mucoviscidosis (cystic fibrosis)
MTR	micromodification of the Takata reaction	mV	millivolt
mtr.	meter (correct: m)	M.V.	Medicus Veterinarius (L); Veterinary Physician
MTS foil	merbromin/tannic acid/silver nitrate foil	MVA	mitral valve area
MTT	malignant trophoblastic teratoma	MVA	modified vaccinia virus Ankara
		MVA	multivariate analysis

mval	millival, milli-equivalent ($=$ mEq)	MWIA	Medical Women's International Association
MVB	mixed venous blood	MWPC	multi-wire proportional
MVB	multivesicular bodies		chamber
MVC	maximal voluntary contraction	MWS	Mallory-Weiss syndrome
MVCAD	multivessel coronary artery disease ($=$ MVD)	MWS	moving window spectrometry
MVCF	mean normalized velocity	MWT	myocardial wall thickness
(card)	of circumferential fiber shortening	mxt.	mixture
		My (ophth)	myopia
MVCI	mitral valve closure index	MyaR	myasthenic reaction
MVD	mitral valve disease	MyG	myasthenia gravis
MVD	multivessel (coronary) disease ($=$ MVCAD)	MyoR, MyR	myotonic reaction
		MZ	monozygotic
MVE	mitral valve excursion		
MVE	Murray Valley encephalitis		
MVES	monomorphous ventricular extrasystoles		

N

MVF	mitral valve flow	N	nausea
MVO	mitral valve opening	N	negative
MVP	mitral valve prolapse	N	neuraminidase
MVPC	multifocal ventricular premature contraction	N (phys)	newton
		N, n (chem)	normal (solution)
MVPI	mitral valve prolapse index	n	nano
MVR (chir)	mitral valve replacement	n	nasal
MVR	myocardial vascular resistance	n (phys)	neutron
		n (gen)	normal chromosome contents
MVRI	mixed vaccine for respiratory infections		
		n	number
MVSD	multiple ventricular septal defect	N. (anat)	nervus (L); nerve
		n.	neutrum, neutral
MVSV	mitral valve stroke volume	NA	nalidixic acid
MVV	Maedi-Visna virus	NA	Narcotics Anonymous
MVV	maximum voluntary ventilation	NA	neutralizing antibody
		NA	nicotinic acid
MW	macroglobulinemia Waldenström	NA	Nomina Anatomica (Basel, Jena, Paris)
MW	megawatt	NA	noradrenaline, norepinephrine, arterenol
MW, mw	microwave		
MW (card)	minute work	NA	nucleic acid
MW	molecular weight ($=$ mol.wt.)	NA	numeric aperture
		NA	nurse's aide
MWCS	midwall circumferential systolic stress	Na	Avogadro's number
MWI	minute work index	NAA	N-acetylaspartate

NAA	naphthalene acetic acid	NAFPD	National Association of Family Planning Doctors (UK)
NAA	neutron activation analysis		
NAA	nicotinic acid amide	NAG	N-acetyl-ß-D-glucosamini-dase
NAA	no apparent abnormalities		
NAACOG	Nurses Association of the American College of Obstetricians and Gynecologists	NAG	non-agglutinating (e.g. NAG vibrios)
		N-agar	nutritional agar
NAACP	National Association for the Advancement of Colored People (USA)	NAGS	N-acetylglutamate synthetase
		NAI	non-accidental injury
NAAP	N-acetyl-4-aminophenazone	NAIDEX	National Aids for the Disabled and Elderly
NAB	novarsenobenzol, neoarsphenamine	NAIS	non-adrenergic inhibitory system
NAC	N-acetyl-L-cysteine	NAL	naso-auricular line
NACL	National Association of Clinical Laboratories (USA)	NAL	National Accelerator Laboratory
		NaLS	sodium laurylsulfate
NACOR	National Advisory Committee on Radiation	NAM	nicotinamide mononucleotide
NAD	nicotinamide-adenine dinucleotide (formerly: DPN)	NAMH	National Association for Mental Health (USA)
NAD	no acute distress	NAMIS	Nifedipine in Acute Myocardial Infarction Study
NAD *(clin)*	no appreciable disease (also: no abnormality demonstrable, nothing abnormal detected)	NAMT	noradrenaline methyltransferase
		NANA	N-acetyl-neuraminic acid
NaDDCT	sodium diethyl-dithiocarbamate	NANB	non-A non-B hepatitis (=HNANB)
NADH	reduced nicotinamide-adenine-dinucleotide (formerly: DPNH)	NAP	N-acetyl-D,L-penicillamine
		NAP	nasion pogonion (angle)
NaDi-reagent	mixture of alpha-naphthol and dimethyl-p-phenylenediamine	NAP	nerve action potential
		NAP	nitrosatin assay procedure
		NAP	Nomina Anatomica Parisiensia
NADL	National Association of Dental Laboratories (USA)	NAP	nucleic acid phosphate
NaDOC	sodium deoxycholate	NAPA	N-acetyl-procainamide
NADP	nicotinamide-adenine-dinucleotide phosphate (formerly: TPN)	NAPA, NAPAP	N-acetyl-p-aminophenol, paracetamol
		NaPAS	sodium salt of p-aminosalicylic acid
NADPH	reduced NADP (formerly: TPNH)	NAPC	National Air Pollution Control
NaDS	sodium dodecylsulfate (electrophoresis)		
Na$_e$	exchangeable sodium	NaPG	sodium pregnanediol glucuronide

NAPNAP	National Association for Pediatric Nurse Associates and Practitioners (USA)	NB	nitrobenzene
		NB	novobiocin
		NB	nota bene (L); note well
NAPNES	National Association for Practical Nurse Education and Service (USA)	NBA	N-bromo-acetamide
		NBA	nitrobenzoic acid
		NBB	normal buffer base
NAPT	National Association of Physical Therapists (USA)	NBC	nuclear, biological, and chemical (weapons) (= ABC)
NAPT	National Association for the Prevention of Tuberculosis (UK)	NBD	neurogenic bladder disturbance
NAR	nasal airway resistance	NBD	4-nitrobenzo-2-oxa-1,3-diazole
NARAL	National Abortion Rights Action League	NBEI	non-butanol-extractable iodine
NARC	National Association for Retarded Children	NBI	no bone injury
		NBL	nasion basion line
NARD	National Association of Retail Druggists	NBM	nothing by mouth
		NBM *(neur)*	nucleus basalis Meynert
NAS	National Academy of Sciences	NBME	National Board of Medical Examiners (USA)
NAS	National Association of Sanitarians	NBP	Nationales Blutdruckprogramm (German National Blood Pressure Intervention Program)
NAS	natural antihistamine substance		
NAS	nickel ammonium sulfate		
NAS	no added salt	NBP	4-(4-nitrobenzyl)-pyridine
NASA	National Aeronautics and Space Administration (Washington)	NBRT	National Board for Respiratory Therapy
		NBS	National Bureau of Standards (USA)
NASDCAE	naphthol-As-D-chloro-acetate esterase	NBS	N-bromosuccinimide
		NBT	nitroblue tetrazolium
NASE	National Association for the Study of Epilepsy	NBTE	non-bacterial thrombotic endocarditis
NASEAN	National Association for State Enrolled Assistant Nurses	NBTNF	newborn, term, normal, female
		NBTNM	newborn, term, normal, male
NASPE	North American Society of Pacing and Electrophysiology	NBT-PABA	N-benzyl-L-tyrosyl-p-aminobenzoic acid (test)
NAVA	National Audio-Visual Association (USA)	NBTR	nitroblue tetrazolium reductase
NAVAC	National Audio-Visual Aids Centre (UK)	NBTS	National Blood Transfusion Service
NAVY	nerve-artery-vein empty space	NC	nitrocellulose
NB	neuroblastoma	NC	nitrochloroform, chloropicrine
NB	newborn		

NC	no change	NCM	nitrocellulose membrane
NC	Nurse Corps	NCMH	National Committee for Mental Health
nc	nanocurie (= nCi)		
Nc.	nucleus (= Nucl.)	NCMHI	National Clearinghouse for Mental Health Information (Dept. of HEW, Washington)
NCA	National Council on Alcoholism		
NCA	neurocirculatory asthenia		
NCA	non-contractile area	NCN	National Council of Nurses
NCA	non-specific cross-reacting antigen		
		NCN	non-collagen nitrogen
NCC	National Cancer Center (of Japan)	N-corticoid	nitrogenous corticoid
		NCP	non-collagen protein
NCCDS	National Cooperative Crohn's Disease Study (USA)	NCP	noscapine
		NCAP	National Coalition for Action in Politics
NCDDG	National Cooperative Drug Discovery Group (USA)	NCRND	National Committee for Research in Neurological Diseases
N-cell	cell with normal number of chromosomes		
		NCRPM	National Commitee on Radiation Protection and Measurements (Washington)
NCEP	National Cholesterol Education Program (USA)		
NCF	neutrophil chemotactic factor	NCS	neocarcinostatin
		NCS	neurotic cervical syndrome
NCFA	neutrophil chemotactic factor of anaphylaxis	NCSC	National Council of Senior Citizens
NCFRF	National Cystic Fibrosis Research Foundation (USA)	NCSNNE	National Commission for the Study of Nursing and Nursing Education (USA)
NCGA	normally connected great arteries	NCTC	National Collection of Type Cultures
NCHS	National Center for Health Statistics	NCV	nerve conduction velocity
		NCV	no commercial value
NCHSR	National Center for Health Services Research	ND	nasal deformity
		ND	natural death
NCI	naphthalene creosote and iodoform	ND	neoplastic disease
		ND	neutral density
NCI	National Cancer Institute (Bethesda)	ND	no date
		ND	normal delivery
nCi	nanocurie	ND	normal dose
NCIB	National Collection of Industrial Bacteria	ND	not detected
		ND	not determined
NCIC	National Cancer Institute of Canada	N.D.	New Drugs
		NDA	National Dental Association (USA)
NCL	National Chemical Laboratory		
		NDA *(pharm)*	New Drug Application
Ncl.	nucleolus		

NDAB	National Diabetes Advisory Board (USA)	NEHDP	National Exercise and Heart Disease Project (USA)
NDBA	N-nitroso-dibutylamine		
NDC	National Drug Code	NEI	National Eye Institute
NDCD	National Drug Code Directory	NEJM	New England Journal of Medicine (official abbreviation: New Engl. J. Med.)
NDD	nutrient-defined diet		
NDDG	National Diabetes Data Group (USA)	NEL	National Epilepsy League (USA)
NDGA	nor-dihydro-guaiaretic acid	NEM	N-ethylmaleinimide
		NEMA	National Eclectic Medical Association
NDMA	N-nitroso-dimethylamine		
NDMA	p-nitroso-dimethylaniline	NEMA	National Electric Manufacturers Association (USA)
NDP	nucleoside diphosphate		
NDS (pharm)	New Drug Submission		
		NEMS	National Emergency Medical Service (USA)
NDT	Neuro-Developmental Treatment	neo	neoarsphenamine
NDT	non-destructive testing	NEP	negative expiratory pressure
NDV	Newcastle disease virus		
NDx	non-diagnostic	NEQ	noise-equivalent number of quanta
NdYAG	neodynium yttrium aluminum granate (laser)		
		ne rep.	ne repetatur (L); do not repeat (Rx)
NE	National Emergency		
NE	neural excitability	NERICP	New England Regional Infant Cardiac Program
NE	neurological examination		
		NES	not elsewhere specified
NE	norepinephrine, noradrenaline (= NA)	NET	(combination of) norephedrine + theophylline
NE	not enlarged		
NE	not examined	n. et m.	nocte et mane (L); night and morning (Rx)
NEA	noise-equivalent absorption		
		NF, N.F.	National Formulary (USA)
NEC	necrotizing enterocolitis	NF	negro female
NEC	non-esterified cholesterol	NF	neutral fat
NEC	not elsewhere classified	NF	neutral filter
NECA	5'-N-ethylcarboxamide adenosine	NF	neutral fraction
		NF	nitrofurantoin
NED	no evident disease	NF	normal flow
NED	normal equivalent deviation	NF	Norme Française; French Norm
NEE	norethisteron enantate	NF	nothing found
NEEP	negative end-expiratory pressure	nF	nanofarad
		NFAC	National Foundation for Asthmatic Children (USA)
NEFA	non-esterified fatty acid (= UFA)		
		NFAT	nuclear factor of activated T-cells
neg.	negative		

NFB	National Federation of the Blind (Canada)	NHANES	National Health and Nutrition Examination Survey (USA)
NFC	National Fertility Center		
NFIP	National Foundation for Infantile Paralysis	NHBPEP	National High Blood Pressure Education Program
NFLPN	National Federation of Licensed Practical Nurses	NHC	3-alpha-naphthyl-4-hydroxycoumarin
NFMR	National Foundation for Metabolic Research (USA)	NHG	normal human globulin
NFN	Nordiske Farmakopénaevn; Northern Pharmacopeia (Scandinavia)	NHI	National Health Insurance
		NHI	National Heart Institute
		NHL	non-Hodgkin lymphoma
		NHLBI	National Heart, Lung, and Blood Institute (Bethesda/ USA)
NFND	National Foundation for Neuromuscular Diseases (USA)		
		NHLI	National Heart and Lung Institute (now: NHLBI)
N-form	"naked" form of Escherichia coli	NHMRC	National Health and Medical Research Council
N-form	normal form of Enterobacteriaceae	NHP	non-heme protein
NFP	"natural" family planning	NH2P3	7,8-dihydroneopterin triphosphate
NFP	nifurprazine		
NFP	nortestosterone furylpropionate	NHR	net histocompatibility rate
		NH region	nodal-His region
NFS	National Fertility Study	NHS	National Health Service (UK)
NFT	nifuratel		
NFTD	normal full term delivery	NHS	normal human serum
NG	new growth	NHSR	National Hospital Service Reserve
NG	neutrophil granulocytes		
NG	nitroglycerin (= NGL)	NHSTA	National Highway Safety Transportation Administration
ng	nanogram ($= 10^{-9}$ g)		
N.g.	Neisseria gonorrhoeae		
NGEA	National Gastroenterological Association (USA)	NI	neutralization index
		NI	no information
NGF	nerve growth factor	NI	non-infectious
NGL	nitroglycerin	NI	not identified
NGP	normal glycoprotein	NIA	National Institute of Aging (USA)
NGS	negative staining procedure		
		NIA	no information available
NGU	non-gonococcal urethritis	Nia	nicotinic acid amide (= NAA)
NH	neonatal hepatitis		
NH	neonatal hyperbilirubinemia	NIAB	National Institute of Agricultural Botany
NH	Nursing Home	NIAID	National Institute of Allergy and Infectious Diseases (Bethesda/ USA)
NH2	7,8-dihydroneopterin		
NHA	National Health Association (UK)		

181

NIAMD	National Institute of Arthritis and Metabolic Diseases (also: NIAMDD = National Institute of Arthritis, Metabolism and Digestive Diseases) (USA)	NINCD	National Institute of Neurological and Communicative Disorders (USA)
NIBCS	National Institute for Biological Control and Standardization (London/UK)	NINDB	National Institute of Neurological Diseases and Blindness (USA)
		NINDS	National Institute of Neurological Diseases and Stroke (USA)
NICHHD	National Institute of Child Health and Human Development (USA)	NIOSH	National Institute for Occupational Safety and Health (USA)
NICM	Nuffield Institute of Comparative Medicine	NIP	mono-nitroiodophenyl
		NIP	normal immunosuppressant protein
NID	normal-weight insulin-dependent diabetic	NIR *(card)*	non-ischemic region
NIDA	National Institute on Drug Abuse (Washington)	NIRMP	National Intern and Resident Matching Program
NIDD, NIDDM	non-insulin-dependent diabetes (mellitus)	NIRNA	non-imaging radionuclide angiography
NIDR	National Institute of Dental Research (USA)	NIRNS	National Institute for Research in Nuclear Science
NIEA	negative inotropic effect of activation		
NIEHS	National Institute of Environmental Health Services (USA)	NIRS	National Institute of Radiological Sciences (USA)
		NIT	naphthyl-isothiocyanate
NIF	negative inspiratory force	NIT	National Intelligence Test
NIF	neutrophil immobilizing (or migration inhibitory) factor	NIT	neuraminidase inhibition test
		NITA	nuclear inclusion type-A viruses
NIGMS	National Institute of General Medical Sciences (USA)	Nitro-BT	nitro blue tetrazolium (= NBT)
NIH	National Institute of Health (Bethesda/USA)	NIVC	normal intraventricular conduction
NIIP	National Institute of Industrial Psychology	NJPC	National Joint Practice Commission (USA)
NIL	nasion-inion line	NK	Nomenklatur-Kommission (G); Commission on Nomenclature (Germany)
NIM	normed information material		
		NKA	natural killer activity
NIMH	National Institute of Mental Health (UK)	NK cells	natural killer cells
		NKCF	natural killer cytotoxic factor
NIMR	National Institute of Medical Research (UK)	NKL	Nemeth-Kellner leukemia
		NL	neutral lipid
		Nl	normal liter

Nl, Nll.	nervulus, nervuli (L); little nerve(s)	NMLCD	National Medical Library and Center for Medical Documentation (Budapest/Hungary)
n.l.	non licet (L); not permitted		
NLA	neuroleptic analgesia, ... anesthesia	NMM	nodular malignant melanoma
NLM	National Library of Medicine	NMMAA	N-monomethyl acetamide
NLN	National League for Nursing	NMN	nicotinamide mononucleotide
NLNE	National League of Nursing Education	NMN	normetanephrine (= NM)
		nmol	nanomol
NLP	Neurolinguistic Programming	NMP	nucleoside monophosphate
NLT	normal lymphocyte transfer	NMPTP	N-methyl-4-phenyl-1,2,3,6-tetra-hydropyridine
nlt	not less than	NMR	nuclear magnetic resonance
NM	negro male		
NM	neomycin	NMR-CT	nuclear magnetic resonance computer tomography
NM	neuromuscular		
NM	night and morning (Rx)		
NM	nitrogen mustard	NMRI	Naval Medical Research Institute (USA)
NM	nodular melanoma		
NM	non-motile (bacteria)	NMS	National Malaria Society (USA)
NM	normetanephrine (= NMN)		
		NMS	National Medical Service (UK)
NM	Nuclear Medicine		
NM, Nm	nux moschata (L); nutmeg	NMS	normal mouse serum
		NMSS	National Multiple Sclerosis Society (USA)
nm	nanometer (= 10^{-9} m)		
nm	nanomolar	NMT	N-methyltransferase
NMA	National Malaria Association	NMT	neuromuscular tension
		NMTS	National Milk Testing Service
NMA	National Medical Association (USA)		
		NMU	neuromuscular unit
NMC	National Medical Center (USA)	Nn.	nervi (L); nerves
		NNA	N-cyclohexyl-N-methyl-C-2-amino-3,5-dibromoben-zyl ammoniumchloride
NMDA	National Medical and Dental Association (USA)		
		NNa	1-nitroso-2-naphthol
NMDA	N-methyl-D-aspartate	NNCD	2-chloro-4-nitrobenzol-diazonium-naphthalene-2-sulfonic acid (reagent)
NMF	non-migrating fraction (of sperm)		
NMGTD	non-metastatic gestational trophoblastic disease	NND	neonatal death
		NND (pharm)	New and Non-official Drugs
NMI	no middle initial		
NMI	nuclear magnetic imaging (= MRI)	NNEB	National Nursery Examination Board

NNIP	di-nitroiodophenyl	NP	nitrophenol
NNIS	National Nosocomial Infections Study	NP	normal plasma
		NP	not practised
NNM	N-nitromorpholin	NP	nucleoplasmic index
NNMC	National Naval Medical Center (USA)	NP	nucleoprotein
		NP	nursing procedure
NN medium	Novy-McNeal medium	Np	neper (napier)
NNN	N-nitroso-nornicotine	n.p.	normal pressure
NNN	Novy-Nicolle-McNeal agar	NPA	National Pharmaceutical Association (USA)
NNP	sodium (natrium) nitro-prusside (= SNP)	NPA	non-palpable arterial pulse
		NPC	nasopharyngeal carcinoma
NNR (pharm)	New and Non-official Remedies	NPC (ophth)	near point of convergence
NNRF	National Neurological Research Foundation (USA)	NPC	nuclear pore complex
		NPD	Niemann-Pick's disease
NO	nitrous oxide	NPH	neutral protamine Hage-dorn, isophane insulin
NOCM	non-obstructive cardiomy-opathy	NPH	normal pressure hydro-cephalus
NOD	non-obese diabetic	NPI	Neuropsychiatric Institute
NOF	National Osteopathic Foundation (USA)	NPJT	non-paroxysmal junctional tachycardia
NOHSN	National Organization of Hospital Schools of Nurs-ing (USA)	NPL	National Physics Labora-tory
		NPL	neoplasma (= NG)
NOP	not otherwise provided for	NPMT	N-pyrrolidine methyltetra-cycline
NOPHN	National Organization for Public Health Nursing	NPN	nitroprusside natrium (sodium)
NOR	noradrenaline (= NA)		
NOR	nucleolus organizer	NPN	non-protein nitrogen
NORC	National Opinion Research Center	NPO	2-(1-naphthyl)-5-phenyl-oxazole
NORD	National Organization for Rare Disorders	NPO	nothing per os
		NPP	nitrophenylphosphate
Norleu	norleucine	NPP	non-palpable peripheral pulse
NOS	not otherwise specified		
NOSIE	nursing observation scale for inpatient evaluation	NPP	nucleus pulposus prolapse
		NPRL	Navy Prosthetics Research Laboratory
NOTB	National Ophthalmic Treatment Board (UK)	NPSVT	non-paroxysmal supraven-tricular tachycardia
NOVS	National Office of Vital Statistics	NPT	nasal provocation test
NP	nasopharynx	NPT	nocturnal penile tumes-cence
NP	near point		
NP	necrotizing pancreatitis	NPT	normal pressure and tem-perature (= NTP)
NP	neuropsychiatry		

NPU	National Pharmaceutical Union (UK)	NRSFPS	National Reporting System for Family Planning Services
NPU	net protein utilization	NS	nephrotic syndrome
NPU	neuropathic plantar ulcer	NS	nervous system
NPX	naproxene	NS	neurosurgery (= NSurg)
NQR *(phys)*	nuclear quadrupole resonance	NS	nodular sclerosis
NR	neurofibromatosis Recklinghausen	NS	normal saline (= NSS)
		NS	normal serum
NR	neutral red	NS *(stat)*	not significant (also: ns, n.s.)
NR	nodal rhythm		
NR	noise-rating number	NS *(chir)*	nylon suture
NR	no recurrence	ns	nanosecond (= 10^{-9} sec)
NR	no response	NSA	Neurological Society of America
NR	normal range		
NR *(neur)*	nucleus ruber (L); red nucleus	NSA	Nikotinsäureamid (= NAA, Nia)
NR	nutritive ratio	NSA	no salt added
N/R, n.r.	no risk	NSA	no significant abnormalities
NRBC	nucleated red blood cells		
NRC	National Research Council	NSAA	non-steroidal (acidic) anti-inflammatory agents
NRC	noise rating curves		
NRC	noise-reduction coefficient	NSABP	National Surgical Advancement in Breast Cancer Project
NRC *(ophth)*	normal retinal correspondence		
NRDC	National Research and Development Corporation	NSAID	non-steroidal anti-inflammatory drugs
NRDL	Naval Radiological Defense Laboratory	NSAR	non-steroidal antirheumatic (drug)
N-reagent	Nessler's reagent	NSC	National Security Council (USA)
N-region	nodal region		
NREH	normal renin essential hypertension (= NRH)	NSC	non-service connected
		NSCC	National Society for Crippled Children
NREM	non-rapid eye movement (phase of sleep)		
		nsCHE	non-specific cholinesterase
N-receptor	nalorphin receptor		
NRH	normal renin hypertension (= NREH)	NSD *(rad)*	nominal standard dose
		NSDP	National Society of Denture Prosthetics
NRM	normal retinal movement		
NRN	noise rating numbers	NSE	National Society for Epileptics (USA)
NRPB	National Radiological Protection Board (UK)		
		NSE	neuron-specific enolase
NRRL	Northern Regional Research Laboratory	nsec	nanosecond
		NSER	normalized systolic ejection rate
NRS	normal rabbit serum		
NRS	Neurological Rating Scale	NSF	National Science Foundation

NSFTD	normal spontaneous full-term delivery	NTA	National Tuberculosis Association (USA)
NSG	neurosecretory granules	NTA	natural thymotoxic auto-antibody
NSHA	non-spherocytic hemolytic anemia	NTA	nitrilo-triacetic acid
NSILA	non-suppressible insulin-like activity	NTA	norethisterone acetate
NSL *(anat)*	nasion to sella (turcica) line	NTA	Nursery Training Association
NSM	neurosecretory material	NTC	Narcotics Treatment Center
NSMR	National Society for Medical Research (USA)	NTC	negative temperature coefficient
NSMVT	non-sustained monomorphic ventricular tachycardia	NTCC *(bact)*	National Type Culture Collection
NSN	nicotine-stimulating neurophysin	NTD	neural tube defect
		NTF	nitrofurantoin (= NF)
NSN	number of similar negative (matches)	NTG	nitroglycerin (= NGL)
NSNA	National Student Nurses' Association	NTIS	National Technical Information Service (formerly CFSTI)
NSO	nucleus supraopticus	NTP	non-invasive temporary pacemaker
NSPB	National Society for the Prevention of Blindness	NTP	normal temperature and pressure
NSPVT	non-sustained polymorphic ventricular tachycardia	NTP	nucleoside triphosphate
		NTPP	nortestosterone phenylpropionate
NSR	normal sinus rhythm	NTR	normal thyroxin rate
NSS	normal saline solution	NTS	nephrotoxic serum
NST	non-stress test	N-type	"nervosa" type of leprosy
NST	nuclear stethoscope	nU	nanounit
NSU	non-specific urethritis	NUAPS	National Unstable Angina Pectoris Study
NSurg	neurosurgery		
NSVT	non-sustained ventricular tachycardia	Nucl.	nucleus (= Nc.)
		NUd *(gen)*	non-union distal
NT	nasotracheal	NUDS	Northwestern University Disability Scale (for Parkinson's disease)
NT	Nelson's test (= TPI)		
NT	neotetrazolium		
NT	neutralization test	NUF	natriuretic factor
NT	normal titer	NUG	necrotizing ulcerative gingivitis
NT	normotensive, normotension		
		NUI	National University of Ireland
NT	nortriptyline		
NT	nystatin	numc	number concentration
n.t.	normal temperature	NUp *(gen)*	non-union proximal
n.t.	not tested	NUpd *(gen)*	non-union proximal-distal
N + T	nose and throat	NUS	National Utility Services

NV, Nv *(ophth)*	naked vision	o- *(chem)*	ortho-
NV	next visit	OA *(obst)*	occipito-anterior
NV	non-venereal	OA	old age
NV	not vaccinated	OA	orotic acid
NV	non-volatile	OA	osteoarthritis
N + V	nausea and vomiting	OA	oxaloacetate
nval	norvaline	OAA	Old Age Assistance
NVD	neck vein distention	OAA	Organisation pour l'Ali-
NVE	native valve endocarditis		mentation et l'Agriculture
NVM *(chem)*	non-volatile matter		(des Nations Unies) (F);
NVP	Nederlandse Vereniging		Food and Agricultural
	voor Proefdierkunde;		Organization of the Unites
	Dutch Society of Labora-		Nations (= FAO)
	tory Animal Science	OAA	oxaloacetic acid
NVR *(card)*	normalized velocity of ven-	OAAD	ovarian ascorbic acid
	tricular relaxation		depletion (test)
NW	naked weight	OAAT	o-amino-azotoluene
NWB	non-weight-bearing	ÖAB	Österreichisches Arznei-
NWF	National War Formulary		buch (G); Austrian Phar-
NWI	net work index		macopeia
NX	nonoxinol-9 (vaginal	OAD *(obst)*	oblique antérieur droit (F);
	spermicide)		right oblique anterior
Nyª factor	Nyberg factor, antigen Nyª		(position of fetus)
NYAS	New York Academy of		(= ROA)
	Science	OAD	occlusive arterial disease
NYD	not yet diagnosed	OAD	ophthalmo-arteriodyna-
NYHA	New York Heart Associa-		mometry
	tion	o.a.d.	once a day
NYP	not yet published	OADC	oleic acid, albumin, dex-
NYU	New York University		trose, catalase (medium)
NZB mouse	New Zealand black mouse	OAF	open air factor
NZVA	New Zealand Veterinary	OAF	osteoclast activating factor
	Association	OAG *(obst)*	oblique antérieur gauche
NZW mouse	New Zealand white mouse		(F); left oblique anterior
			(position of fetus)
			(= LOA)
		OAP	o-aminophenol
		OAP	occlusion d'artère pulmo-
			naire (F); pulmonary arte-
			rial occlusion
		OAP	oedème aigu du poumon
			(F); acute pulmonary
			edema
		OAP	Old Age Pension
O *(ophth)*	oculus (L); eye	OAP	ophthalmic artery pressure
O *(dent)*	occlusal	OAP	oscillatory afterpotential
O	opening	OAS	Old Age Security
O	opium		
O, o	oral		

O

OAS	Organization of American States	OCD	ovarian cholesterol depletion
OAS	overall survival	OCG	oral cholecystogram
OASDHI	Old Age, Survivors, Disability and Health Insurance	OCM	obliterative cardiomyopathy
OASI	Old Age and Survivors Insurance	OCMT	orthodromic circus movement tachycardia
OASP	organic acid soluble phosphorus	OCS	oxycorticosteroids
OAT	o-acetyl-L-tyrosine	OCT	ornithine carbamoyl transferase
ÖAW	Österreichische Akademie der Wissenschaften (G); Austrian Academy of Sciences (Vienna)	OCT	oxytocin challenge test
		OCV *(otol)*	ordinary conversational voice
OB	obstetrics	OD	occupational disease
o.B.	ohne Befund (G); no pathologicalal finding	OD	oculus dexter (L); right eye
		OD	optical density
OBCC	Obstetrical Complications Clinic	OD	originally derived
		OD	osteochondrosis dissecans
obd.	obduce (L); cover (or coat) with (Rx)	OD	out-of-date
		OD	outside diameter
OBE	Office of Biological Education	OD	overdose
		O.D.	Doctor of Optometry
O.B.E.	Order of the British Empire	o.d.	once daily
		ODA *(obst)*	occiput dexter anterior (L); right occipitoanterior (position of fetus) (=ROA)
OBG	Obstetrician-Gynecologist		
OB/GYN	Obstetrics and Gynecology		
obl.	oblique	ODAC	on-demand analgesia computer
OBS	organic brain syndrome	ODC	ornithine decarboxylase
obs.	obsolete	ODC	orotidine-5-phosphate decarboxylase
obst.	obstetrical		
OC, oc *(dent)*	occlusocervical	ODC	oxygen dissociation curve
		ODG	ophthalmodynamogram
OC	office call	ODM	ophthalmodynamometry
OC	only child	ODN	overt diabetic nephropathy
OC	opening click	ODP *(obst)*	occiput dexter posterior (L); left occipitoanterior (position of fetus) (=ROP)
OC	oral contraceptives		
OC	oxacillin		
OC	oxygen consumption	ODQ	on direct questioning
O+C	onset and course (of a disease)	ODSG	ophthalmic Doppler sonogram
occ.	occasionally	ODT *(obst)*	occiput dexter transversus (L); right occipitotransverse (position of fetus) (=ROT)
occ.	occipital		
OccTh	occupational therapy		
OCD	Office of Civil Defence	OE	on examination

OE	oral examination	OHI	Occupational Health Institute (USA)
OE	otitis externa	OHI	ocular hypertension indicator
Oe *(phys)*	oersted (unit)	OHI	oral hygiene index
Oe	oestrogen (= E)	OHL	oral hairy leukoplakia
O + E	observation and examination	OHLG	o-hydroxylysyl glycoside
OECD	Organization for Economic Cooperation and Development	OHP	hydroxyprogesterone
		OHP	Ontario Heart Project
OECQ	Organisation Européenne pour le Contrôle de Qualité (F); European Organization for Quality Control	OHP	oxygen under high pressure
		OHPGDH	15-hydroxyprostaglandin dehydrogenase
		OI	obstruction index
OED *(rad)*	optimum erythemogenic dose	OI	opportunistic infections
		OI	opsonic index
OEE	outer enamel epithelium	OI	orgasmic impairment
OEMG	oculo-electromyogram	OI	oscillometric index
OER	oxygen enhancement ratio	OI	oxygen intake
		OIA	occlusion intestinale aigue (F); acute intestinal occlusion
OER	oxygen excretion rate		
OERTC	European Organization for Research on Treatment of Cancer	OIB	Oxford inflating bellow
		OIC, Oic	osteogenesis imperfecta congenita
OF	occipito-frontal (diameter)		
O/F	oxidation/fermentation	OICM	Office Intercantonal de Contrôle des Medicaments (F); Intercantonal Drug Control Office (Berne/ Switzerland)
OFA	oncofetal antigens (cp. OFMA)		
OFD	oral-facial-digital syndrome		
OFMA	oncofetal membrane antigens	OIE	Office International des Epizooties (F); International Office of Animal Epidemics (Paris)
OFP	oncofetal protein		
OG	Obstetrics-Gynecology		
OG *(dent)*	occlusogingival	OIH	ovulation-inducing hormone
O-g	zero-gravity		
OGTT, oGGT	oral glucose tolerance test	OIS	optic information-processing system
OH	occupational health	OIT *(psych)*	organic integrity test
OH	occupational history	OIT	Organisation Internationale du Travail (F); International Labor Organization (Geneva) (= ILO)
OH	Outpatient Hospital		
OHC	outer hair cells		
OHCS	hydroxycorticosteroids (11-OHCS, 7-OHCS)		
		OIT, Oit	osteogenesis imperfecta tarda
OHD	organic heart disease		
6-OHDA	6-hydroxydopamine	OIT	oxygen insufficiency theory
OHF	Omsk hemorrhagic fever		

OKN	optokinetic nystagmus	OMP-A	antisense oligodeoxynucle-
OKT	ornithine keto-azide trans-		oside methylphosphonate
	aminase	om.quad.hor.	omni quadrante hora (L);
OL	oculus laevus (L); left eye		every quarter of an hour
	(=OS)		(Rx)
Ol.	oleum (L); oil	OMS	Organisation Mondiale de
OLA *(obst)*	occiput laevus anterior (L);		la Santé (F); World Health
	left occipitoanterior (posi-		Organization (Geneva)
	tion of fetus) (=LOA)		(=WHO)
OLB	open lung biopsy	OMS	osteomyelosclerosis
OLP *(obst)*	occiput laevus posterior	OMS	Osteopathic Medicine and
	(L); left occipitoanterior		Surgery
	(position of fetus) (=LOP)	OMSA	otitis media suppurativa
Ol.res.	oleoresin		acuta
OLT *(obst)*	occiput laevus transversus	OMT	o-methyltransferase
	(L); left occipitotransverse	ON	orthopedic nurse (=ORN)
	(position of fetus) (=LOT)	o.n.	omni nocte (L); every night
OM	occipito-mental (diameter)		(Rx)
OM	Occupational Medicine	ONA	osteonecrose aseptique
OM	oleandomycin		(F); aseptic bone necrosis
OM	osteomyelitis	onc	oncogen
OM	otitis media	O.N.C.	Orthopedic Nursing Certi-
o.m.	omni mane (L); every		ficate
	morning (Rx)	Oncorna	oncogenic RNA viruses
OMC	open mitral commissuro-	viruses	
	tomy	O.N.D.	Ophthalmic Nursing
OMCS	oculo-muco-cutaneous		Diploma
	syndrome (practolol)	ONU	Organisation des Nations
OMCT	o-methylcatechol transfer-		Unies (F); United Nations
	ase		Organization (=UNO)
OME	otitis media with effusion	OOB	out of bed
OMF	osteomyelofibrosis	OOD	osteo-onychodysplasia
OMGE	Organisation Mondiale de	ÖOG	Österreichische Ophthal-
	Gastro-Entérologie (F);		mologische Gesellschaft
	World Organization of		(G); Austrian Ophthalmo-
	Gastroenterology		logical Society
om.hor.	omni hora (L); every hour	OOLR	Ophthalmology, Otology,
	(Rx)		Laryngology, Rhinology
OMI	old myocardial infarction	OOR	orbicularis oculi reflex
OMI	oocyte maturation inhib-	OP	occipito-posterior
	itor	OP	occiput position
OMP	oligodeoxynucleoside	OP	Operationssaal (G); ope-
	methylphosphonate		rating room, ... theatre
OMP	orotidine monophosphate	OP	operative procedure
OMP *(imm)*	outer membrane protein	OP *(pharm)*	original package
OMPA	octamethyl pyrophosphor-	OP	osmotic pressure
	amide	OP	outpatient

OP	ovine prolactin	OR	Orthopedic Research
Op.	operation	O/R	oxidation/reduction
op.	opus (L); work	ORA	operating room attendant
O₂P	oxygen pulse	ORANS	Oak Ridge Analytical Systems
O+P	ova and parasites		
OPC	Outpatient Clinic (=OPD)	ORCA	Organization for Caries Research
op.cit.	opus citatum (L); the work cited	ORD	optic rotation dispersion
		ORE	oil retention enema
OPCS	Office of Population Censuses and Surveys	OREF	Orthopedic Research and Education Foundation
OPD	optical path difference	orf *(gen)*	open reading frame
OPD	ostium primum defect, atrial septal defect	org.	organic
		ORIF *(orth)*	open reduction with internal fixation
OPD	Outpatient Department		
OPD	outpatient dispensary	ORL	otorhinolaryngology (=ENT)
Op.Dent.	operative dentistry		
OPD syndrome	otopalatodigital syndrome	ORN	operating room nurse
		ORN	orthopedic nurse
		ORN	osteoradionecrosis
OPG	oculopneumoplethysmography	Orn.	ornithine
		OROS	Oral Osmotic Therapeutic System
OPG	oxypolygelatin		
O-phase	original phase (of the freshly recovered influenza virus A)	ORPHEUS	on-line system for real-time processing of His electrocardiograms and assorted universal signal parameters
OPM	operation microscope		
opp.	opposite, opposed		
OPPA	cytotoxic combination therapy with Oncovin (vincristine), procarbazine, prednisone, and adriamycin (doxyrubicin)	ORS	oral surgeon
		ORS	Orthopedic Research Society
		ORS	orthopedic surgeon
OPRT	orotate phosphoribosyl transferase	ORT	object relations technique (Murray-Phillipson)
OPS	organic psychic syndrome	ORT	operating room technician
		ORT *(clin)*	oral rehydration therapy
OPS	Outpatient Service	ORTHO	American Orthopsychiatric Association (=AOA)
OPSI	overwhelming postsplenectomy infection		
		ORVID	on-line roentgen video display including documentation (system)
OPSR-BQA	Office of Professional Standards Review, Bureau of Quality Assurance		
		OS	oculus sinister (L); left eye (=OL)
OPT	o-phthalic acid aldehyde		
opt.	optics, optical	OS *(card)*	opening snap
opt.	optimum, optimal	OS	Osgood-Schlatter (syndrome)
OPV	oral polio vaccine (Sabin)		
OR	operating room	OS	osteogenic sarcoma

OSA *(obst)*	occiput sinister anterior (L); left occipitoanterior (position of fetus) (= LOA, OLA)
OSA	Optical Society of America
OSC	overdrive suppression of conduction
OSF	overgrowth stimulating factor
OSHA	Occupational Safety and Health Administration (USA)
osm	osmol
OSP *(obst)*	occiput sinister posterior (L); left occipitoposterior (position of fetus) (= LOP, OLP)
OSRD	Office of Scientific Research and Development (USA)
OSS	Office of Strategic Services (USA)
OST *(obst)*	occiput sinister transversus (L); left occipitotransverse (position) (= LOT, OLT)
OST	Office of Science and Technology
OSTS	Office of State Technical Services
OSU	Ohio State University (Columbus)
OSUK	Ophthalmological Society of the United Kingdom
OT *(psych)*	object test
OT	occupational therapy
OT *(anat)*	old term
OT	old tuberculin
OT	optical tract
OT	orotracheal
OTA	Office of Technology Assessment
OTA	operative transluminal angioplasty
OTA	orthotoluidine arsenite (test)
OTC	ornithine transcarbamylase

OTC *(pharm)*	over the counter (i.e. no prescription needed)
OTC	oxytetracycline
OTCA	operative transluminal coronary angioplasty
OTD *(rad)*	organ tolerance dose
OTEC	ocean thermal energy conversion
OTM	orthotoluidine manganese sulfate
OTR	ovarian tumor registry
O.T.R.	Occupational Therapist, Registered
O.T.Reg.	Occupational Therapist, Registered (Canada)
OU	oculus uterque, oculi unitas (L); both eyes
OUS	oculo-urethrosynovial syndrome (Reiter)
OV	office visit
OV	ovalbumin
OV	overventilation
OW	out-of-wedlock
O/W	oil-in-water (emulsion)
Ox.	oxymel
OXC	oxacillin
OYE	old yellow enzyme
oz.	ounce
oz.ap.	ounce apothecary's
oz.av.	ounce avoirdupois

P

P	paralysis
P *(gen)*	parental generation
P	partial pressure
P *(stat)*	percentile
P	percussion
P *(phys)*	permeability
P	peyote, Lophophora williamsii
P	pharmacopeia
P	phenolphthalein

P	plasma	PA	pression artérielle (F); arterial pressure
P *(phys)*	poise (unit of dynamic viscosity)	PA	primary appearance (syphilis stage 1)
P	pole	PA	prior to admission
P	position	PA *(pharm)*	prolonged action
P *(phys)*	power	PA	proprietary association
P	premolar	PA	proteolytic activity
P *(ophth)*	presbyopia	PA	psychoanalysis, psychoanalyst
P	pressure		
P	protein	PA	psychogenic aspermia
P	pulse	PA	pulmonary area
P *(pharm)*	pulvis (L); powder	PA	pulmonary artery ($=$AP)
P *(ophth)*	punctum proximum (L); near point ($=$PP, pp)	PA, pa *(dent)*	pulpo-axial
P	pupil	P_A	alveolar pressure
P	pico- ($=$factor 10^{-12})	Pa	pascal
p *(phys)*	pond	P_a	arterial pressure
p *(stat)*	probability	p.a.	post applicationem (L); after administration
p *(gen)*	protein (e.g. p17, p24)		
P. *(anat)*	pars (L); part	p.a. *(chem)*	pro analysi (L); with highest degree of purity
P. *(bact)*	Pasteurella		
P.	plexus		
p.	page	p.a.	pro anno (L); per year
p- *(chem)*	para-	p-a, P-A *(rad)*	posterior-anterior
p$^+$	proton		
P1, P2 *(gen)*	first, second parental generation, etc.	P+A	percussion and auscultation
P2 *(card)*	second pulmonic heart sound	PAA *(pharm)*	partial agonist activity
PA	atrial pressure	PAA	poliomyelitis anterior acuta
PA	paralysis agitans		
PA	peptone agar	PAA	polyacrylamide
PA	peridural anesthesia	PAA	polyacrylic acid
PA	pernicious anemia	PAA	pyridine-acetic acid
PA	phosphatase activity	PAAG	pregnancy-associated alpha$_2$-glycoprotein ($=$PAG)
PA	phosphatidic acid		
PA	phosphoarginine		
PA	photoallergenic	PAB, PABA	p-aminobenzoic acid
PA	physician's assistant	PABS	p-aminobenzene sulfonamide, sulfanilamide
PA	plasma activity		
PA	plasminogen activator	PAC	(analgesic preparation consisting of) phenacetin, aspirin, and caffeine ($=$APC)
PA	platelet adhesiveness		
PA	polyvalent antigen		
PA, pA	postnatal asphyxia		
PA	prealbumin		
PA	precipitating antibodies		
PA	prenylamine		

PAC	cytotoxic combination therapy with cis-platinum, adriamycin, and cyclophosphamide	PAF	paroxysmal atrial flutter
		PAF *(clin)*	percussion, auscultation, fremitus
PAC	pivampicillin	PAF	platelet-activating factor
PAC	plasma aldosterone concentration	PAF	platelet-aggregating factor
		PAF	pulmonary arteriovenous fistula
PAC	premature atrial contraction	PAFA	platelet-aggregating factor of anaphylaxis
PAC *(psych)*	parent-adult-child	PAG	phono-angiography
PACIA	particle counting immunoassay	PAG	polyacrylamide gel
		PAG	pregnancy-associated alpha$_2$-glycoprotein ($=$PAAG)
PACO$_2$	alveolar carbon dioxide partial pressure		
paCO$_2$	arterial carbon dioxide partial pressure	PAG	primary antrum gastritis
		PAGE	polyacrylamide gel electrophoresis
PACS	Picture Archiving and Communication System	PAGIF	polyacrylamide gel isoelectric focusing
PACWP	pulmonary artery capillary wedge pressure ($=$PAWP, PCWP)	PAH	p-aminohippuric acid ($=$PAHA)
PAD	(combination drug containing) phenacetin, aspirin, and desoxyephedrine	PAH	polycyclic aromatic hydrocarbons
		PAHA	p-aminohippuric acid ($=$PAH)
PAD	partial antibiotic decontamination	PAHO	Pan-American Health Organization
PAD	percutaneous abscess drainage	PAI	platelet aggregation inhibition
PAD	peripheral arterial disease	PAI	porphyria acuta intermittens
PAD	premature atrial depolarization	PAI	pyruvate, adenine, and inosine
PAD	pression auriculaire droite (F); right atrial pressure	PAK	peritoneal artificial kidney
PAD, PAd	pulmonary artery pressure, diastolic ($=$PADP, PAPD)	PAL	Pathology Laboratory
PAD	pulsatile assist device	PAL	posterior axillary line
PAD	pyridine-2-aldoxim-dodeka-iodide	PAL	pyridoxal-5-phosphate ($=$PALP, PLP)
PADP	pulmonary artery diastolic pressure	PALI	programmed accelerated laboratory investigation
p.ae.	partes aequales (L); in equal parts (Rx)	PALP	pyridoxal-5-phosphate ($=$PAL)
PAEDP	pulmonary artery end-diastolic pressure	PALS	prison-acquired lymphadenopathy syndrome
PAESP	pulmonary artery end-systolic pressure	PAM	penicillin-G aluminum monostearate

PAM	phenylalanine mustard, melphalan	PAP	pulmonary alveolar proteinosis
PAM	piracetam	PAP	pulmonary artery pressure
PAM	pression artérielle moyenne (F); mean arterial pressure	pap.	papilla
		PAPase	phosphatidic acid phosphohydrolase
PAM, PAm	pulmonary artery mean pressure (= MPAP, PAMP)	PAPD, PApd	pulmonary artery pressure, diastolic (= PADP)
PAM	pulse amplitude modulation	PAPM, PAPm	pulmonary artery pressure, mean
PAM	pyridine-2-aldoxim-N-methyliodide, pralidoxim	Papova	papilloma-polyoma-vacuolating agent (group of viruses)
PAMA	Pan-American Medical Association	PAPP	p-aminopropiophenone
PAMBA	p-aminomethyl-benzoic acid	PAPS	Pacific Association of Pediatric Surgeons
PAMC	Pakistan Army Medical Corps	PAPS	3'-phospho-adenosine-5'-phosphosulfate
PAMIE (psych)	Physical and Mental Impairment of Function Evaluation	PAPS, PAPs	pulmonary artery pressure, systolic (= PASP)
PAMN	propionylatropine methylnitrate	PAPVC	partial anomalous pulmonary venous connection
PAMP	pulmonary artery mean pressure	PAP virus	primary atypical pneumonia virus, Eaton virus
PAMSA	p-aminomethyl-salicylic acid (= Homo-PAS)	PAR	postanesthetic recovery
		PAR	pulmonary arteriolar resistance
PAN	peroxyacetyl nitrate	PARIS	Persantin-Aspirin Reinfarction Study
PAN	polyacryl nitrile		
PAN	polyarteritis nodosa	P_{art}	arterial pressure
PAN	pyridyl azonaphthol	PARU	postanesthetic recovery unit
P-antigen	Price antigen		
PAO	peak acid output	PAS	p-aminosalicylic acid (= PASA)
PAo, pAO	aortic pressure	PAS (psych)	Problem Appraisal Scales
PAO_2	alveolar oxygen partial pressure	PAS	Professional Activities Study
paO_2	arterial oxygen partial pressure	PASA	p-aminosalicylic acid (= PAS)
PAOP	pulmonary artery occluded pressure	P'ase	phosphatase (= Ptase)
PAP, Pap	Papanicolaou (e.g. PAP smear, PAP test)	PASP	pulmonary artery systolic pressure (= PAPS)
PAP	peroxidase-antiperoxidase	PAS reaction	periodic acid Schiff reaction
PAP	primary atypical pneumonia	pass.	passive
PAP	prostatic acid phosphatase	PAT	paroxysmal atrial tachycardia

PAT	photometric aggregation test	PBE	proton balance equation
PAT	platelet aggregation test	PBF	peripheral blood flow
PAT	pregnancy at term	PBF	pigment of filtered broth
pat.	patient	PBF	ponction biopsie du foie (F); needle biopsy of the liver
pat.	patent(ed)		
PATE	Psychodynamic and Therapeutic Education		
Path.	pathogenesis, pathology	PBF	pulmonary blood flow
PAV	cytotoxic combination of procarbazine, alkeran (melphalan), and vinblastine	PBG	porphobilinogen
		PBG	progesterone-binding globulin
		PBI	phenethyl biguanide, phenformin
PAVB	paroxysmal atrioventricular block	PBI	protein-bound iodine
PAVC	partial atrioventricular canal (= PCAVC)	PBK	phosphorylase-b-kinase
		PBL	peripheral blood lymphocytes
PAVF	pulmonary arteriovenous fistula	PBMC	peripheral blood mononuclear cells
PAW (card)	proximal anterior wall	PBNAA	partial body neutron activation analysis
PAW,	pulmonary artery wedge		
PAWP	pressure	PBO	penicillin in beeswax
P_{aw}	airway pressure	PBO	2-phenyl-5-(4-biphenyl)-1,3,4-oxadiazole (= PBD)
PB	Pharmacopoeia Britannica (= BP, B.Ph., Ph.B.)		
PB	phenobarbital	PBP	penicillin-binding proteins
PB	phonetically balanced	PBPI	penile-brachial pressure index
PB	plasma blasts		
PB	pressure breathing	PBPV	percutaneous balloon pulmonary valvuloplasty
Pb	presbyopia		
PBA	Pressure Breathing Assister	PBR	Paul-Bunnell reaction
PBA (dent)	pulpobucco-axial	PBS	phosphate buffered saline
PBAN	polybutadiene acrylnitrile	PBS	polybutadiene styrene
PBB	peribronchial biopsy	PBSP	prognostically bad signs in pregnancy
PBB	polybromated biphenyls		
PBBO	2-(p-biphenylyl)-6-phenylbenzoxazole	PBV	pulmonary blood volume
		pBV	pulsating blood volume
PBC	penicillin-binding component	PBW (dent)	posterior bite wing
		PBZ	phenylbutazone
PBC	point of basal convergence	PBZ	pyribenzamine
PBC	primary biliary cirrhosis	PC	packed cells
PBD	2-phenyl-5-(4-biphenyl)-1,3,4-oxadiazole (= PBO)	PC	paper chromatography
		PC	parent cells
		PC	peak clipping
PBE (vet)	Perlsucht-Bazillenemulsion (G); bovine tuberculosis bacillary emulsion	PC (anat)	pedunculus cerebri
		PC	pericyte
		PC	penicillin
		PC	phosphocholine

PC	phosphocreatine	PCB	pentachlorobenzene (insecticide)
PC	Physicians Corporation		
PC	plasmocyte	PCB	polychlorinated biphenyls
PC	platelet concentrate	PCB	potatoes, carots, bovine
PC	pneumotaxic center	medium	bile (medium)
PC	polycarbonate	PCC	pheochromocytoma
PC	pondus civile (L); avoirdupois weight	PCC	phosphate carrier compound
PC	portocaval	PCC	Poison Control Center
PC, p.c.	postcoital	PCc	periscopic concave
PC	precordium	PCD	polycystic disease
PC	present complaint	PCE	polyarthrite chronique évolutive (F); progressive rheumatoid arthritis
PC	process control		
PC	propicillin		
PC	pulmonary capillary (pressure)	PCE	pseudocholine esterase (= PCHE)
P.c.	Pneumocystis carinii	PCEC	chicken embryo fibroblast vaccine (for rabies)
p.c. *(pharm)*	post cenam, post cibum, post cibos (L); after meals (Rx)		
		P-cells	pacemaker (or pale) cells (in the sinus node)
p.c.	post cohabitationem (L); after intercourse	PCF	pharyngoconjunctival fever
p.c.	post conceptionem (L); after conception	PCF	prothrombin converting factor; factor VII, proconvertin (= SPCA)
PCA	parietal cell antibodies		
PCA	passive cutaneous anaphylaxis	PCG	pancreatocholangiography
		PCG	penicillin G
PCA	patient controlled analgesia	PCG	phonocardiogram
		PCH	paroxysmal cold hemoglobinuria
PCA	pentachloroanisol (pesticide)		
		PCH	pheochromocytoma
PCA	peptone-casein hydrolysate	PCh	phosphatidyl choline
PCA	perchloric acid	PCHE	phosphocholine esterase
PCA	portocaval anastomosis (= PCS)	PCHE	pseudocholine esterase (= CHE)
PCA	posterior cerebral artery	pCi	picocurie
PCAg	plasma cell antigen	PCIC	Poison Control Information Center
PCA pressure	pulmonary capillary arterial pressure		
		PCIS	post cardiac injury syndrome
PCAVB	permanent complete atrioventricular block		
		PCK	phosphoenol pyruvate carboxykinase (= PEPCK)
PCAVC	partial common atrioventricular canal		
		PCL	paced cycle length
PCB	near point of convergence to the intercentral line	PCL	persistent corpus luteum
		PCM	paracetamol (= NAPAP)
		PCM	protein calorie malnutrition
PCB *(obst)*	paracervical block		

PCM, PCm	pulmonary capillary mean pressure	PCT	proximal convoluted tubule
PCM	pulse-code modulation	pct.	per cent (%)
PCMB	p-chloromercuribenzoate	PCTFE	polychlorotrifluoro-ethyl-
PCMO *(mil)*	Principal Colonial Medical Officer		ene
		PCTNH	non-hereditary porphyria
PCMV	premature closure of the mitral valve		cutanea tarda
		PCTS	symptomatic porphyria
PCN	penicillin (= PC)		cutanea tarda
PCN	percutaneous nephrolithot-omy (= PCNL)	PCV	packed cell volume (in ml/dl blood)
PCN	pregnenolone carbonitrile	PCV	penicillin V
PCNL	percutaneous nephrolithot-omy (= PCN)	PCV	polycythaemia vera
		PCV	porcine circovirus
PCNV	Provisional Committee on Nomenclature of Viruses	PCVP	pulmonary capillary venous pressure
		PCWP	pulmonary capillary wedge pressure
pCO₂	carbon dioxide partial pressure	PCx	periscopic convex
PCOB	Permanent Central Opium Board (Geneva)	PCZ	procarbazine
		PD	Dublin Pharmacopoeia
PCOD	polycystic ovarian disease; Stein-Leventhal's syn-drome	PD	papillary diameter
		PD	paralytic dose
		PD	Parkinson's disease
PCP	pentachlorophenol	PD	pars distalis (of the pitu-
PCP	1-(1-phenylcyclohexyl)-piperidine		itary gland)
		PD	peridural
PCP	pneumocystis carinii pneu-monia	PD	peritoneal dialysis
		PD	phase discriminator
PCP, pcP	primary chronic polyarthri-tis, polyarthritis chronica progressiva	PD	phenyldichlorarsin
		PD	phosphate dextrose
		PD	potential difference
PCP	pulmonary capillary pres-sure	PD	present disease
		PD	pressor dose
PCPA	p-chlorophenylalanine	PD	prism diopter (= prdpt)
pcpn.	precipitation	PD	pre- or protodiabetes
PCPS	peroral cholangiopancrea-toscopy	PD	provocation dose
		PD	psychotic depression
pcpt.	perception	PD, pd *(dent)*	pulpodistal
PCR	Perth Coronary Register		
PCR	plasma clearance rate	PD	pulse difference
PCS, PC shunt	portocaval shunt (= PCA)	PD	pupillary distance
		PD	pyrimidine derivative
pcs.	preconscious	Pd	diastolic (arterial) pressure
PCT	peak concentration time	P.D.	Pharmaciae Doctor (L); Doctor of Pharmacy (= Phar.D.)
PCT	plasmacrit test		
PCT	porphyria cutanea tarda		

P.D.	Philosophiae Doctor (L); Doctor of Philosophy (usually: Ph.D.)	PD medium	phosphate-dextrose medium
p.d.	pro die (L); per day	PDP	paracetamol-dextropropoxyphen
p.d.	pro dosi (L); per dose	PDP (obst)	prematurity-dysmaturity prevention program
PDA	parenteral drug abuser		
PDA	patent ductus arteriosus (Botalli)	PDP	pulmonary driving pressure
PDA	pediatric allergy	PDPA	pulmonary artery diastolic pressure
PDA	peridural anesthesia		
PDA (card)	posterior descending artery	pdpt	prism diopter (= PD, prdpt)
PDAB	p-dimethylamino-benzaldehyde (= DMAB, PDMB)		
		PDQ	Prescreening Developmental Questionnaire
PDB	p-dichlorobenzene	PDR	Pediatric Radiology
PDC	Pediatric Cardiology	PDR	Physician's Desk Reference
PDC	preliminary diagnostic clinic		
		PDR	proliferative diabetic retinopathy
PDC	pyridinol carbamate		
PDC	pyridyl carbinol	pdr.	powder
PDC	pyruvate decarboxylase	PDS	Physician Depression Scale
PDCA	peroral direct cholangioscopy		
		PDS	polydextrane sulfate
PDE	paroxysmal dyspnea on exertion	PDS	prednisone
		PDS	phyton-dextrose-serum
PDE	phosphodiesterase	medium	substrate
PDE	pulsed Doppler echocardiography	PDT	photodynamic therapy
		PDTA	1,2-propylenediamine tetra-acetic acid
PDETA	pentamethyl diethyl triamine		
PDF (card)	protodiastolic filling	PDV (vet)	pustulous dermatitis virus (poxvirus of sheep)
PDFR	peak diastolic filling rate		
PDGA	pteroyldiglutamic acid	PE	Edinburgh Pharmacopoeia
PDGF	platelet-derived growth factor	PE	palmar erythema
		PE	paper electrophoresis
PDH	past dental history	PE	parallel-elastic element
PDH	pyruvate dehydrogenase	PE	pericardial effusion
P_{diast}	diastolic pressure	PE (stat)	permissible error
P-diol	pregnanediol	PE	pharyngo-esophageal
PDM	progressive muscular dystrophy	PE	phenylephrine
		PE	phosphoryl-ethanolamine
PDM	pulse duration modulation	PE	physical examination
PDMB	p-dimethylamino-benzaldehyde (= DMAB, PDAB)	PE	placebo effect
		PE	polyethylene
		PE	potential energy
		PE	powdered extract
PDME	phosphatidyl dimethyl ethanolamine	PE	pre-erythroblast
		PE (stat)	probable error

PE	psychomotor epilepsy	PEPCK	phosphoenol pyruvate carboxykinase (= PCK)
PE	pulmonary embolism		
Pe	pressure on expiration	PEPR	Precision Encoder and Pattern Recognizer
p.e.	par example (F); for example (= e.g.)		
		PEQ	phenanthrene quinone
PEA	phenethyl alcohol	PER	peak ejection rate
PEA	phenethylamine	PER, per	perchlorethylene
PEB	pentobarbital	PERRLA	pupils equal, round, react to light and accommodation
PECO	carbon monoxide expiration pressure		
PECT	positron emission computerized tomography	PES	photoelectron spectroscopy
PED	patient's evaluation by doctor	PES (card)	programmed electrostimulation
PED	pre-ejection diameter	PESP	post-extrasystolic potentiation
PEd	physical education		
PEEP	positive end-expiratory pressure	PET	partial exchange transfusion
PEF	peak expiratory flow	PET	positron emission tomography
PEF	psychiatric evaluation form		
PEFR	peak expiratory flow rate	PET (obst)	pre-eclamptic toxemia
PEFV	partial expiratory flow volume curve	PET	proteolytic enzyme test
		PETN	pentaerythritol tetranitrate
PEG	Paul-Ehrlich-Gesellschaft (G); Paul Ehrlich Society (Germany)	PETP	polyethylene terephthalate
		PETT	positron emission transverse (or transaxial) tomography
PEG	pneumencephalography		
PEG	polyethylene glycol	PEV	peak expiratory velocity
PEI	phosphate excretion index	PEV	pulmonary extravascular volume
PEIP	positive end-inspiratory pressure		
		PEX	peak exercise
PEL	permissible exposure limits	p.ex.	par example (F); for example (= e.g., p.e.)
PELS	propionyl erythromycin lauryl sulfate		
		PF	partial filling
PEM	photoelectron emission microscope	PF	peak flow
		PF	permeability factor
PEM	protein energy malnutrition	PF	phenol formaldehyde
		PF	plantar flexion
PEMF	pulsating electromagnetic fields	PF	platelet factor
		PF	potentiating factor (lymphokine)
PENG	photoelectronystagmogram		
PEP	phosphoenol pyruvate	PF	proflavin
PEP	photic evoked potential	PF	pulmonary factor
PEP	polyestradiol phosphate	PF	pulse frequency
PEP (card)	pre-ejection period	PF	Purkinje fibers
PEPC	polyphenyl phosphatidyl choline	Pf.	Pfeifferella
		PFA	p-fluorophenylalanine

PFA	phosphonoformic acid, phosphonoformiate	PG	prostaglandin
PFA	1-phosphofructaldolase	PG	proteoglycane
PFA3	mixture of saturated picric acid, formol, acetic acid, and urea (for histological fixation)	PG	pyogenic granuloma
		6-PG	6-phosphogluconate
		pg	picogram
		PGA	phosphoglyceric acid
		PGA	3-phosphoglycerin aldehyde
PFB	posterior fascicular block		
PFC	persistent fetal circulation (syndrome)	PGA	polyglycolic acid
		PGA	prostaglandin A
PFC	plaque-forming cells	PGA	pteroylglutamic acid
PFD	primary flash distillate	PGAD,	phosphoglycerin aldehyde
PFER	peak fractional ejection rate	PGADH	dehydrogenase
		PGB	prostaglandin B
PFI	peak flow index	6-PGD,	6-phosphogluconate dehy-
PFI	posterior fossa index	6-PGDH	drogenase
PFK	phosphofructokinase	PGDH	prostaglandin dehydroge-
PFM	peak flow meter		nase
PFM	pulse frequency modulation	PGDF	Pilot Guide Dog Foundation
PFO	patent foramen ovale	PGE	prostaglandin E
PFP	platelet-free plasma	P-generation	parental generation
PFR	peak filling rate	(gen)	
PFR	peak flow rate	PGF	prostaglandin F
PFT	peak flow time	PGFM	prostaglandin F metabo-
PFT	pulmonary function test		lite
PF test	Picture Frustration Test (of Rosenzweig)	PGG	prostaglandin G
		PGH	pituitary growth hormone, somatotrophin
16-PF test	16 Personality Factors Test (of Cattell)		
		PGH	prostaglandin H
PFU	plaque-forming unit	PGI	phosphoglucose isomerase
PFU	pock-forming unit	PGI	prostaglandin I
PFV	peak flow velocity		$(PGI_2 = prostacyclin = PGX)$
PFV	physiological full value		
PG	paralysie générale (F); general paralysis	PGK	phosphoglycerate kinase
		PGL	persistent (or progressive) generalized lymphadenop-
PG	pentagastrin		athy
PG	peptidoglycane		
PG	Pharmacopoeia Germanica ($=$ DAB, Ph.G.)	PGLUM, PGM	phosphoglucomutase
		PGM	phosphoglycerate mutase
PG	phosphogluconic acid	PGN	primary chronic glomeru-
PG	phosphoglycerate		lonephritis
PG	pneumography	PGO spikes	ponto-geniculo-occipital
PG	postgraduate		spikes
PG	pregnanediol glucuronide	PGP	paralysis generalisata pro-
PG	progesterone		gressiva
PG	propylgallate		

PGP	phosphoglycerate phosphate	PHB	p-hydroxybenzoic acid
PGP	polyglycerophosphatide	Ph.B.	Pharmacopoeia Britannica ($=$ BP, P.Ph. PB)
PGR	psycho-galvanic response	Ph.B.	Philosophiae Baccalaureus (L); Bachelor of Philosophy
PGSI	prostaglandin synthetase inhibitor		
PGTT	prednisone glucose tolerance test	PHB(A)	polyhydroxybutyric (acid)
		PHBE	p-hydroxybenzoic acid ester
PGU	postgonococcal urethritis		
PGUT	phosphogalactose uridyl transferase	Ph.Belg.	Pharmacopoeia Belgica
		PHC	pheneticillin
PGV	proximal gastric vagotomy	PHC	posthospital care
PGX	prostacyclin	PHC	primary hepatocellular carcinoma
PH	passive hemagglutination ($=$ PHA)		
		PHC	psychose hallucinatoire chronique (F); chronic hallucinatory psychosis
PH	past history		
PH	phenylalanine hydroxylase		
PH	portal hypertension	Ph.C.	Pharmaceutical Chemist
PH	prolactin hormone	Ph^{1}c	Philadelphia chromosome, minute chromosome
PH	Public Health		
pH	pondus hydrogenii (L); hydrogen ion concentration	PHC syndrome	Böök syndrome (with missing premolar teeth, hyperhidrosis, and premature canities)
ph	phot (unit of photochemical energy)		
PHA	passive hemagglutination ($=$ PH)	PHD	post-heparin diamine oxidase
PHA	phenylalanine	PHD	potentially harmful drug
PHA	phytohemagglutinin ($=$ PhHA)	PHD	Public Health Department
		Ph.D.	Philosophiae Doctor (L); Doctor of Philosophy ($=$ P.D.)
PHA	Port Health Authorities		
PHA	primary habitual abortion	Ph.Dan.	Pharmacopoeia Danica
PHA	pulse height analyzer	PHE	post-heparin esterase
pHa	arterial pH	Phe	phenylalanine
PHAL	preleukemic acute human leukemia	Ph.Eur.	Pharmacopoeia Europaea
		Ph.Fenn.	Pharmacopoeia Fennica
PHAR	phytohemagglutination reaction	PHG	pertussis hyperimmunoglobulin
Pharm.B.	Pharmaciae Baccalaureus (L); Bachelor of Pharmacy	Ph.G.	Graduate of Pharmacy
		Ph.G.	Pharmacopoeia Germanica ($=$ DAB, PG)
Pharm.C.	Pharmaceutical Chemist		
Pharm.D.	Pharmaciae Doctor (L); Doctor of Pharmacy	Ph.Gall.	Pharmacopoeia Gallica
		Phgly	phenylglycine
Pharm.G.	Graduate in Pharmacy	PHH	progressive hypergammaglobulinemic hepatitis
Pharm.M.	Pharmaciae Magister (L); Master of Pharmacy		
PHB	phenobarbital	Ph.H., Ph.Helv.	Pharmacopoeia Helvetica

PhHA	phytohemagglutinin (=PHA)	Ph.Suec.	Pharmacopoeia Suecica
Ph.Hung.	Pharmacopoeia Hungarica	PHT	phenytoin
PHI	past history of illness	PHTS	Psychiatric Home Treatment Service
PHI	phosphohexose isomerase	PHV	peak height velocity
PHI	Public Health Institute	Phys.Ed.	Physical Education
Ph.I.	Pharmacopoeia Internationalis	Phys.Med.	Physical Medicine
Ph.Ind.	Pharmacopoeia Indica	Phys.Ther.	Physical Therapy
PHK cells	postmortem human kidney cells	phys.dis.	physical disability
PHLA	post-heparin lipolytic activity	physS	physiological saline
		PI	inspiration pressure
PHLS	Public Health Laboratory Service (UK)	PI	pancreatic insufficiency
		PI	parodontopathy index
PHM	pulmonary hyaline membranes	PI	penetration index
		PI	perfusion index
Ph.M.	Pharmaciae Magister (L); Master of Pharmacy	PI (psych)	personality and interest (test)
PHMI	picolino-hydroxamate methyliodide	PI	Pharmacopoeia Internationalis (=Ph.I.)
PHN	Public Health Nursing	PI	phosphatidyl inositol
PHNO	(+)-4-propyl-9-hydroxy-naphthoxazine	PI	present illness
		PI	primary infection
Ph.Nord.	Pharmacopoeia Nordica (=NFN)	PI (psych)	proactive inhibition
		PI	prognostic index
PHP	post-heparin phospholipase	PI	progression index
		PI	prostacyclin
PHP	prepaid health plan	PI	protamine insulin
PHP	pseudohypoparathyroidism	PI	protease inhibitor
PHPAA	p-hydroxyphenyl-acetic acid	PI	protective index
		PI (pharm)	Protocol International (F)
PHPLA	p-hydroxyphenyl-lactic acid	PI	pulmonary insufficiency
		PI	pulsatility index
Ph.Pol.	Pharmacopoeia Polonica	pI	pH of the isoelectric point of a substance in solution
PHPPA	p-hydroxyphenyl-pyruvic acid	Pi	P inorganic
PHPT	primary hyperparathyroidism	Pi	pressure of inspiration
PHS	periarthritis humeroscapularis, adhesive capsulitis, "frozen shoulder"	p.i.	per inhalationem (L); by inhalation
		p.i.	post infectionem (L); after infection
PHS	Physicians Health Study (USA)	p.i.	post injectionem, post infusionem (L); after injection, after infusion
PHS	primary hypoventilation syndrome	PIA	(-)-N^6-phenylisopropyl adenosine
PHS	Public Health Service	PIA	photoelectronic intravenous angiography

PIA	postinfectious or parainfectious arthritis	PIH	pregnancy-induced hypertension
PIB	polyisobutylene	PIH	preoperative isovolemic hemodilution
PIBI	polyisobutylene isoprene	PIH	prolactin inhibiting hormone (=PIF)
PIC	Population Investigation Committee	PIHPS	pregnancy-induced hypertension - preeclampsia syndrome
PIC	protease inhibitor complex	pil.	pilula, pilulae (L); pill(s)
PICA	posterior inferior cerebellar artery	PIM	pimaricin
PICO	inspiratory carbon monoxide pressure	PIN	Personal Identification Number
Picodna	small DNA viruses (from: pico = small; DNA = deoxyribonucleic acid)	PIND *(imm)*	premunity inducer
		P-index	prostatic index
		pINN	proposed INN
Picorna	group of entero, EMC, and FMD viruses (from: pico = small; RNA = ribonucleic acid)	PIO	5-phenyl-2-imino-4-oxo-oxazolidine
		PIP	peak inspiratory pressure
PICSO	pressure-controlled intermittent coronary sinus occlusion	PIP	phosphatidyl inositol diphosphate
		PIP	proximal interphalangeal (joints)
PICU	pulmonary intensive care unit	PIP	psychotic inpatient profile
PID	Patient Identification Number	PIRP *(pharm)*	Provisional International Reference Preparation
PID	patient-related information and documentation	PIS	Pathology Information System
PID *(gyn)*	pelvic inflammatory disease	PIS	Provisional International Standard
PID	photoionization detector	PIS	pulmonary immune system
PID	prolapsed intervertebral disc	PISCES	percutaneously inserted spinal cord electrostimulator
PIE	positive inotropic effect	PIT	pacing-induced tachycardia
PIE	pulmonary infiltration with eosinophilia	PIT	Personality Inventory Test (Eysenck) (=PI)
PIE	pulmonary interstitial emphysema	PITR	plasma iron turnover rate
PIEA	positive inotropic effect of activation	PIV	parainfluenza virus
PIF	prolactin inhibiting factor (=PIH)	PIVKA	protein induced by vitamin K absence
PIF	proliferation inhibiting factor	PJRT	permanent junctional reciprocating tachycardia
PIF	prostatic interstitial fluid	PJS	Peutz-Jeghers syndrome
PIFR	peak inspiratory flow rate	PK	Prausnitz-Küstner (reaction)
PIH	phenylisopropyl hydrazine	PK	psychokinesis

PK	pyruvate kinase	PL-reaction	periodic acid leukofuchsin reaction (= PAS reaction)
pk	peck (measure, in the U.S. for dry, in the UK for fluid substances)	PLRV	potato leaf roll virus
		PLS	persistent lymphadenopathy syndrome
PKI	pyruvate kinase isoenzyme		
PKR	Prausnitz-Küstner reaction	PLSVC	persistent left superior vena cava
PKU	phenylketonuria		
PL	perception of light	PLT	pancreolauryl test
PL	phospholipids	PLT group	psittacosis-lymphogranuloma-trachoma group of viruses (cp. PLGV)
PL	placental lactogen (= HPL)		
PL	plasma lipids	PLV	phenylalanine, lysine, vasopressin
PL	ponction lombaire (F); lumbar puncture spinal tap		
		PLV	posterior wall of left ventricle
PL	programming language		
PL, pl *(dent)*	pulpolingual	P_{LV}, pLV	left ventricular pressure
PLA	passive latex agglutination	plv.	pulvis (L); powder
PLA	phospholipase A	pLVED	left ventricular end-diastolic pressure
PLA, pla *(dent)*	pulpolinguoaxial		
		PLVP	peak left ventricular pressure
PLA, pla *(dent)*	pulpolabial		
		pLVS	left ventricular systolic pressure
P_{LA}, pLA	left atrial pressure		
PLAW	posterior left atrial wall	PLVW	posterior left ventricular wall
PLB	percutaneous liver biopsy		
PLD	phospholipase D	PLW	phospholipid-water preparation
PLD	polymorphous light dermatosis (= PMLE)		
		PLW syndrome	Prader-Labhart-Willi syndrome
PLD	potentially lethal damage		
PLF	pulmonary lesion factor	PM	pacemaker
PLGV	psittacosis-lymphogranuloma venereum (cp. PLT group)	PM	panmyelopathy
		PM	papillary muscle (of the heart)
PLH	posterior lobe of hypophysis, posterior pituitary gland	PM	pellicular membrane
		PM	perinatal mortality
		PM	petit mal (F); mild form of epilepsy
PLH	pulmonary lymphoid hyperplasia		
		PM	phase modulation
PLI	posterolateral infarction (= PLMI)	PM	photometer
		PM	photomultiplier
PLL	phase-locked loop	PM	Physical Medicine (= Phys.Med.)
PLMI	posterolateral myocardial infarction (= PLI)		
		PM	poids moleculaire (F); molecular weight (= mol.wt.)
plnn	pathologic lymph nodes		
PLN test	popliteal lymph node test		
PLP	pyridoxal phosphate (= PAL, PALP)	PM	poliomyelitis
		PM	polymyositis

PM, p.m.	post meridiem (L); in the afternoon	PMB	postmenopausal bleeding
PM	post mortem (L); after death, autopsy	PMC	phenylmercuric chloride
		PMC	promyelocyte
PM *(pharm)*	Praescriptiones Magistrales (Switzerland)	PMC	pseudomembranous colitis
		PMCA	polymethylchloroacrylate
PM *(dent)*	premolar	PMD	primary myocardial disease
PM	presystolic murmur		
PM	preventative medicine	PMD	private medical doctor
PM	prostatic massage	PMD	progressive muscular dystrophy
PM, pm *(dent)*	pulpomesial		
		PMD	psychose maniaque depressive (F); manic-depressive psychosis
PM	pulse modulation		
PM *(card)*	punctum maximum (L); point of maximal impulse or intensity (= p.m., PMI)	PMDPT vaccine	poliomyelitis-measles-diphtheria-pertussis-tetanus vaccine
		PME	phosphomonoester
Pm	mean (arterial blood) pressure	PME	polymorphonuclear eosinophils
P.m. *(bact)*	Pasteurella multocida	PME	progressive myoclonic encephalopathy
p.m.	pondus medicinale (L); medicinal weight		
		PMEA	9-(2-phosphonylmethoxy-ethyl)-adenine
p.m.	post menstruationem (L); after the period	PMEDAP	9-(2-phosphonylmethoxy-ethyl)-2,6-diaminopurine
p.m.	post mortem (L); after death, autopsy	PMEMAP	9-(2-phosphonylmethoxy-ethyl)-2-aminopurine
p.m.	punctum maximum (= PM, PMI)	PMF	progressive massive fibrosis
PMA	Pharmaceutical Manufacturers Association	PMG	photomotograph
		PMG	postmenopausal gonadotrophin (= HMG)
PMA	phorbol-12-myristate-13-acetate		
		PMH	past medical history
PMA *(psych)*	Primary Mental Abilities Test	PMI	previous medical illness
		PMI	phosphomannose isomerase
PMA	progressive muscular atrophy (= PMD)	PMI *(card)*	point of maximal intensity (= PM, p.m.)
PMA	pyridylmercuric acetate	PMI	posterior myocardial infarction
PMA index	papillary, marginal, alveolar index (of gingival diseases)		
		PMI syndrome	postmyocardial infarction syndrome
PMAOA	platelet monoamine oxidase activity	PML	pemoline
PMB	p-mercuric benzoate	PML	polymorphonuclear leukocytes
PMB	polychrome methylene blue		
		PML	posterior mitral leaflet (= PMVL)
PMB	polymorphonuclear basophils		

PML, PMLE	progressive multifocal leu- koencephalopathy	PN	peptone nutritional solu- tion
PMLE	polymorphous light exan- them (= PLD)	PN	perceived noise
		PN	percussion note
PMMA	polymethylmethacrylate	PN	periarteritis nodosa
PMN	polymorphonuclear neu- trophils	PN	peripheral nerve
		PN	platelet-rich normal plasma
PMNR	periadenitis mucosa necro- tica recurrens	PN *(chem)*	Polenske number
PMO	phenylmethyl oxadiazole	PN	postnatal
PMO	Principal Medical Officer	PN	Practical Nurse
pmol	picomol	PN	protein nitrogen
PMP *(obst)*	persistent mentoposterior (position of fetus)	PN	psychoneurotic
		PN	pyelonephritis
PMP	previous menstrual period	Pn	pneumonia
PMPEA	p-methoxyphenyl ethyla- mine	p.n.	postnatal
		p.n.	pro narcosi (L); for anes- thetic use
PMQ	Pasteur-Meyerhof quotient		
PMR	palmomental reflex	P+N	Psychiatry and Neurology
PMR	perinatal mortality rate	PNA	Paris Nomina Anatomica (1955)
PMR	Physical Medicine and Rehabilitation	PNA	peanut agglutinin
PMR	polymyalgia rheumatica	PNA	pentose nucleic acid (= RNA)
PMR	proton magnetic resonance		
PMRAFNS	Princess Mary's Royal Air Force Nursing Service	PNA	plasma noradrenaline
		PNA	prenylamine
³¹P-MRS	³¹P magnetic resonance spectroscopy	PNAQ *(psych)*	positive-negative ambiva- lent quotient
PMRS	Physical Medicine and Rehabilitation Service	PNB	pudendal nerve blockade
		PNBT	p-nitroblue tetrazolium
PMS	phenazine methosulfate	PNC	penicillin
PMS *(pharm)*	postmarketing study	PNC *(biochem)*	purine nucleotide cycle
PMS	postmenopausal syndrome	PND	paroxysmal nocturnal dyspnea
PMS	premenstrual syndrome (= PMT)	PND	postnasal drainage
PMS	pregnant mare serum	PN-db	perceived noise decibels (= dBPN)
PMSF	phenylmethane sulfonyl- fluoride	PNDMA	p-nitroso-dimethylamine
PMSF *(urol)*	progressive motility sus- taining factor	PNDS	Paranoid Neurosis Depres- sion Scale
PMSG	pregnant mare serum gonadotrophin	P.Ned.	Nederlandsche Pharmaco- pee; Dutch Pharmacopeia
PMT	premenstrual tension	Pneu	pneumothorax
PMV	posterior mitral valve	PNF	proprioceptive neuromus- cular facilitation
PMVL	posterior mitral valve leaf- let (= PML)	PNH	non-hereditary porphyria

PNH	paroxysmal nocturnal hemoglobinuria	POF	pyruvate oxidation factor
PNI	peripheral nerve injury	PofE	portal of entry
PNI	postnatal infection	POG	pression d'oreillette gauche (F); left atrial pressure (= LAP)
PNMT	phenylethanolamine N-methyltransferase		
PNO	Principal Nursing Officer	pol	polymerase
PNP	p-nitrophenol	Poly-A	polyadenylic acid
PNP	polyneuropathy	Poly-IC	polyribo-inosinic-cytidylic acid
PnP	pneumoperitoneum		
PNPase	polynucleotide phosphory-lase	Poly-ICLC	polyribo-inosinic-cytidylic acid-L-lysine complex
PNPB	positive-negative pressure breathing (= APN, PNPR, PNPV)	POM	polymyxin
		POMB	polymyxin B
		POME	polymyxin E, colistin
PNPG	p-nitrophenylglycerin	POMP	cytotoxic combination therapy of acute leukoses with prednisone, Oncovin (vincristine), methotrexate, and Purinethol (mercap-topurine)
PNPP	p-nitrophenylphosphate		
PNPR	positive-negative pressure respiration (= APN, PNPB, PNPV)		
PNPS	p-nitrophenylsulfate		
PNPV	positive-negative pressure ventilation (= APN, PNPB, PNPR)	POMP	principal outer-membrane protein
		POMR	problem-oriented medical record
PNS	paraneoplastic syndrome		
PNS	parasympathetic nervous system	POMS *(psych)*	Profile of Mood States
PNS	peripheral nervous system	POP *(obst)*	persistent occipito-poste-rior (position)
PNU	protein nitrogen unit		
Pnx	pneumothorax	POP	plasma osmotic pressure
PO	period of onset	POP	plaster of Paris
PO	phone order	p.op.	post operationem (L); postoperative (= p.o.)
p.o.	per os (L); by mouth		
p.o.	post operationem (L); postoperative	POPS	Project on Preterm and Small-for-Gestational-Age Infants (The Netherlands, 1983)
PO$_2$	oxygen partial pressure		
POA	paraosteoarthropathy		
POA	primary optic atrophy	POR	problem-oriented record
POB	penicillin, oil, beeswax	PORP	partial ossicular replace-ment prosthesis
POB	phenoxybenzamine		
POC	potential-operated channel	pos.	position
POC *(obst)*	products of conception	pos.	positive
POD	peroxidase	POSM	patient-operated selector mechanism
POD	pression d'oreillette droite (F); right atrial pressure (= RAP)		
		POSS	proximal over-shoulder strap
PODx	preoperative diagnosis	post.	posterior

208

post sing.sed.liq.	post singulas sedes liquidas (L); after each loose bowel movement (Rx)	p.p.a.	phiala prius agitata (L); shake before use (Rx)
POV	pentoxyverine	PPAP	peak pulmonary artery pressure
POVT	puerperal ovarian vein thrombosis	PPB	positive pressure breathing
POW	prisoner of war	ppb	parts per billion (= concentration 10^{-9})
PP	partial pressure		
PP	pellagra preventing (factor) (= PPF)	PPBF	Pan-American Pharmaceutical and Biochemical Federation
PP *(imm)*	percentage of positive cells	PPB test	Purdue pegboard test
PP	pericardial pressure	PPC	pentose phosphate cycle
PP	placenta protein	PPC *(clin)*	postoperative pulmonary complications
PP	pluripara, multipara		
PP	polypeptide	PPC	progressive patient care
PP	polypropylene	PPC	pulmonary capillary pressure
PP	posterior pituitary		
PP	postprandial	PPCA	plasma prothrombin conversion accelerator, factor VI, accelerin
PP	primipara		
PP	private patient		
PP	private practice	PP cells	pancreatic polypeptide-secreting cells
PP	proactivator plasminogen		
PP	progressive paralysis	PPCF	plasma prothrombin conversion factor, factor V
PP	protoporphyria		
PP	pulse pressure	PPCV	pulmonary capillary venous pressure
PP, pp *(ophth)*	punctum proximum (L); near point of accommodation		
		PPD	p-phenylenediamine (oxidase)
PP	pyrophosphate (= PYP)		
pp.	paginae (L); pages	PPD	progressive perceptive deafness
p.p.	per primam (intentionem sanationis) (L); primary healing of a wound		
		PPD	purified protein derivative (tuberculin)
p.p.	post partum (L); after delivery	PPDS	purified protein derivative-standard
p.p.	pro parte (L); per part	PPE	pentosane polysulfoester
PPA *(clin)*	palpation, percussion, and auscultation	PPF	pasteurized plasma protein fraction
PPA	phenoxypropylamide	PPF	pellagra preventive factor, nicotinic acid
PPA	phenylpropanolamine hydrochloride		
		PPFA	Planned Parenthood Federation of America
PPA	phenylpyruvic acid		
PPA	Pittsburgh pneumonia agent, Legionella	PPG	photoplethysmography
		PPH	phenylpropyl hydrazine
PPA	prephase accelerator	PPH	postpartum hemorrhage
P_{PA}, pPA	pulmonary artery pressure	PPH	precapillary pulmonary hypertension

PPH	primary pulmonary hypertension	PPS	postperfusion syndrome, mononucleosis after transfusion ($=$PTM)
P-phenomenon	Polcak phenomenon	PPS	protein polysaccharide
PPHP	pseudo-pseudohypoparathyroidism	PPSA	Pan-Pacific Surgical Association
PPi	pyrophosphate inorganic	PPSB	prothrombin (factor II), proconvertin (VII), Stuart-Prower factor (X), and antihemophilic factor B (IX)
PPL	penicilloyl polylysine		
PPL	posterior pulmonary leaflet		
PPLO	pleuropneumonia-like organisms, mycoplasmas		
PPLP	peak pleural pressure	P/p system	blood group system containing factor P
PPM *(card)*	posterior papillary muscle		
ppm	parts per million ($=$concentration 10^{-6})	PPT	partial prothrombin time
		PPT	prednisone provocation test
PPMA	post-poliomyelitis progressive muscular atrophy	PPT	pyrexin provocation test
PPMI	progressive pacemaker inhibition	Ppt.	precipitate
		ppt	parts per trillion ($=$concentration 10^{-12})
PPN *(psych)*	Patient Progress Note		
PPNG	penicillinase-producing Neisseria gonorrhoeae	PPTL *(gyn)*	postpartum tubal ligation ($=$PPS)
PPO	2,5-diphenyloxazole	PP type	pink puffer type (in pulmonary emphysema with severe dyspnea) (cp. BB)
PPO	peak pepsin output		
PPO	pleuropneumonia organisms		
PPO	polyphenyloxide	PPU	persistent proteinuria
PPP	paroxypropione, p-hydroxypropiophenone	PPV	positive pressure ventilation ($=$PPB)
PPP	platelet-poor plasma	PPV	pulmonary venous pressure
3-PPP	propyl-3-(3-hydroxyphenyl)-piperidine	PPVL	posterior pulmonary valve leaflet ($=$PPL)
PPPPP(P)	pain, pallor, paresthesia, pulselessness, paralysis (and prostration) – symptoms and signs of acute peripheral arterial occlusion	PPVO	premature pulmonary valve opening
		PPX	pipecolylxylidine
		PQ	permeability quotient
		PR	pallida reaction
PPR	Price precipitation reaction	PR	paramagnetic resonance
PPS	pain-producing substance	PR	partial remission
PPS	pentosane polysulfoester ($=$PPE)	PR	patient relations
		PR	percentile rank
PPS	phosphoribosyl-1-pyrophosphate synthetase	PR	peripheral resistance
		PR	phenol red
PPS	plasma protein solution	PR	pityriasis rosea
PPS *(gyn)*	postpartum sterilization ($=$PPTL)	PR	polyarthrite rhumatisme (F); rheumatoid arthritis ($=$RA)

PR	pregnancy rate	PRF	prolactin-releasing factor (= PRH)
PR	premières règles (L); first menstrual period, menarche	PRF	pulse repetition frequency
		PRH	prolactin-releasing hormone (= PRF)
PR	pressoreceptor		
PR	production rate	PRI *(card)*	pressure-rate index
PR	progressive resistance	PRIF, PRIH	prolactin-release inhibiting factor, ... hormone
PR	prothrombin ratio		
PR	Puerto Rico (virus strains)	prim.	primary
PR	pulse rate	PRIND	prolonged reversible ischemic neurological deficits
PR, pr *(ophth)*	punctum remotum (L); far point of accommodation		
Pr *(ophth)*	presbyopia	PRINS	partially reversible ischemic neurologic symptoms
Pr *(ophth)*	prism		
Pr	prolactin	prion	Prusiner's term for a suspected infectious protein
Pr	propane		
p.r.	per rectum (L); rectally	PRIS	protective response inducing substance
p.r.	post radiationem (L); after radiation		
		PRIST	paper radioimmunosorbent test
PRA	phosphoribosylamine		
PRA	plasma renin activity	PRL	prolactin
P_{RA}, pRA	right atrial pressure	PRM	paromomycin
praec.	praecipitatus (L); precipitate (= ppt.)	PRM	primidone
		p.r.n.	pro re nata (L); if necessary, as needed
PRAS *(bact)*	prereduced anaerobically sterilized		
		Pro	proline
p.rat.aet.	pro ratione aetatis (L); proportional to age	Proc.	procedure
		Proc. *(anat)*	process
PRAVT	pre-entry AV tachycardia	PROCAM	Prospective Cardiovascular Study of Münster (Germany)
PRB	Prosthetics Research Board		
PRBBB	proximal right bundle branch block	Procs.	proceedings
		Prof.	professor
PRC	plasma renin concentration	prof.	professional
PRC	polymerase chain reaction	prof.	profound
PRD	partial reaction of degeneration	PROM *(obst)*	premature rupture of the membranes
prdpt	prism diopter	PROMIS	problem-oriented medical information system
PRE	photon relaxation enhancement		
		prox.	proximal
PRE	progressive resistive exercise	PRP	platelet-rich plasma
		PRP	progressive rubella panencephalitis
PR-enzyme	prosthetic group removing enzyme		
		PRP	psychotic reaction profile
prep.	preparation	PRPP	phosphoribosyl pyrophosphate
PRESYS	Prevention and Rehabilitation System		

PRPP-AT	phosphoribosyl pyrophosphate amidotransferase	p.s.	per secundam (intentionem sanationis) (L); secondary healing of a wound
PRS	Pierre-Robin syndrome		
PRS	procto-recto-sigmoidoscopy	P+S	paracentesis and suction
		P+S	Physicians and Surgeons
PRSP	prereading screening procedures	PSA	Psychological Society of America
PRT	pacemaker re-entry tachycardia	PSAN	polystyrene acrylnitrile
		PSAn	psychoanalysis, psychoanalyst
PRT	phosphoribosyl transferase		
		PSAT	percent saturation of transferrin
prt	protease		
PRU	peripheral resistance unit	PSB	parasympathetic blockade
PRV	posterior wall of right ventricle	PSC	Porter silver chromogens
		PSC	proscillaridine
P$_{RV}$, pRV	right ventricular pressure	PSC, PSCC	posterior subcapsular cataract
PRVED	right ventricular end-diastolic pressure		
		PSE *(psych)*	point of subjective equality
PS	paradoxical sleep phase	PSE	portosystemic encephalopathy; encephalopathia hepatica
PS	Parapsychological Society (USA)		
PS	Parkinson's syndrome	PSER	peak systolic ejection rate
PS	pathological staging		
PS	patient's serum	PSF	pleuritis serofibrinosa
PS *(pharm)*	penicillin-sulfonamide combination	PSF	point spread function
		PSF reaction	polarographic serum filtrate reaction
PS	Pferdestärke (G); horse power (=CV, HP)		
		PSG	prednisolone stearoylglycolate
PS	phenolsteroid		
PS	phosphatidyl serine, cephalin	PSGB	Pharmaceutical Society of Great Britain
PS	photo systems	PSGBI	Pathological Society of Great Britain and Ireland
PS	physical status		
PS	plastic surgery	PSH	périarthrite scapulo-humérale (F) (=vd. PHS syndrome)
PS	poids spécifique (F); specific weight		
PS	polystyrene	PSH	post-stimulation histogram
PS	ponction sternale (F); sternal puncture	PSI	Pharmaceutical Society of Ireland
PS	post scriptum	PSI	posterior sagittal index
PS	pregnant serum	PSI	presynaptic inhibition
PS	pregnenolone sulfate	PSI	Problem Solving Information
PS	pulmonary stenosis		
Ps	prescription (=Rx)	psi	pounds per square inch
Ps	systolic (arterial) pressure	PSIL	preferred-frequency speech interference level
Ps.	Pseudomonas	PSL	prednisolone

PSL sol	potassium, sodium chloride, sodium lactate solution		PST	paroxysmal supraventricular tachycardia (= PSVT)
PSM	pression systémique moyenne (F); mean systemic (arterial) pressure (= MAP)		PST	penicillin, streptomycin, tetracycline
			PST	pentobarbital sleeping time
			PST *(psych)*	picture story test
PSMA	progressive spinal muscular atrophy, Duchenne-Aran syndrome		PSTH	post-stimulus time histogram
			P-substance	protein substance
PSMF	protein-substituted modified fasting		PSV	proximal selective vagotomy
PSNI	Pharmaceutical Society of Northern Ireland		PSVT	paroxysmal supraventricular tachycardia (= PST)
p.sol.	partly soluble		PSW	Psychiatric Social Worker
PSP	pancreatic stone protein		PSWS *(card)*	peak systolic wall stress
PSP	peak systolic pressure		PSYCHIS	Psychiatric Information System
PSP	phenolsulfonphthaleine, phenol red (= PR)		P_{syst}	systolic (arterial) blood pressure (= Ps)
PSP *(card)*	post-stimulation potentiation		P-system	blood group system containing factor P
PSP	postsynaptic potential		PT	parathyroid
PSp	pneumothorax spontané (F); spontaneous pneumothorax		PT	paroxysmal tachycardia
			PT	passage time
			PT	peak time
PSPA	systolic pulmonary artery pressure		PT	phototoxicity
			PT	physical therapy
PSPP	presqualene pyrophosphate		PT	plasmolysis test
			PT	pneumotachograph
P/S quotient	ratio of polyene to saturated fatty acids		PT	precipitation test
			PT	primary tumor
PSR	pelvispondylite rhumatismale (F); ankylosing spondylitis, Bechterew's disease		PT	propylthiouracil (= PTU)
			PT	prothrombin time
			PT	psychotherapy
PSRO	Professional Standards Review Organization (USA)		PT	pulmonary trunk
			PT	pulmonary tuberculosis
			pt.	part
PSRS	Psychiatric Self-Rating Scale		pt.	patient
			pt.	point
PSS	physiological saline solution		pt	pint
			p.t.	post transfusionem (L); after transfusion
PSS	physiological stability score		PTA	patient-triggered analgesia
PSS	progressive systemic sclerosis		PTA	percutaneous transluminal angioplasty (= PTCA)
PSS	Personality Scale System			
PsSS	Psychiatric Status Schedule		PTA	peritonsillar abscess

PTA	Pharmaceutical-Technical Assistant	PTH	phenylthiohydantoin
PTA	phosphotransacetylase	PTH	posttransfusion hepatitis
PTA	plasma thromboplastin antecedent, factor XI, Rosenthal factor	PTH	prothionamide (= PTA)
		PTJC	percutaneous transjugular cholangiography
PTA	posttraumatic amnesia	PTJV	percutaneous transtracheal jet ventilation
PTA	primary tubular acidosis		
PTA	prior to admission	PTL	posterior tricuspid leaflet
PTA	prothionamide (= PTH)	PTL group	psittacosis-trachoma-lym-
PTAP	purified toxoid precipi-		phogranuloma group of
	tated by aluminum phos-		viruses (= PLT group)
	phate	PTM	phenyltrimethylammonium
Ptase	phosphatase	PTM	posttransfusion mononu-
PTB	patella tendon bearing		cleosis (= PPS)
PTB	prior to birth	PTM	pressure time per minute
PTB	prothrombin	PTM	pulse-time modulation
PTB	pulmonary tuberculosis	PTM x ESV	pressure time per minute x
PTC	percutaneous transhepatic		endsystolic volume
	cholangiography	PTO (vet)	Perlsucht-Tuberkulin origi-
PTC	phenylthiocarbamide		nal (G)
PTC	plasma thromboplastin	PTO, p.t.o.	please turn over
	component, factor IX,	PTP	posttetanic potentiation
	Christmas factor	PTR	patella tendon reflex
PTC	positive temperature coef-	PTR	percutaneous transluminal
	ficient		recanalization
PTC	posttraumatic cephalgia	PTR (vet)	Perlsucht-Tuberkulin-Rest
PTC	primary traumatic coma		(G)
PTCA	percutaneous transluminal	PTR	plasma transfusion reac-
	coronary angioplasty		tion
PTCD	percutaneous transhepatic	PTR	pulmonary total resistance
	cholangio-drainage	PTRD	percutaneous transluminal
PTCR	percutaneous transluminal		renal (artery) dilatation
	coronary recanalization	PTS (otol)	permanent threshold shift
PTD	percutaneous transhepatic	PTS	postthrombotic syndrome
	drainage	pts.	patients
PTD	permanent total disability	PTT	partial thromboplastin
PTE	parathyroid extract		time
PTEN	pentaerythrityl tetranitrate	PTU	propylthiouracil
	(= PETN)	PTV	posterior tibial vein
P-test	Prokop test	PTX	pengitoxin
PTF	plasma thromboplastin	PTX	pentoxyphylline
	factor, factor X	PTx	parathyroidectomy
PTF	proximal tubular flow	PTZ	pentylene tetrazole
PTFE	polytetrafluoro-ethylene	PU	peptic ulcer
PTH	parathyroid hormone, par-	PU	per urethram (L); via the
	athormone		urethra
		PU	pregnancy urine

PUC *(obst)*	premature uterine contractions	PVC	pression veineuse centrale (F); central venous pressure
PUD	peptic ulcer disease		
PuD	pulmonary disease	PVC	pulmonary venous capillary pressure
PUFA	polyunsaturated fatty acid		
PUH	pregnancy urine hormone	PVCAC	polyvinylchloride acetate
pulm.	pulmonary	PVCO	pulmonary venous channel obstruction
pulv.	pulvis (L); powder		
PUO	pyrexia of unknown origin	PVCP	pulmonary venous capillary pressure
PUPP	pruritic urticarial papules and plaques of pregnancy	PVD	peripheral vascular disease
PUR	polyurethane	PVD	pulmonary vascular disease
PUT	phosphate uridyl transferase		
		PVDC	polyvinylidene chloride
PUVA	psoralen ultraviolet A (psoriasis therapy)	PVE	prosthetic valve endocarditis
PV	paraventricular	PVES	polymorphous ventricular extrasystole
PV	pemphigus vulgaris		
PV	plasma volume	PVE	postvaccinal encephalitis
PV	polycythaemia vera	PVF	polyvinyl formol
PV	polyoma virus	PVF	primary ventricular fibrillation
PV	portal vein		
PV	pression veineuse (F); venous pressure	PVFS	(chronic) postviral fatigue syndrome
PV	pression ventriculaire (F); ventricular pressure	PVL	Panton-Valentine leukocidin (= P.V.)
PV	primary vaccine	PVM	pneumonia virus of the mouse
PV	pulmonary vein		
P.V.	Panton-Valentine leukocidin (= PVL)	p.v.n.	per vias naturales (L); through natural ways
P/V	pressure/volume	PVNO	polyvinylpyridine-N-oxide
P + V *(chir)*	pyloroplasty and vagotomy	PVO	pulmonary venous obstruction
p.v.	per vaginam (L); via the vagina		
		PVO_2	venous oxygen pressure
p.v.	post vaccination	PVP	polyvinylpyrrolidone
PVA	polyvinyl alcohol (= PVAL)	PVPH	primary vascular pulmonary hypertension
PVA	polyvinyl acetate (= PVAC)	PVR	peripheral vascular resistance
PVA	pulmonary valve atresia	PVR	pulmonary vascular resistance
PVAC	polyvinyl acetate (= PVA)		
PVAL	polyvinyl alcohol (= PVA)	PVS *(gyn)*	prostaglandin vaginal suppositories
PVB	premature ventricular beat (= PVC)	PVT	paroxysmal ventricular tachycardia
PVC	polyvinyl chloride		
PVC	premature ventricular contraction (= PVB)	PVT	pressure, volume, temperature

PW	pulse width	Q	quinacrine, mepacrine
PWA	person with AIDS	Q	quotient
PWAR	posterior wall of aortic root	q	Quadrat (G); square
PWC	physical working capacity	QAC	quaternary ammonium compound
PWI *(card)*	posterior wall infarction	QALY	Quality Adjusted Life-Year (with reference to health care cost)
PWLA	posterior wall of left atrium		
PWM	pokeweed mitogen	QAP	Quality Assurance Program
PWP	pulmonary wedge pressure		
PWS	pickwickian syndrome	QAP	quinine, atebrin, plasmoquine (for malaria)
PWT	posterior wall thickness		
PWT	pulse wave time	QAR	quantitative autoradiography
PWV	pulse wave velocity		
PX	physical examination	QARANC	Queen Alexandra's Royal Army Nursing Corps
PX	pyridoxine		
Px	pneumothorax	QARNNS	Queen Alexandra's Royal Naval Nursing Service
PXDH	pancreatic xanthine dehydrogenase		
		QC	Quality Control
PXE	pseudoxanthoma elasticum	QC	quinaldinum caeruleum (L); quinaldine blue
Py	pyrimidine nucleoside		
PYA	psychoanalysis	QCH	Queen Charlottes's Hospital
PyC	pyogenic culture		
PYG	peptone-yeast-glucose (agar)	QCIM	Quarterly Cumulative Index Medicus
PYGM	peptone-yeast-glucose-maltose (agar)	QCThr	quantitative computerized tomography with high resolution special scanner
PYM	Psychosomatic Medicine		
PyP	pyridoxamine phosphate	QCTwb	quantitative computerized tomography with whole body scanner
Pyr	pyridine		
PZ	pancreozymin (cholecystokinin)		
		q.d.	quaque die (L); every day
PZA	pyrazinamide	q.e.d.	quod erat demonstrandum (L); which was to be demonstrated
PZC	perphenacine		
PZI	protamin zinc insulin		
PZ-protein	pregnancy zone protein	QEONS	Queen Elizabeth's Overseas Nursing Service
		Q-fever	query fever, Queensland fever, Queensland tick typhus

Q

Q	quality factor (or index)	q.h.	quaque hora (L); every hour
Q *(phys)*	quantity (of electricity, light, warmth)	q.2h., q.3h.	quaque secunda hora, quaque tertia hora (L); every two (three) hours
Q	quartile	Q.H.N.S.	Queen's Honorary Nursing Sister

Q.H.P.	Queen's Honorary Physician	qual.anal.	qualitative analysis
Q.H.S.	Queen's Honorary Surgeon	quant.anal.	quantitative analysis
		QUI	Queen's University of Ireland
q.i.d.	quater in die (L); four times a day (Rx)	quot.op.sit	quoties opus sit (L); as often as is needed
QIDN	Queen's Institute of District Nursing	q.v.	quantum vis (L); as much as you like
QIE	quantitative immune electrophoresis	q.v.	quod vide (L); which see
QKM	quantitative kinetic microfluorometry		
q.l.	quantum libet (L); as much as is desired (Rx)		

R

QM	quinacrine mustard (staining of chromosomes)	
q.m.	quaque mane (L); every morning	R *(stat)*	coefficient of correlation
QMT	quantitative muscle test	R *(clin)*	quotient réspiratoire (F); respiratory quotient
q.n.	quaque nocte (L); every night	R *(chem)*	radical
QNB	(3H)-quinuclidinyl benzylate	R *(stat)*	range
		R *(phys)*	Rankine (temperature scale)
QNS	quantity not sufficient	R *(phys)*	Réaumur (temperature scale)
Q.N.S.	Queen's Nursing Sister (of the QIDN)	R *(bact)*	resistence factor
QO₂	oxygen quotient	R *(phys)*	Reynolds' number (= Re)
q.o.d.	every other day (Rx)	R *(chem)*	ribose
QP	quanti-Pirquet reaction	R *(rad)*	roentgen
q.p.	quantum placet (L); as much as is desired	R *(bact)*	rough
		R *(chem)*	rubber
qqh	quaque hora (L); hourly (= q.h.)	R *(phys)*	Rydberg's constant
q.q.h.	quaque quarta hora (L); every four hours (Rx)	R. *(pharm)*	radix (L); root (= Rad.)
		R. *(anat)*	ramus (L); branch
q.r.	quantum rectum (L); correct quantity	R. *(bact)*	Rickettsia
		r *(chem)*	racemic
QR	quinaldine red	r *(gen)*	resistance allele (gene of blood group O)
QRZ	Quaddel-Resorptionszeit (G); weal absorption time	r *(pharm)*	resistance rate
		+ R *(otol)*	Rinne positive
QS	Queckenstedt's sign	− R *(otol)*	Rinne negative
QS	Quecksilbersäule (G); mercury column	RA	radioactive
		RA	réserve alcaline (F); alkaline reserve
q.s.	quantum satis (L); sufficient quantity	RA	residual air
QT	Quick's test	RA	rheumatoid arthritis
qt	quart	RA	right arm

QO_2 oxygen quotient

RA	right atrium
RAA	rhumatisme articulaire aigu (F); acute articular rheumatism
RAA	right atrial appendage
RAAA	ruptured aneurysm of the abdominal aorta
RAAS	renin-angiotensin-aldosterone system
RAC	right atrial contraction
rac-	racemate
RACAT	rapid-acquisition computed axial tomography
RA-cell	rheumatoid arthritis cell
RACGP	Royal Australian College of General Practitioners
RACO	Royal Australian College of Ophthalmologists
RACOG	Royal Australian College of Obstetricians and Gynaecologists
RACP	Royal Australian College of Physicians
RACS	Royal Australasian College of Surgeons
RAD	ramus anterior dexter (L); atrial branch
RAD	right anterior descending (artery)
RAD	right axis deviation
rad	radiation absorbed dose (=rd)
rad	radiant
Rad.	radix (L); root (=R.)
rad.	radial
R.a.d. (anat)	ramus atrialis dexter
RADA (obst)	right acromio-dorsoanterior (position of fetus)
RADA	rosin amine-D-acetate
RADAR	Radio Detecting and Ranging
RADC	Royal Army Dental Corps
RADP (obst)	right acromiodorsoposterior (position of fetus)
RADP (card)	right atrial diastolic pressure
RAE	right atrial electrogram

RAEB	refractory anemia with excess of blasts
RAEF	right atrial ejection fraction
RaEm	radium emanation
RAER	right atrial expansion rate
RAERP	right atrial effective refractory period
RAESV	right atrial end-systolic volume
RAFMS	Royal Air Force Medical Services
RAGGS	rheumatoid agglutinating serum (vd. RAS)
RAH	right atrial hypertrophy
RAI	radioactive iodine
RAITI	right atrial inversion time index
RAIU	radioactive iodine uptake
RAM	Random Accessory Memory (of a computer)
RAMC	Royal Army Medical Corps
RAMP (card)	right atrial mean pressure
RANA	rheumatoid arthritis associated nuclear antigen
RANDO	radiation analogue dosimetry system
R-antigen	"rough" antigen
RAO (rad)	right anterior oblique (projection)
RAP (card)	rate-adapted pacing
RAP	right atrial pressure
RAP (mil)	Regimental Aid Post
RARE	rapid acquisition relaxation enhanced
RAS	rapid atrial stimulation
RAS	renin-angiotensin system
RAS	reticular activating system (=ARAS, ARS)
RAS	reticulo-endothelium activating serum (=ACS, ARES, SARC)
RAS	rheumatoid arthritis serum (vd. RAGGS)
RAS	rien à signaler (F); no abnormal finding

R.a.s. *(anat)*	ramus atrialis sinister	RC	respiratory center
RASER	roentgen amplification by stimulated emission of radiation	RC	retention catheter
		RC	reticulocyte count
		RC	root canal
RASP	right atrial systolic pressure	RC	rythme cardiaque (F); cardiac rhythm
RAST *(imm)*	radio-allergosorbent test		
RA-test	rheumatoid arthritis test	R_c	receptors in cytoplasm
RATG	rabbit antithymocyte globulin	R.c. *(anat)*	ramus circumflexus
		RCA	red cell agglutination
RAV	Rous-associated viruses	RCA	right coronary artery
RAVA	regurgitant aortic valvular area	R.c.a. *(anat)*	ramus coni arteriosi
		RCAMC	Royal Canadian Army Medical Corps
RAVC	Royal Army Veterinary Corps	RCBF	regional cerebral blood flow
R.a.v.d.	ramus atrioventricularis dexter		
		RCBF	regional cortical blood flow
RAVO	right atrioventricular orifice		
		RCC	Radio-Chemical Center
R.a.v.s.	ramus atrioventricularis sinister	RCC	right coronary cusp
		RCCA	right common carotid artery
R_{aw}	airway resistance		
RB	résistance bronchique (F); bronchial resistance	RCD	relative cardiac dullness
		RCD	relative cross-sectional area difference
RB	rose bengal		
Rb	ribosome ($=$ Rib)	RCD	resistance-condenser-diode
RBBB	right bundle branch block	R.c.d.	ramus circumflexus dexter
RBC	red blood cell (or corpuscle)	rcdr	recorder
		RCF	relative centrifugal force
RBC	red blood count	rcfm	"reconfirm"
RBD	relative biological dose	RCG	radiocirculography
RBD	right border of dullness	RCGP	Royal College of General Practitioners
RBE	relative biological effectiveness		
		RCH	recto-colite hémorragique (F); hemorrhagic proctocolitis
RBF	renal blood flow		
RBFD	renal blood flow distribution		
		RCLAAR	red cell linked antigen-antiglobulin reaction
RBNA	Royal British Nurses' Association		
		RCM	red cell mass
RBP	retinol-binding protein	RCM	reinforced clostridial medium
RBV	regional blood volume		
RC	red cell	RCM	restrictive cardiomyopathy
RC	Red Cross	RCM	right costal margin
RC *(phys)*	resistance capacitance	RCM	Royal College of Midwives
RC	résistance capillaire (F); capillary resistance	RCN	Royal College of Nursing
		RCOG	Royal College of Obstetricians and Gynaecologists
RC	resistance x compliance (of the lungs)		
		R_{cor}	coronary reserve

R_{cor}	coronary resistance	rd	rad (radiation absorbed dose)
RCP	Royal College of Physicians	R + D	Research and Development
RCPSC	Royal College of Physicians and Surgeons of Canada	RDA	ramus descendens anterior (= LAD, RIA, RIVA)
RCR	renal clearance rate	RDA	recommended daily (or dietary) allowance
RCR	Royal College of Radiologists	RDA *(obst)*	right dorso-anterior (position of fetus)
RCS	rabbit aorta contracting substance	RDBBB	rate-dependent bundle branch block
RCS	Red Cross Society (UK)	RDE	receptor destroying enzyme
RCS	reticulum cell sarcoma	RDF	redistribution factor
RCS	retrocardial space	RDH	Registered Dental Hygienist
RCS	Royal College of Surgeons		
R.c.s.	ramus circumflexus sinister	RDH	ribitol dehydrogenase
		rDNA	recombinant DNA
RCSC	Royal College of Surgeons of Canada	RDP *(obst)*	right dorso-posterior (position of fetus)
RCSE	Royal College of Surgeons of Edinburgh	RDS	respiratory distress syndrome
RCSI	Royal College of Surgeons of Ireland	R_{ds}	downstream resistance
RCT	Race-Coombs test	RDSS	Regenerative Dialysis Supply System
RCT *(clin)*	radiation and chemotherapy	RDT	regular dialysis treatment
RCT	radionuclide computerized tomography	RDW	red cell distribution width
RCT	red colloidal test	RDX	trimethylene trinitramine
RCT *(psych)*	Rorschach Content Test	RE	expiratory resistance
RCT technique	resistance-condenser-transistor technique	RE	radium emanation (= Em, RaEm, Rn)
RCU	Respiratory Care Unit	RE	rectal examination
RCVS	Royal College of Veterinary Surgeons	RE	resting energy
		RE	reticuloendothelium
RCWI	right ventricular cardiac work index (= RVWI)	RE	right eye (= OD)
		Re *(phys)*	Reynolds' number (= R)
RCX	right circumflex branch (of coronary artery)	R + E *(ophth)*	round and equal (pupils)
RD	reaction of degeneration	REAC	relative erythrocyte aggregation capacity
RD	Registered Dietitian		
RD *(ophth)*	retinal detachment	rec.	recens (L); fresh
RD	retinopathia diabetica	rec.	recurrent
RD *(dent)*	rubber dam	RECG	radio-electrocardiography
Rd *(phys)*	rutherford (unit of radioactivity)		
rd	radiant (= rad)	rect. *(pharm)*	rectificatus (L); rectified, purified

rectss. *(pharm)*	rectificatissimus (L); highly purified	RES	reticuloendothelial system (=RHS)
RED	réflexe électrodermal (F); electrodermal reflex	Res.	research
red.in pulv.	reductus in pulverem (L); reduced to a powder	RES-viruses	respiratory-enteric orphan viruses, REO-viruses
redox	reduction oxidation	RET	repetitive extrasystole threshold
REF	regional ejection fraction	ret	roentgen equivalent therapy
REF	renal erythropoietic factor		
REG	Radiation Exposure Guide	ret.	retarded
REG	radio-encephalogram	ret.	retired
REG	rheo-encephalogram	REV	reticuloendotheliosis virus
REIA	radio-enzyme immunoassay	Rev.	review
		rev.	reverse
REL	rate of energy loss	RF, rf	radiofrequency (therapy)
REM	rapid eye movement (sleep)	RF	recognition factor
		RF	regeneration factor
REM	Rasterelektronenmikroskopie (G); scanning electron microscopy (=SEM)	RF	regurgitant fraction
		RF	Reitland-Franklin (unit)
		RF	rejection fraction
rem *(rad)*	roentgen equivalent man (or mammal)	RF	relative flow (rate)
		RF	releasing factor
rem.	remanentia (L); remainder (Rx)	RF	renal function
		RF *(gen)*	replicative form
rem.	remedy	RF *(card)*	residual fraction
REMAB *(rad)*	radiation equivalent manikin absorption	RF *(gen)*	resistance factor
		RF	respiratory failure
REMCAL *(rad)*	radiation equivalent manikin calibration	RF	reticular formation
		RF	rheumatic fever
R-enzyme	amylopectin-1,6-glucosidase	RF	rheumatoid factor
		RF	riboflavin
REO-viruses	respiratory-enteric orphan viruses, RES-viruses	RF	risk factor
		R_F	rate of flow (in chromatography)
REP	retrograde pyelogram		
rep	roentgen equivalent physical	R_f	retention factor
		RFA *(obst)*	right fronto-anterior (position of fetus)
rep.	repetatur (L); let it be repeated (Rx)	RFA	roentgen fluorescence analysis
rep.	report		
repPT	repeated puncture technique	R factor *(bact)*	resistance transfer factor
RER	rough endoplasmic reticulum	RF_{AO}	aortic regurgitation fraction
RERF	Radiation Effects Research Foundation	RFB	respiratory biofeedback
		RFC	rosette-forming cells
RERP	retrograde effective refractory period	RFF	rapid filling fraction
		RF-FSH	FSH-releasing factor

RFI	regurgitant fraction index	RHCSA	Regional Hospitals Consultants' and Specialists' Association
RFI	renal failure index		
RFL *(obst)*	right fronto-lateral (position of fetus)	RHD	relative hepatic dullness
RF-LH	LH-releasing factor	RHD,	rheumatic heart disease
RFLP *(gen)*	restriction fragment length polymorphism	RhDH	
		RHF	right heart failure
RFLS	rheumatoid factor-like substance	Rh fever	East Coast or East African fever transmitted by Rhipicephalus
RF method	Reitmann-Frankel method (for GOT, GPT)	Rh fever	Rhodesian fever (sleeping sickness)
RFN	Registered Fever Nurse		
RFP	rapid filling phase	RHI	right heart insufficiency (=RHF)
RFP *(obst)*	right fronto-posterior (position of fetus)		
		RhIG	Rh₀ (D) immune globulin
RFPS	Royal Faculty of Physicians and Surgeons (Glasgow)	rH indicator	redox indicator
		Rhiz.	Rhizobium
		rhiz.	rhizome
RFS	relapse-free survival	RhLA	rhesus leukocyte antigen
RFT	radio-fibrinogen test	rhm	roentgen hour meter
RFT	rapid filling time	RHR	resting heart rate
RFT *(obst)*	right fronto-transverse (position of fetus)	RHS	reticulohistiocytic system (=RES)
RFW	rapid filling wave (of the apex cardiogram)	rHuEPO	recombinant human erythropoietin
RGC	radio-gas chromatography	RI	radiation intensity
RGC	retinal ganglion cell	RI	reduction index
RGE	relative gas expansion	RI	refractive index
RGN	Registered General Nurse	RI	Regan's isoenzyme
RGPD	range-gated pulsed Doppler (echocardiogram)	RI	regeneration index
		RI	regurgitant index
RH	radiant heat	RI	release-inhibiting
RH	reactive hyperemia	RI *(gen)*	replicative intermediate (product)
RH	relative humidity		
RH	releasing hormone (=RF)	RI	respiratory illness
RH	right-handed	RI	respiratory index
RH *(ophth)*	right hyperphoria	RI	respiratory insufficiency (=RF)
Rh	rhesus (blood group system)		
		RI *(psych)*	retroactive inhibition
Rh.	Rhipicephalus	RIA	radio-immunoassay
RHA	Regional Health Authority	RIA	reversible ischemic attack
RhA	rheumatoid arthritis (=RA)	R.i.a.	ramus interventricularis anterior (=LAD, RIVA)
RHB	Regional Hospital Board	RIA-DA	radio-immunoassay double antibody (procedure)
RHC	resin hemoperfusion column		
RHC	right hypochondrium	RI-agents,	respiratory illness agents (adeno viruses)

RIAGT	radio-immune antiglobulin test	RIPH	Royal Institute of Public Health
Rib	ribose	RIPHH	Royal Institute of Public Health and Hygiene
Rib	ribosome		
Ribu	ribulose (= Ru)	RIPT	radio-immunoprecipitation test (= RIPA)
RIC	rectangular impulse characteristics	RIRB	radio-iodinated rose bengal
RIC	Royal Institute of Chemistry	RIS	respiratory insufficiency syndrome
RICU	Respiratory Intensive Care Unit	RISA	radio-immunosorbent assay (= RIST)
RID	radio-immunodiffusion	RISA	radio-iodine serum albumin (= RIHSA)
RIEP	radio-immune electrophoresis	RIST	radio-immunosorbent test (= RISA)
RIF	renal interstitial fluid		
RIF	resistance inducing factor (leukovirus)	RIT	radio-iodinated triolein
RIF	rifampicin (= RIFA, RMP)	RITC	rhodamine isothiocyanate
RIF	right iliac fossa	RIVA	ramus interventricularis anterior (= R.i.a., LAD)
RIFA	rifampicin (= RIF, RMP)		
RIFC	rat intrinsic factor concentrate	RIVC	right inferior vena cava
RIG(H)	rabies immune globulin (human)	RI-viruses	respiratory illness viruses (= RI-agents)
RIH	right inguinal hernia	RIVP	ramus interventricularis posterior (= R.i.p.)
RIHSA	radio-iodinated human serum albumin (= RISA)	RIVT	right idiopathic ventricular tachycardia
RI-insulin	rare immunogenic insulin	RKI	Robert Koch Institute (Berlin/Germany)
RIMA	right internal mammary artery	RkVA *(rad)*	reactive kilovolt-ampère
RIMR	Rockefeller Institute for Medical Research	RKY	roentgen kymography
		RL	Radiologic Laboratory
RIN	radio-isotope nephrography (= ING)	RL, Rl	rales
		RL	reduction level
RIND	reversible ischemic neurological deficits	RL	Ringer lactate (solution)
		Rl	roentgen liter
RING	radio-isotope nephrogram	RLAS	rapid left atrial stimulation
rINN	recommended INN	RLBCD	right lower border of cardiac dullness
RIP	radio-immunoprecipitation		
RIP	renin inhibitory peptide	RLC	residual lung capacity
RIP	respiratory inductive plethysmography	RLD	related living donor
		RLD	ruptured lumbar disc
R.i.p.	ramus interventricularis posterior (= RIVP)	RLE	right lower extremity
		RLF	retrolental fibroplasia
RIPA	radio-immunoprecipitation assay (= RIPT)	RLL	right lower lobe (of the lung)
		RLM	rat liver mitochondria

RLP	rat liver protein	RMR *(ophth)*	right medial rectus (muscle)
RLPV	right lower pulmonary vein	RMS *(rad)*	root mean square (also: r.m.s.)
RLQ	right lower quadrant		
RLSh	right-left shunt	RMS	Royal Microscopial Society (Oxford)
RLV	Rauscher leukemia virus		
RM	radical mastectomy	R.m.s.	ramus marginalis sinister, obtuse marginal branch
RM	range of movement (= ROM)		
RM	reactive monocytosis	RMSF	Rocky Mountain spotted fever
RM	respiratory movement		
R_m	magnetic resistance	RMSSD *(card)*	root mean square of successive differences
R_m	relative mobility (electrophoresis)		
		RMSV *(card)*	right maximal spatial vector
R.m.	ramus marginalis		
RMA *(obst)*	right mento-anterior (presentation of fetus)	RMT *(obst)*	right mento-transverse (position of fetus)
RMBF	regional myocardial blood flow	RMTC	rhesus monkey tissue culture
RMCA	right middle cerebral artery	rMTR	(mean) relative mortality rate
RMCD	rat mast cell degranulation (test)	RMV	respiratory minute volume
RMD	retromanubrial dullness	RN	receptors in the cell nucleus
R.m.d.	ramus marginalis dexter	RN *(anat)*	red nucleus
Rm-factor	Romunde factor, antigen Rm	R.N.	Registered Nurse
		Rn	radium emanation (= Em, RaEm, RE)
RMK	rhesus monkey kidney		
RML *(obst)*	right mediolateral (episiotomy)	RNA	radionuclide angiography
RML	right midle lobe (of the lung)	RNA	ribonucleic acid
		RNA *(bact)*	rough, non-capsulated, avirulent
RMM	Read Mostly Memory		
RMN	Registered Mental Nurse (UK)	R.N.A.	Registered Nurse Anesthetist
R.M.O.	Regimental Medical Officer	RNase	ribonuclease
		R.n.a.v.	ramus nodi atrioventricularis
R.M.O.	Regional Medical Officer (UK)		
RMO	Resident Medical Officer	RNCA	radionuclide cineangiogram
RMP	Regional Medical Program		
RMP	regional myocardial perfusion	RND *(ophth)*	radionucleotide dacryography
RMP	resting membrane potential	RNDr.	Rerum Naturalium Doctor (L); Doctor of Sciences
RMP	rifampicin		
RMP *(obst)*	right mento-posterior (presentation of fetus)	RNG	radionephrography (= ING)
RMPA	Royal Medico-Psychological Association (UK)	RNIB	Royal National Institute for the Blind

RNID	Royal National Institute for the Deaf
R.N.M.D.	Registered Nurse for Mentally Defectives
R.N.M.S.	Registered Nurse for Mentally Subnormal
RNP	ribonucleophosphate
RNP	ribonucleoprotein
RNPAg	ribonucleoprotein antigen
RNS	Ribonukleinsäure (G); ribonucleic acid (= RNA)
R.n.s.	ramus nodi sinuatrialis
RNV	radionuclide venography
RNV,	radionuclide ventriculogra-
RNVG	phy
RO	routine order
R/O	rule out
ROA *(obst)*	right occipito-anterior (position of fetus)
ROC	receiver operating characteristics
ROC	receptor-operated channel
ROCM	restrictive obliterative cardiomyopathy
ROI	region of interest
Ro-joint *(dent)*	rotation joint
ROL *(obst)*	right occipito-lateral (position of fetus)
ROM	range of motion
ROM	Read Only Memory (in computer processing)
ROP *(obst)*	right occipito-posterior (position of fetus)
ROS	review of systems
ROSV	right oblique subxiphoid view
ROT	réflexes ostéo-tendineux (F); tendon reflexes
ROT	remedial occupational therapy
ROT *(obst)*	right occipito-transverse (position of fetus)
ROV	respiratory orphan virus
RP	radial pulse
RP	radiophotography
RP	rapid processing

RP	rectum prolapse
RP	refractory period
RP	Reiter's protein
RP	résistance périphérique (F); peripheral resistance
RP	retinitis pigmentosa
RP	retrograde pyelogram
RP	rhinopharyngitis
Rp.	recipe (L); take (Rx)
R-1-P	ribose-1-phosphate
R-5-P	ribose-5-phosphate
RPA	Renal Physicians' Association (USA)
RPA	right pulmonary artery
RPAV	right pulmonary artery volume
RPCF	Reiter protein complement fixation (test)
RPD *(anat)*	right posterior descending (artery), ramus interventricularis posterior (= R.i.p., RIVP)
RPE	ratings of perceived exertion
RPE	resonance paramagnétique électronique (F); electron spin resonance (= ESR)
RPE	retinal pigment epithelial cells
RPEP	right ventricular pre-ejection period
RPF	relaxed pelvic floor
RPF	renal plasma flow
RPF	retroperitoneal fibrosis
RPG	Radiation Protection Guide
RPG	réflexe psycho-galvanique (F); psychogalvanic reflex
R.Ph.	Registered Pharmacist
RPHA	reverse passive hemagglutination
RP index	respiratory/pulse index
RPL *(rad)*	radiophotoluminescence
R.p.l.d.	ramus posterolateralis dexter

225

R.p.l.s.	ramus posterolateralis sinister	RRL	Registered Record Librarian
RPM	repetitive pulse method	RRM	rhino-rheomanometry
RPM	retropulsive petit mal	rRNA,	ribosomal ribonucleic acid
rpm	revolutions per minute	rRNS	
RPMI	Roswell Park Memorial Institute	RRP	relative refractory period
RPO	right posterior oblique (position)	RRT	resazurin reduction time
RPP	retropubic prostatectomy	RS	rauwolfia serpentina
RPP *(card)*	rate-pressure product	RS	reading of standard (cp. RU)
RPP	renal perfusion pressure	RS	recipient's serum
RPP	retropneumoperitoneum	RS	reinforcing stimulus
RPPL	right posterior pulmonic leaflet	RS	resorcinol sulfur
		RS	Reye's syndrome
RPPR	red cell percursor production rate	RS	right septal border (in the echocardiogram)
RPR	radius periosteal reflex (=BPR)	RS	Ringer's solution
		Rs	resolution of separation (electrophoresis)
RPRC test	rapid plasma reagin card test	r.s.	renovetur semel (L); to be repeated once (Rx)
RPR test	rapid plasma reagin test		
RPS	renal pressor substance	R/S	reaction/stimulus ratio
RPS	repetitive pulse sequence	RSA	rabbit serum albumin
RPS *(psych)*	Rockland-Pollin Scale	RSA	relative specific radioactivity
rps	rotations (revolutions) per second	RSA	respiratory syncytial agents, RS-viruses
R.P.T.	Registered Physical Therapist	RSA *(obst)*	right sacro-anterior (position of fetus)
RPV	right portal vein	R.s.a.	ramus septalis anterior
RQ	recovery quotient	RSB	Rechtsschenkelblock (G); right bundle branch block (=RBBB)
RQ	respiratory quotient		
RR	radiation response		
RR	recovery room	RSB *(mil)*	Regimental Stretcher Bearer
RR	respiratory rate		
RR	Riva-Rocci (sphygmomanometer)	RSC	Reed-Sternberg cells
		RScA *(obst)*	right scapulo-anterior (position of fetus)
Rr. *(anat)*	rami (L); branches	R.S.C.N.	Registered Sick Children's Nurse
R+R	rate and rhythm (of pulse)		
RRA	radioreceptor assay	RScP *(obst)*	right scapulo-posterior (position of fetus)
RRC	routine respiratory care		
RRC	Royal Red Cross	RS dissociation	rough-smooth dissociation
RRE *(ophth)*	regular, round and equal (pupils)		
RRF	radionuclide regurgitant fraction	RSIVP	rapid sequence intravenous pyelogram

RSL *(obst)*	right sacro-lateral (position of fetus)	RT	recovery time
RSM	Royal Society of Medicine (UK)	RT	recreational therapy
		RT	rectal temperature
RSMT	radioselenium methionine test	RT	reduction time
		RT *(gen)*	resistance transfer
RSNA	Radiological Society of North America (USA)	RT	respiratory therapy
		RT	retransfusion
RSNRT	relative sinus node recovery time	RT	reverse transcriptase
		RT	room temperature
RSO	Resident Surgical Officer	R_T	total resistance (of the lungs)
RSP	receptor-specific protein		
RSP *(obst)*	right sacro-posterior (position of fetus)	R.T.	Registered Technician
		RTA	renal tubular acidosis
R.s.p.	ramus septalis posterior	RTA	road traffic accident
RSPCA	Royal Society for the Protection and Care of Animals	RTB	radio-iodine labelled toluidine blue
		RTBS	real-time B-scan
RSPH	Royal Society for the Promotion of Health	RTC	return to clinic
		RTD	routine test dilution
RSPK	recurrent spontaneous psychokinesis	R_{Te}	total expiratory resistance
		RTF *(gen)*	resistance transfer factor
RSR	regular sinus rhythm	R_{Ti}	total inspiratory resistance
RSS *(stat)*	relative score sums	RTL *(rad)*	radiothermoluminescence
RSSE	Russian spring-summer encephalitis	R.T.N.	Registered Technician – Nuclear Medicine
RST	radiosensitivity testing	RTOG	Radiation Therapy Oncology Group
RST	reticulospinal tract		
RST *(obst)*	right sacro-transverse (position of fetus)	rt-PA	recombinant tissue-type plasminogen activator
RSV *(card)*	relative stroke volume	RTPCFR	Reiter treponema protein complement fixation reaction
RSV	Rous sarcoma virus		
RSVC	right superior vena cava	RTR	Recreational Therapist Registered
RSVI	regurgitant stroke volume index	RTR	red blood cell turnover rate
RS-viruses	respiratory-syncytial viruses (= RSA, CCA)	R.T.R.	Registered Technologist Radiographer
RSVT	recurrent supraventricular tachycardia	RTS	radiotelemetric system
RSWI	right ventricular stroke work index	RT_3U	triiodothyronine (T_3) resin uptake
RT	radio-isotope technique	RU	rat unit
RT	radiotherapy	RU	reading of unknown (cp. RS)
RT	radium therapy		
RT	reaction time	RU	roentgen unit
RT	reading test	Ru	ribulose (= Ribu)
RT	recirculation time	RUE	right upper extremity

RUI	Royal University of Ireland	RVEF	right ventricular ejection fraction
RUL	right upper lid	RVERP	right ventricular effective refractory period
RUL	right upper lobe (of the lung)	RVESL	right ventricular end-systolic fiber length
RUO	right ureteral orifice		
RUOQ	right upper outer quadrant	RVESV	right ventricular end-systolic volume
Ru-5-P	ribulose-5-phosphate		
Ru-1,5-P$_2$	ribulose-1,5-diphosphate	RVET	right ventricular ejection time
RUPV	right upper pulmonary vein		
		RVF	Rift Valley fever
RUQ	right upper quadrant	RVG	radionuclide ventriculography
RV	rat virus		
RV	regurgitant volume	RVG	renovasography
RV	reserve volume	RVH	right ventricular hypertrophy
RV	residual volume		
RV	right ventricle	RVI	right ventricular infarction
RV	rubella vaccine	RVICT	right ventricular isovolumic contraction time
RVA	renal vascular resistance		
RVA	résistance des voies aériennes (F); airway resistance	RVLG	right ventrolateral gluteal
		RVMAP	right ventricular monophasic action potential
RVA(E)	right ventricular apical (electrocardiogram)	RVMWI	right ventricular minute work index
RVAC	retrograde ventriculo-atrial conduction	RVO	relaxed vaginal outlet (= RPF)
RVAW	right ventricular anterior wall	RVO	Regional Veterinary Officer
RVC	relative velocity of contraction	RVOT	right ventricular outflow tract
RVCD	right ventricular conduction defect	RVOTO	right ventricular outflow tract obstruction
RVD	relative vertebral density	RVP	right ventricular pressure
RVD	renovascular disease	RVPC	right ventricular premature contraction
RVD	right ventricular diameter		
RVD	right ventricular dysplasia	RVPD	repetitive ventricular premature depolarization
R.v.d.	ramus ventricularis dexter		
RVE	right ventricular enlargement	RVPEP	right ventricular pre-ejection period
RVEDD	right ventricular end-diastolic diameter	RVR	renal vascular resistance
		RVR	repetitive ventricular response
RVEDL	right ventricular end-diastolic fiber length		
		RVRA	renal venous renin activity
RVEDP	right ventricular end-diastolic pressure	RVRT	repetitive ventricular response threshold
RVEDV	right ventricular end-diastolic volume	RVS	relative value scale
		RVS	reported visual sensation

RVSP	right ventricular systolic pressure
RVSTI	right ventricular systolic time intervals
RVSV	right ventricular stroke volume
RVSV	right ventricular systolic volume
RVSWI	right ventricular stroke work index (= RSWI)
RVT	renal venous thrombosis
RVV	right ventricular volume
RVWT	right ventricular wall thickness
RW	réaction de Wassermann (F); Wassermann reaction (= WaR)
RWM *(card)*	regional wall motion
RW-test	Rideal-Walker test
Rx	(symbol for) prescription

S

S *(anat)*	sacral (segment)
S	saline
S	saturation
S	scale
S	sensation
S	septum
S	serum
S *(pharm)*	signa (L); mark, label (Rx)
S	single
S	sinus
S *(bact)*	smooth
S	soluble
S	sound
S	substrate
S	Svedberg unit
S	syndrome
S	synthesis
s	scruple
s	second (= sec)
s	sedimentation constant

s *(gen)*	selection coefficient
s	semis (L); half
s	sinister (L); left (= sin.)
s *(phys)*	spherical (= sph.)
s *(gen)*	stem line
s *(chem)*	symmetric isomer
s.	sive, seu (L); or
SA	salicylamide
SA	salicylic acid
SA	sarcoma
SA	serum albumin
SA	sinoatrial
SA	sinus arrhythmia
SA	Society of Apothecaries (UK) (= SOA)
SA *(chem)*	soluble in alkaline solution
SA	spatial average
SA	specific activity
SA	sulfadiazine
SA	sulfanilamide
SA	surface area
SA *(pharm)*	sustained action
s.a.	secundum artem (L); according to the art
s.-a.	semi-automatic
S + A	sugar and acetone
SAA	sinoatrial arrhythmia
SAA	Society for Applied Anthropology
SAAT	serum aspartate amino-transferase (= SGOT)
SAB	Society of American Bacteriologists
SAB	subarachnoidal bleeding (= SAH)
SA block	sinoatrial block
SABP	systemic arterial blood pressure
SABP	systolic arterial blood pressure (= SAP)
SABS	South African Bureau of Standards
SAC	sérum antiréticulaire-cytotoxique (F); antireticular cytotoxic serum (= ACS, ARES, RAS, SARC)

SAC	Society for Analytical Chemistry	SAJ	sinoatrial junction
SACE	serum angiotensin converting enzyme	SAKK	Schweizerische Arbeitsgruppe für Klinische Krebsforschung (G); Swiss Working Group for Clinical Cancer Research
SACH	Small Animal Care Hospital		
SACT	sinoatrial conduction time	SAL	serum antilymphocytes
SAD	seasonal affective disorder	SAL	signal-averaged lead
SAD	small airway disease	s.a.l.	secundum artis leges (L); according to the rules of the art
SAD	sudden (coronary) artery death		
SAD	sugar, acetone, diacetic acid (test)	S-ALAT	serum alanine aminotransferase (= GPT, SGPT)
SADA	serum adenosine desaminase	Salm.	Salmonella
SADC	succinyl amino-dodecyl cellulose	SALP	signal-averaged late potentials
SAE	surface averaging electrogram	SAM	S-adenosyl-L-methionine
		SAM	scanning acoustic microscope
SAF	scrapie-associated fibrils	SAM	sex arousal mechanism
SAF	spinal anterior flexion	SAM	systolic anterior movement (of mitral valve)
SAFA	soluble antigen fluorescent antibody (test)	SAMA	serum agar measuring aid
SAFT	Societé des Accumulateurs Fixes et de Traction (pacemaker battery)	SAMA	Student American Medical Association
SAFUR	Scottish Automated Follow-up Register Group	SAMI	serum agar measuring integrator
SAG	saline-adenine-glucose (medium)	SAMI	socially acceptable monitoring instrument
SAG	Swiss type of agammaglobulinemia	SAMJ	South African Medical Journal (official abbreviation: S. Afr. med. J.)
S-α_2 globulin	slow alpha$_2$ globulin	SAMMI	South African Medical Military Institute (Pretoria)
SAGM	saline-adenine-glucose-mannitol (medium)	SAN	sinoatrial node
SAH	S-adenosyl-L-homocysteine	SANA	sinoatrial node automaticity
SAH	subarachnoidal hemorrhage	SANRT	sinoatrial node recovery time
SAHC	succinyl aminohexyl cellulose	S-antigen	soluble antigen
		SAP	subsidiary atrial pacemaker
SAI	sulfanilaminoimidazole	SAP	systemic arterial pressure
SAIB	sucrose acetate isobutyrate	SAP	systolic arterial pressure (= SABP)
SAICAR	succino-5-amino-4-imidazole carboxamide ribotide	SAPS	Simplified Acute Physiological Score
SAIDS	simian AIDS		

SAQ	self-administered question-naire	sat.sol.	saturated solution
SAR	search and rescue	SATT	sérum antitétanique (F); tetanus serum
SAR *(psych)*	sexual attitude reassess-ment	SAU	statistical analysis unit
SAR	specific absorption rate	SAVE	Survival and Ventricular Enlargement Study (to improve outcome of chronic heart failure)
SAR *(dent)*	structure activity relation-ship		
SAR *(psych)*	subordination-authority relation	SAVS	supravalvular aortic steno-sis
SAR	sulfarsphenamine, sulfars-enobenzene	SAX	short axis
SAR	Synthetic Aperture Radar	SB	saddle block
SAR	systemic arteriolar resis-tance	SB	serum bilirubin
		SB	shortness of breath
SARC	sérum antiréticulaire-cyto-toxique (F); antireticular cytotoxic serum (=ACS, ARES, RAS, SAC)	SB	sinus bradycardia
		SB	spontaneous breathing
		SB	standard bicarbonate, alka-line reserve
		SB	standard strain Bryan
SAS *(psych)*	Self-Rating Anxiety Scale	SB	Stanford-Binet (intelli-gence test)
SAS	Society of Applied Spec-troscopy (USA)		
		SB	stillbirth
SAS	Statistical Analysis System (Cary, NC, USA)	sb *(phys)*	stilb
		S.B.	Scientiae Baccalaureus (L); Bachelor of Science
SAS	sterile aqueous suspension		
SAS	subaortic stenosis	SBA *(mil)*	sick bay attendant
SAS	subarachnoidal space	SBA	soybean agglutinin
SAS	sulfasalazine	SBAP	systolic brachial artery pressure
S-ASAT	serum aspartate amino-transferase (=GOT, SGOT)		
		SBE	shortness of breath on exertion
SASOG	South African Society of Obstetricians and Gynae-cologists	SBE	sporadic bovine encepha-lomyelitis
		SBE	subacute bacterial endo-carditis
SASP *(pharm)*	salazosulfapyridine	SBF	small bowel factor
SAT *(psych)*	School Ability Test	SBF	systemic blood flow
SAT	sine acido thymonucleini-co (L); without DNA	SBG	selenite brilliant green
		SBI	soybean inhibitor
SAT	sodium ammonium thio-sulfate	SBI	sterol biosynthesis inhibi-tion (=EBI)
SAT	Standard Anagram Task	SBL	State Bacteriological Labo-ratory (Stockholm/Swe-den)
sat.	saturated		
SATL	sodium ammonium thio-sulfate		
		SBMV	southern bean mosaic virus
SATL	surgical Achilles tendon lengthening	SBNS	Society of British Neuro-logical Surgeons

SBOM	soybean oil meal	SCAT	sheep cell agglutination test (=SBR)
SBP	spontaneous bacterial peritonitis	scat. *(pharm)*	scatula (L); box
SBP	steroid-binding plasma protein	SCB	Société de Chimie Biologique (F); Society of Biochemistry (France)
SBP	suprapubic bladder puncture	SCB	strictly confined to bed
SBP	systolic blood pressure	SCC	Services for Crippled Children
SBPR	systolic blood pressure response	SCC	severe common cold
SBPS	sinubronchopulmonary syndrome	SCC	short-circuit current
SBR	sheep blood cell agglutination reaction (=SCAT)	SCC	squamous cell carcinoma
		SCCK	secretin-cholecystokinin test
SBR	Société Belgique de Radiologie (F); Belgian Society of Radiology	SCCL	small cell carcinoma of the lung
SBR	Society for Biological Rhythm	SCD	sickle cell disease
		SCD	subacute coronary disease
SBR	strict bed rest	SCD	sudden coronary death
SBR	styrene-butadiene rubber	Sc.D.	Scientiae Doctor (L); Doctor of Science
sbt	subtilis	ScDA *(obst)*	scapulo-dextra anterior (position of fetus)
SBTI	soybean trypsin inhibitor		
SC	sacrococcygeal	ScDP *(obst)*	scapulo-dextra posterior (position of fetus)
SC	secretory component		
SC *(obst)*	sectio caesarea (L); cesarian section	SCE	saturated calomel electrode
		SCFA	short-chain fatty acid
SC	self-care	SCG	sodium cromoglycate
SC	semilunar (valve) closure	SChE	serum cholinesterase
SC	serum calcium	S-chromo-some	chromosome with subterminal centromere
SC	service connected		
SC	sex chromatin	SCI	Science Citation Index
SC	short circuit	SCI	Science of Creative Intelligence
SC	sickle cell		
SC	silicone coated	SCI *(psych)*	Structured Clinical Interview
SC	stimulus, conditioned		
SC	subclavian artery	SCI	Swedish Carnegie Institute (Stockholm)
SC	sugar coated		
Sc	scanner	SCID	severe combined immune deficiency
sc, s.c.	subcutaneous		
SCA	sickle cell anemia	SCIPP	sacrococcygeal to inferior pubic point
SCA	single channel analyzer		
SCA	sperm-coating antigen	SCK	serum creatine kinase
SCAD	suspected coronary artery disease	SCKT	secretin-cholecystokinin test
		SCL	scleroderma
SCAT *(psych)*	School and College Ability Test	SCL	shortest cycle length

SCL	symptom check list
ScLA *(obst)*	scapulo-laeva anterior (position of fetus)
ScLP *(obst)*	scapulo-laeva posterior (position of fetus)
SCM	splenius cervicis muscle
S.C.M.	State Certified Midwife
SCMC	spontaneous cell-mediated cytotoxicity
SCMC	spontaneous cytotoxicity (of normal human lympho-cytes) against a human melanoma cell line
SCMC test	sperm cervical mucus con-tact test
Scop.	scopolamine
SCOR	Specialized Center of Research (San Diego/ USA)
Scot. *(ophth)*	scotoma
SCP	secondary chronic polyar-thritis
SCP	single cell protein
SCP	spinal cord protein
SCP	supernormal conduction period
scp	spherical candle power
SCPPV	synchronized continuous positive pressure ventila-tion
SCR	Society for Clinical Research
scr	scruple
SCRAP	Simple Complex Reaction-Time Apparatus
SCS	Society of Clinical Sur-gery
SCT	serial computerized tomog-raphy
SCT	staphylococci clumping test
SCT	sugar-coated tablet
SCTZ	5-(2-chlorethyl)-4-methyl-thiazole
SCU	Special Care Unit
SCUBA	self-contained underwater breathing apparatus
scuPA	single-chain urokinase plasminogen activator
SCUR	Society for Cutaneous Ultrastructure Research
SCV	simultaneous compression and ventilation (in cardio-pulmonary resuscitation)
SCV *(bact)*	smooth, capsulated, viru-lent
SCZ *(card)*	secondary concealment zone
SD	scleroderma (=SCL)
SD	senile dementia
SD	septal defect
SD	serological determinant
SD	short-term dialysis
SD *(rad)*	skin dose
SD	sphincter dilatation
SD	spontaneous delivery
SD *(stat)*	standard deviation
SD	streptodornase, streptococ-cal deoxyribonuclease
SD *(card)*	stroke dimension
SD	subclinical diabetes
SD	sudden death
SD *(psych)*	systematic desensitization
SD	systolic discharge
SD	systole duration
Sd *(psych)*	stimulus drive
SDA *(obst)*	sacro-dextra anterior (posi-tion of fetus)
SDA	semihydro-ascorbate
SDA	specially denatured alco-hol
SDA	specific dynamic action
SDA	succinate dehydrogenase activity
SD-antigens	serologically defined anti-gens
SDAT	senile dementia of Alzhei-mer type (also: ATSD)
SDB	selective decontamination of the bowels
SDBP	supine diastolic blood pressure
SDC	succinyl dicholine, suxa-methonium

SDE	specific dynamic effect (=SDA)	SEA	sheep erythrocyte agglutination
SDF	slow death factor	SEA *(physiol)*	spontaneous electrical activity
SDH	L-serine dehydratase		
SDH	sorbitol dehydrogenase (now: iditole dehydrogenase)	SEAS	sympathetic-ergotropic-adrenergic system
		SEAT	sheep erythrocyte agglutination test (=SBR, SCAT)
SDH	subdural hematoma		
SDH	succinate dehydrogenase	SEBM	Society of Experimental Biology and Medicine (UK)
SDI	selective dissemination of information		
SDP *(obst)*	sacro-dextra posterior (position of fetus)	SEC	secondary electron conduction
SDP	seduheptulose diphosphate	SEC *(pharm)*	soft elastic capsules
SDP	slow diastolic depolarization	sec.	secondary
		sec	second(s) (=s)
SDS	School Dental Service	SED *(rad)*	skin erythema dose
SDS *(psych)*	Self-Rating Depression Scale	SEEG	stereoelectroencephalogram
SDS	simple descriptive scale	SEER	Surveillance, Epidemiology, and End Results (program in the USA for testicular cancer)
SDS	sodium dodecyl sulfate		
SDS	Specific Diagnosis Service		
SDS	Symptoms of Depression Scale		
		SEF	sodium excreting factor, aldosterone
SDSE	sodium dodecyl sulfate electrophoresis		
SDS-PAGE	sodium dodecyl sulfate polyacrylamide gel electrophoresis	SEG	Schweizerische Entomologische Gesellschaft (G); Swiss Entomological Society
SD spike	soma-dendritic spike (of a nerve cell)		
		SEG	sonoencephalogram, echoencephalogram
SDT *(obst)*	sacro-dextra transversa (position of fetus)	segs	segmented neutrophils
SDZ	sulfadiazine	SEH	Société Européenne d'Hématologie (F); Sociedad Europea de Hematologia (S); European Society of Hematology
SE	saline enema		
SE	sanitary engineering		
SE *(imm)*	Schutzeinheit (G); protective unit		
		^{75}SeHCAT	^{75}seleno-homocholic acid taurin (retention test)
SE *(anat)*	sphenoethmoidal (suture)		
SE	spherical equivalent	SEK	Sektion Experimentelle Krebsforschung (G); Section for Experimental Cancer Research (of the German Cancer Society)
SE *(rad)*	spin echo		
SE	stage of exhaustion		
SE *(stat)*	standard error		
SE	staphylococcal extract		
SE	sulfoethyl	SEM	scanning electron microscope
SE	systemic lupus erythematosus (=LED, SLE)		
		SEM	standard error of the mean

SEM	systolic ejection murmur	SF	shipping fever (a type of rhinopharyngobronchitis) (cp. SF4 virus)
SEMI	subendocardial myocardial infarction		
SEN	State Enrolled Nurse	SF *(card)*	shortening fraction
SENS	sensitivity test	SF *(bact)*	sodium azide fecal
SEP	Société Européenne de Pneumologie (F); European Society of Pneumology (=ESP)	SF	spinal fluid
		SF	Streptococcus faecalis
		SF	sulfation factor
		SF	synovial fluid
SEP	somatosensory evoked potential (=SSEP)	Sf	Svedberg flotation (unit)
		s.f.	sub finem (L); at the end
SEP	Symposium of European Pedopsychiatrists	SFB	superior fascicular block
		SFC	spinal fluid count
SEP	systolic ejection period	s.f.c.a.	sub finem coquendi adde (L); add at the end of boiling (Rx)
SEPCR	Societas Europaea Physiologiae Clinicae Respiratoriae (L); European Society of Clinical Respiratory Physiology		
		SFCI	Société Française de Chirurgie Infantile (F); French Society of Surgery in Children
SE-PV	polyoma virus detected by Stewart and Eddy	SFEA	Société Française d'Experimentation Animale (F); French Society of Experiments in Animals
seq.luce	sequenti luce (L); the following day		
SER	smooth endoplasmic reticulum	SFH	stroma-free hemolysate
		SFL	Sexual Freedom League
SER	subendocardial resection	SFl	synovial fluid
SER	systolic ejection rate	SFMC	soluble fibrin monomer complex
Ser	serine		
ser.	series, serial	SFO	Société Française d'Ophtalmologie (F); French Society of Ophthalmology (Paris)
SERP	segmental early relaxation phenomenon		
SES	socioeconomic status		
SES	supraventricular extrasystole (=SVES)	SFO *(anat)*	subfornical organ
		S-form *(bact)*	smooth form
SETD	sulfaethyl thiadiazole	SFP *(card)*	slow filling phase
SETS	staphylogenic epidermolytic toxic syndrome	SFP *(rad)*	steady-state free precession (=SSFP)
SEV	surface epithelial volume	SFR	stroke with full recovery
SEVM	systolic endocardial velocity maximum	SF solution	saponide-ferricyanide solution
SEZ	sulfethoxypyridazine	SFT	Sabin-Feldman test
SF	salt free	SFV	Semliki forest virus
SF	scarlet fever	SF4 virus	shipping fever virus (=parainfluenza virus type 3)
SF	seminal fluid		
SF	serum fibrinogen		

SFW	shell fragment wound	SGP	Society of General Physiologists
SFW	slow filling wave (in the apical cardiogram)	SGPT	serum glutamic pyruvic transaminase
SG	secretory granula	SGR	Sachs-Georgi reaction
SG	serum glycoside	SGRNM	Schweizerische Gesellschaft für Radiologie und Nuklearmedizin (G); Swiss Society of Radiology and Nuclear Medicine
SG (card)	spatial ventricular gradient		
SG	specific gravity		
SG	sphygmogram		
SG	structural gene		
SG	sulfaguanidine		
S-G	Sachs-Georgi (reaction)	SGRS (psych)	Stockton Geriatric Rating Scale
S.G.	Surgeon General		
SGA (obst)	small for gestational age	SGTT	steroid glucose tolerance test
SGG	Schweizerische Gesellschaft für Gynäkologie (G); Swiss Society of Gynecology	SGUB	Schweizerische Gesellschaft für Unfallmedizin und Berufskrankheiten (G); Swiss Society of Traumatology and Occupational Diseases
SGH	Schweizerische Gesellschaft für Hämatologie (G); Swiss Society of Hematology		
SGIM	Schweizerische Gesellschaft für Innere Medizin (G); Swiss Society of Internal Medicine	SGUMB	Schweizerische Gesellschaft für Ultraschall in der Medizin und Biologie (G); Swiss Society of Ultrasound in Medicine and Biology
SGK	Schweizerische Gesellschaft für Kardiologie (G); Swiss Society of Cardiolgy	SGV	salivary gland virus
		SGV	selective gastric vagotomy
SGKCH	Schweizerische Gesellschaft für Klinische Chemie (G); Swiss Society of Clinical Chemistry	SGXT	supine graded exercise testing
		SH	serum hepatitis
		SH	social history
SGMG	Schweizerische Gesellschaft für Medizinische Genetik (G); Swiss Society of Medical Genetics	SH	somatotrop(h)ic hormone (=STH)
		SH (chem)	sulfhydryl
		SH	surgical history
SGN	secondary chronic glomerulonephritis	Sh.	Shigella (=Shig.)
		Sh (vet)	sheep
SGO	Society of Gynecological Oncology	S+H	speech and hearing
		SHA (otol)	sinusoidal harmonic acceleration
SGO	Surgeon-General's Office	SH-Ag	serum hepatitis antigen, Australia antigen
SGOT	serum glutamic-oxalacetic transaminase		
		SHB (card)	supra-His block
SGP	Schweizerische Gesellschaft für Phlebologie (G); Swiss Society of Phlebology	SHBD	serum hydroxybutyrate dehydrogenase

236

SHBE	surface His bundle electrogram	SI	shock index
SHBG	sex hormone binding globulin	SI	soluble insulin
		SI *(imm)*	staining intensity
SHCO	sulfated hydrogenated castor oil	SI	stroke index
		SI	subendocardial ischemia
SHD	sudden heart death	SI *(dent)*	summa incisivorum
SHDI	supraoptical hypophyseal diabetes insipidus	SI	sympathetic inhibition
		SI	Système Internationale
SHE	standard hydrogen electrode		d'Unités (F); International System of Measurement and Units
SHE	super high frequency	SIA	Société Internationale
SHEP	Systolic Hypertension in the Elderly Program (USA)		d'Acupuncture (F); International Society of Acupuncture
SHG	scatter histogram		
SHG diet	Sauerbruch-Hermannsdorfer-Gerson diet (in Tbc)	SIA	synalbumin-insulin antagonism
SHHD	Scottish Home and Health Department	SIADH	syndrome of inappropriate ADH-secretion
Shig.	Shigella (=Sh.)	SIAS	severe intra-abdominal sepsis
SHML	sinus histiocytosis with massive lymphadenopathy	SIB	Société Internationale de Biometrie (F); International Society of Biometry
SHMO	Senior Hospital Medical Officer	SIC	Société Internationale de Cardiologie (F); Internationale Society of Cardiology
SHN	subacute hepatic necrosis		
SHO	Senior Health Officer		
SHO	Senior House Officer	SIC	Société Internationale de Chirurgie (F); International Society of Surgery
SHR	spontaneously hypertensive rats		
SHRT	solufibrin hirudine reaction test	sicc.	siccus, siccatus (L); dry, dried
SHS	supine hypotensive syndrome	SICOT	Société Internationale de Chirugie, Orthopédie et Traumatologie (F); Society of Surgery, Orthopedics, and Traumatology
SHT *(gyn)*	Sims-Huhner test		
SH virus	serum hepatitis virus, hepatitis B virus (HBV)		
ShW *(phys)*	short wave	SID	Society for Investigative Dermatology
S-hypercorticism	Cushing's syndrome I (S=sugar hormone)		
		s.i.d.	semel in die (L); once daily (Rx)
SI	sacroiliac		
SI	safety index	SIDA	syndrôme d'immunodéficit acquis (F); síndroma de inmunodeficiencia adquirida (S); AIDS
SI	saline infusion		
SI	saturation index		
SI	selectivity index		
SI	septum interventriculare		
SI	serum iron		

SIDH	Société Internationale pour les Droits de l'Homme (F); Sociedad Internacional para los Derechos Humanos (S); International Society for Human Rights (=IGFM, ISHR)
SIDS	sudden infant death syndrome
SIECUS	Sex Information and Education Council of the United States
SIF	serum inhibitory factor
SIF	somatotrop(h)in release-inhibiting factor (=SIH, SRIF, SRIH)
SIg	standard immunoglobulin
sig.	signa, signetur (L); mark, label (Rx)
SIgA	secretory active immunoglobulin A
SIGE	Société Internationale de Gastro-Entérologie (F); Sociedad Internacional de Gastro-Enterología (S); International Society of Gastroenterology
sig.n.pr.	signa nomine proprio (L); label with the correct name (Rx)
SIH	Société Internationale d'Hématologie (F); International Society of Hematology
SIH	somatotrop(h)in release-inhibiting hormone (=SIF, SRIF, SRIH)
SII	Science Impact Index (=SCI)
SIL	Société Internationale de la Lèpre (F); International Leprosy Society
SIL	Société Internationale de Limnologie (F); International Society of Limnology

SIL	speech interference level;
SILA	suppressible insulin-like activity
SIM	Society of Industrial Microbiology
SIMA	secondary ion microanalysis
SIMG	Société Internationale des Médecins Generales (F); International Society of General Practitioners
SIMI	Società Italiana di Medicina Interna; Italian Society of Internal Medicine
SIMS	secondary ion mass spectrometry
SIMV	synchronized intermittent mandatory ventilation
sin.	sinister (L); left
SINA	N-morpholino-N-nitroso-amino-acetonitrile
SINE	Subjective Index of Nervous Excitation States
SINH	streptomycin isonicotinic acid hydrazide, streptoniazide
si non val.	si non valeat (L); if not sufficient (Rx)
SINR	Swiss Institute of Nuclear Research
SIOP	Société Internationale d'Oncologie Pédiatrique (F); International Society of Pediatric Oncology
si op.sit	si opus sit (L); if necessary
SIP	Sociedad Interamericana de Psicología (S); Interamerican Society of Psychology
SIPE	Société Internationale de Psychopathologie de l'Expression (F); International Society of Psychopathology of Expression

SIPPV	synchronized intermittent positive pressure ventilation	SIW	self-inflicted wound
		SJA	St. Jude aortic valve prosthesis
SIPRI	Stockholm International Peace Research Institute	SJP	small junction potentials
		SJMP *(card)*	St. Jude medical prosthesis
Sir.	sirupus (L); syrup	SK	serum kallikrein
SIRA	Scientific Instrument Research Association (UK)	SK	streptokinase
		Sk-Ag	skin antigen
SIRMN	Società Italiana di Radiologia e Medicina Nucleare; Italian Society of Radiology and Nuclear Medicine	SKAT	Sex Knowledge and Aptitude Test
		SKF	Smith Kline and French
		SKI	Schweizerisches Krankenhausinstitut (G); Swiss Hospital Institute
SIRS	soluble immune response suppressor		
		SKI	Sloan-Kettering Institute (New York)
SIRT	simultaneous iterative reconstruction technique		
		SL	sarcolysin
SIS	scintigraphic ischemic score	SL *(otol)*	sensation level
		SL	Shepherd-Linn (unit)
SIS	sterile injectable suspension	SL	sodium lactate
		SL	spironolactone
SISI *(otol)*	short increment sensitivity index	SL	streptolysin
		SL	sympatholytic (agent)
SiSV	simian sarcoma virus	s.l.	secundum legem (L); according to the rules
SIT	Stanford Intelligence Test (=SB)		
		s.l.	sublingual
SITEMS	Société Internationale de Traumatologie et de Médecine Sport d'Hiver (F); International Society of Traumatology and Medicine in Winter Sports	SLA *(obst)*	sacro-laeva anterior (position of fetus)
		SLA	serum lipase activity
		SLAM	scanning laser acoustic microscope
		SLB	short leg brace
SITS	Société Internationale de Transfusion Sanguine (F); International Society for Blood Transfusion	SLD, SLDH	serum lactate dehydrogenase
		SLE	St. Louis encephalitis
		SLE	systemic lupus erythematosus
SIU	Société Internationale d'Urologie (F); Sociedad Internacional de Urología (S); International Society of Urology	S-line *(dent)*	Steiner line
		SLM	sound level meter
		SLP *(obst)*	sacro-laeva posterior (position of fetus)
SIV	septum interventriculare	SLR	Streptococcus lactis R
SIV	simian immune deficiency virus	SLS	salt-loosing syndrome
		SLS	segment long-spacing (collagen fibers)
si vir.perm.	si vires permittant (L); if strength permits	SLS	Stein-Leventhal syndrome
SIVT	septal idiopathic ventricular tachycardia	SLS	streptolysin S

SLT *(obst)*	sacro-laeva transversa (position of fetus)	SMI	Senior Medical Investigator
SLT *(lab)*	serum lability tests	SMI	silent myocardial ischemia (or infarction)
SLT	single load test		
SM	simple mastectomy	SMI	sustained maximum inspiration
SM	somatomedin		
SM	spectrometry	SMJ	Society of Medical Jurisprudence (USA)
SM	stereomicroscope		
SM	streptomycin	SMMV	synchronized mandatory minute ventilation
SM	sustained medication		
SM	sympathomimetic (agent)	SMO	Medical Officer of Schools
SM	systolic murmur	SMO *(mil)*	Senior Medical Officer
S.M.	Scientiae Magister (L); Master of Science	SMOG	(artificial word made of) "smoke" and "fog"
SMA	sequential multiple analysis	SMOH	Society of Medical Officers of Health
SMA	smooth muscle antibody	SMOH	Senior Medical Officer of Health
SMA	surface modulating assembly		
		SMON	subacute myelo-optic neuropathy (Japan)
SMAc	stabilized metabolic acidosis	SMOP	sulfamethoxypyrazine (=SMP)
SMAF	smooth muscle activating factor	SMoRV	squirrel monkey retrovirus
SMAF	specific macrophage arming factor	SMP	sulfamethoxypyrazine (=SMOP)
SMB	standard mineral base (medium)	SMR	standard mortality rate
		SMR	submucous resection
SMBG	self-monitoring of blood glucose	SMS	serial myocardial scintigram (=MS)
SMC	Scientific Manpower Commission	SMS	Service Médico-Social (F); Medical Social Service
SMC	sensorimotor cortex	SMS	somnolent metabolic state
SMC	smooth muscle cell	SMSA	Standard Metropolitan Statistical Areas (USA)
SMC	succinyl monocholine		
SMD	submanubrial dullness	SMV	synchronized mandatory ventilation
SMD	sulfamethyldiazine		
SMDC	sodium-N-methyl dithio-carbamate	SMZ	sulfamethoxazole
		SN	serum neutralization
S-M change	change from "smooth" to "mucous" form (in bacterial cultures)	SN	sinus node
		SN	Staff Nurse
		SN	Student Nurse
		SN	subnormal
SMER	Société Médicale Internationale d'Endoscopie et de Radio-Cinématographie (F); International Medical Society of Endoscopy and Cinematoradiography	SN	substantia nigra
		s.n.	secundum naturam (L); according to nature
		s.n.	suo nomine (L); under the patient's own name

SNA	système nerveux autonome (F); autonomic nervous system (=ANS)
SNAGG	serum normal agglutinant
SNC	système nerveux central (F); central nervous system (=CNS)
SNCP *(card)*	supernormal conduction period
SND	single needle dialysis
SNDO	Standard Nomenclature of Diseases and Operations (USA)
SNE	subacute necrotizing encephalomyelopathy
SNF	Skilled Nursing Facililty
SNFF	single nephron filtration fraction
SNFG	Société Nationale Française de Gastroenterologie; French National Society of Gastroenterolgy
SNGFR	single nephron glomerular filtration rate
SNIPA	seronegative inflammatory polyarthritis
SNM	Society of Nuclear Medicine (USA)
SNMER	systolic normalized mean ejection rate
SNMT	Society of Nuclear Medicine Technologists
SNOP	Systematized Nomenclature of Pathology (CAP)
SNP	seronegative polyneuropathy
SNP	sodium nitroprusside
SNRT *(card)*	sinus node recovery time (=SRT)
SNS	Society of Neurological Surgeons
SNS	sympathetic nervous system
SNV	Schweizerische Normen-Vereinigung (G); Swiss Union of Standards
SNV	système nerveux vegetatif (F); autonomous nervous system (=ANS, SNA)
SO	salpingo-oophorectomy
SO	spheno-occipital
SO	supraoptic
SOAP *(clin)*	subjective and objective assessment and plan
SOB	shortness of breath
SOBELPHA	Société Belge de Pharmacologie (F); Belgian Society of Pharmacology
SOBEVECO	Société Ophthalmologique Belge des Vers de Contact (F); Belgian Ophthalmological Society for Contact Lenses
Soc.Sec.	Social Security
SOD	superoxide dismutase
SODH	sorbitol dehydrogenase
SOG	Schweizerische Ophthalmologische Gesellschaft (G); Swiss Ophthalmological Society
SOG	Società Ostetrica e Ginecologia (I); Society of Obstetrics and Gynecology (Italy)
SOI	systolic output index
SOL	space-occupying lesion
Sol.	solution
Sol.aq.	solutio aquosa (L); aqueous solution
SOLAS	Scientific Organization of Laboratory Animal Societies
solv.	solve (L); dissolve (Rx)
SOLVD	Studies of Left Ventricular Dysfunction (to test the effect of ACE inhibition)
SOM	secretory otitis media
SOM	Society of Occupational Medicine (UK)
SOMOS	Society of Military Orthopedic Surgeons
SON *(psych)*	Snijders-Oomen Non-Verbal Intelligence Test

SON	superior olivary nucleus	SPAF	spontaneous paroxysmal atrial fibrillation
SOP	standard operative procedure	SP$_{AO}$	systolic aortic pressure
SOP	suboccipital puncture	SPAP	systolic pulmonary artery pressure
SOPHE	Society of Public Health Education (USA)	SPC	salicylamide, phenacetin, caffeine
SOPS	somnolent-ophthalmoplegic syndrome	SPC	serum prolactin concentration
s.op.s.	si opus sit (L); if necessary (=s.o.s.)	SPCA	serum prothrombin conversion accelerator, factor VII, proconvertin
SOR	serum opacity reaction		
SOR	Society of Rheology (USA)	SPCA	Society for the Prevention of Cruelty to Animals
sor *(gen)*	short open reading frame		
S-O-R *(psych)*	stimulus-organism-response	SPC cell	sickleform particles containing cell
SorbD	sorbitol dehydrogenase	sp.cd.	spinal cord
SOREM	sleep onset rapid eye movements	SPE	sécrétion pancréatique externe (F); excretory pancreatic function
SOS	"save our souls"		
s.o.s.	si opus sit (L); if necessary (=s.op.s)	Spec.	species (=sp.)
		Spec.	specimen
SOSAI	Springfield Outpatient Symptom and Adjustment Index	spec.	specific
		SPECT	single photon emission computerized tomography
SOTT	synthetic medium old tuberculin trichloroacetic acid precipitated	S-period	synthesis period of DNA (=S-phase)
		SPET	secretin-pancreozymin evocation test (=SPT)
SP	sampling pump		
SP	serum phosphorus	SPF	spectrophotofluorometer
SP	sphingomyelin	SPF	specific pathogen-free (laboratory animals)
SP	summation potential		
SP	subclavian puncture	sp.fl.	spinal fluid
SP	suprapubic	SPG	splenoportography
SP	systolic pressure	sp.gr.	specific pravitiy
Sp.	Spirillum	sph.	spherical
sp.	species	S-phase	synthesis phase of DNA (=S-period)
sp.	spinal		
sp.	spirit	SPI	serum-precipitable iodine
S-7-P	sedulose-7-phosphate	SPI	stroke power index
S-1,7-P$_2$	sedulose-1,7-diphosphate	SPI	serum precipitable iodine
SPA	serum phenylalanine	SPI	Structured Psychological Interview
SPA	single photon absorptiometry		
		SPID	Russian acronym for AIDS
SPA	spondylitis ankylosans, ankylosing spondylitis	SPIH	superimposed pregnancy-induced hypertension
SPA	suprapubic aspiration		
sp.act.	specific activity	Spir.	spirit (=Sp.)

SPK	serum pyruvate kinase	SR	sedimentation rate ($=$ESR)
SPL	serum prolactin level	SR	Senior Registrar
SPL	sound pressure level	SR	sensitization response
SPL	spironolactone	SR	sex ratio
spl.	simplex (L); simple	SR	sigma reaction
SPM	spectinomycin	SR *(card)*	sinus rhytm
SPP *(psych)*	Sexualitiy Preference Profile	SR *(gen)*	sister chromatide reunion
SPP	suprapubic prostatectomy	SR	stage of resistance
SpP *(dent)*	spina plane	SR	stimulus-response
spp.	species	SR	startle reflex (Moro)
SpPn	spontaneous pneumothorax	SR	stomach rumble
		SR	synaptic reaction
SPPS	stable plasma protein solution	SR	systems review
		sr *(phys)*	steradiant
SPR	Society for Pediatric Research (USA)	SRA	Science Research Association
SPR	Society for Psychic Research (UK, USA)	SRA	serum renin activity
		SRA	skin-reactive antigen
SPRINT	Secondary Prevention Reinfarction Nifedipine Trial (conducted in Israel)	SRA	splenorenal anastomosis ($=$SR shunt)
		SRAS *(psych)*	Self-Rating Anxiety Scale
SPRT *(stat)*	Sequential Probability Ratio Test	SR_{aw}	specific airway resistance
SPS	sulfasalazine	SRBC	sheep red blood cells
SPS	sulfite polymyxin sulfadiazine agar	src *(gen)*	sarcoma-inducing oncogen
		SRCA	specific red cell adherence
SPT	secretin-pancreozymin test ($=$SPET)	S-R change	change from "smooth" to "rough" form (in bacterial cultures)
spt.	spirit ($=$Sp., Spir.)	SRCL	sinus rhythm cycle length
SPTI	systolic pressure time index	SRD	specific radiation dose
		SRE *(stat)*	standardized regression effects
SPV	selective proximal vagotomy	SRE	système réticulo-endothelial (F); reticulo-endothelial system ($=$RES)
SPVD	Society for the Prevention of Venereal Diseases (UK)	SRF	salmonella resistance factor
SPV reaction	sulfophosphovanillin reaction	SRF	skin reactive factor
SPZ	sulfinpyrazone	SRF	somatotrop(h)in releasing factor ($=$STH-RF)
SQ	suspension quotient		
sq	subscutaneous ($=$sc, s.c.)	SRFW	Schweizerische Rettungsflugwacht (G); Swiss Rescue Air Service
s.q.	sufficient quantity		
SQUID	superconducting quantum-interference device	SRH	somatotrop(h)in releasing hormone ($=$SRF)
SR	sarcoplasmic reticulum		
SR	secretion rate		

SRH	sulforizine hydrazide	SS	Sézary syndrome
SRH	système réticulo-histiocytaire (F); reticulohistiocytic system (=RHS)	SS	single-stranded (DNA)
		SS	Sjögren's syndrome
		SS	soap suds
SRI	systemic resistance index	SS	sparingly soluble
SRID	simple radial immunodiffusion	SS *(psych)*	standard score
		SS	sterile solution
SRIF	somatotrop(h)in release-inhiting factor (=SIF, SIH, SRIH)	SS	steroid sulfatase
		SS	stimulator substance
		Ss.	subjects
SRIH	somatotrop(h)in release-inhibiting hormone (=SIF, SIH, SRIF)	ss.	semis (L); half
		SSA	skin-sensitizing antibodies
		SSA	Smith surface antigen
SRK	Schweizerisches Rotes Kreuz (G); Swiss Red Cross (=CRS)	SSA	Social Security Act (USA, 1972)
		SSA	Social Security Administration
SRM	spiramycin		
SRM	standard reference material	SS agar	salmonella-shigella agar
SRM	steroroentgenometry	SSB *(derm)*	skin surface biopsy
SRMC	Southern Regional Medical Consortium	SSBH	sex steroid binding hormone
S.R.N.	State Registered Nurse	SSC	sensitized sheep cells
sRNA	soluble ribonucleid acid	SSC	Specialist Short Course (UK)
SR psychology	stimulus response psychology		
		SSCQT	Selective Service College Qualifying Test
SRS	slow reacting substance		
SRS	Social and Rehabilitation Service (USA)	SSCr *(dent)*	stainless steel crown
		SSC test	sensitized sheep cell test
SRS	Swedish Radiological Society	SSD *(rad)*	source-skin distance
		SSD	sulfisomidine
SRSA	slow reacting substance of anaphylaxis	SSE	saline solution enema
		SSE	soap suds enema
SR shunt	splenorenal shunt (=SRA)	SSEA	sensitized sheep erythrocyte agglutination (=SSC test)
SRT *(rad)*	saturation recovery index		
SRT	sedimentation rate test		
SRT	sinus node recovery time (=SNRT)	SSEH	spontaneous spinal epidural hematoma
SRT	speech reception threshold	SSEP	somatosensory evoked potential (=SEP)
SR teeth	solvent resistant (artificial) teeth	SSER	somatosensory evoked reaction
SRV	simian retrovirus	SSF	Society for the Study of Fertility
SS	saline soak		
SS	saliva sample	SSF	supersonic frequency
SS	saturated solution	SSFP *(rad)*	steady-state free precession (=SFP)
SS	securité sociale (F); social security		
SS	serum sickness		

SSKI	saturated solution of potassium iodide
SSLE	subacute sclerosing leukoencephalitis
SSM	superficial spreading melanoma
s.s.n.	signetur suo nomine (L); label with proper name
SSO	Société Suisse d'Odontologie (F); Società Svizzera di Odontologia (I); Swiss Society of Odontology
SSP	salazosulfapyridine
SSP	Shwartzman-Sanarelli phenomenon
SSP	Société Suisse de Pharmacie (F); Swiss Society of Pharmacy
SSP	supersensitive perception
ssp	subspecies
SSPE	subacute sclerosing panencephalitis
SSPG	steady-state plasma glucose
SSPI	steady-state plasma insulin
SSR	sulfide silver reaction
SSS (card)	sick sinus (node) syndrome
SSS	specific soluble substance
SSS	sterile saline soak
sss	stratum super stratum (L); layer on layer
s.st.	sensu strictiori (L); in the strict sense
SS syndrome	saliva-sudoriparous syndrome
SST	somatostatin
SSU	self-service unit
SSV	short saphenous vein
s.s.v.	sub signo veneni (L); under a poison label (Rx)
ST (rad)	scatter tomography
ST	sedimentation time
ST	skin test
ST	slight trace
ST (psych)	standardized test
ST	standard temperature
ST	sulfathiazole

ST	supraventricular tachycardia (= SVT)
ST	surface tension
ST	survival time
St	stat (unit of radioactivity)
St	stoke (unit of viscosity)
St	subtype
st.	stet, stent (L); let it stand (Rx)
STA	secondary tubular acidosis
STA	serotype antigen
STA	serum thrombotic accelerator activity activation product
STA	stearylmethyl ammonium
STA	superficial temporal artery
Staph.	Staphylococcus
STARS	Solar Thermal Aerostat Research Station
Stat.	statistics
stat.	statim (L); immediately (Rx)
stat. (phys)	static
stb	stillborn
STBG	stercobilinogen
STD	sexually transmitted disease
STD	skin test dose
STD	standard test dose
STEM	scanning transmission electron microscopy
STEN	staphylogenic toxic epidermal necrolysis
STH	somatotrop(h)ic hormone
STH-RF	STH-releasing factor
StHS	stabilized human serum
STI	serum trypsin inhibitor
STI	soybean trypsin inhibitor
STI	systolic time interval
STIA	Scientific, Technological, and International Affairs
STIF	soft tissue interstitial fluid
STK, sTK	serum thymidine kinase
STL	swelling, tenderness, limitation
STLV	simian T-cell lymphotropic virus (-I, -III)

STME (card)	symptom-tolerated maximum exercise	SU-NH- (chem)	sulfanilamido-
STNR	symmetrical tonic neck reflex	SUNY	State University of New York (Albany)
STP	serenity-tranquility-peace (action of hallucinogens)	SUP	selective ultraviolet phototherapy
STP	specific tear protein	SUp (gen)	sister union proximal
STP	standard temperature and pressure	sup.	superior
		SUpd (gen)	sister union proximal-distal
STP	sternal puncture	SUPHEPA	N-succinyl-L-phenylalanine-p-nitroanilide
STPD	standard temperature pressure dry	Supp.	suppositories
STPI	Science and Technology Policy Implementation	SUR	serological universal reaction
Str., Strept.	streptococci	SUS	Society of University Surgeons
str.	stroke		
STS	serological (or standard) test for syphilis	SUS	suppressor sensitive
		Susp.	suspension
STS	Society of Thoracic Surgeons (USA)	SUT	systolic upstroke time
		SV	sarcoma virus
STS	Space Transportation System	SV	satellite virus, subvirus
		SV	scalp vein
STT	sensitization test	SV	sedimentation volume
STTI	systolic tension time index	SV	selective vagotomy
		SV	simian virus
STU	skin test unit	SV	single vibrations
S-type (psych)	synesthesia-prone personality	SV	sinus venosus
		SV	snake venom
SU	sensation unit	SV	stroke volume
SU	stress ulcer	s.v.	spiritus vini (L); ethyl alcohol
SU	strontium unit ("sunshine unit")		
		SVA	selective visceral angiography
SU	sulfonylurea		
SU- (chem)	sulfanilyl-	SVA	sinus of Valsalva aneurysm
SUA	serum uric acid	SVA	Statens Veterinärmedicinska Anstalt; State Institute of Veterinary Medicine (Uppsala/Sweden)
SUD (rad)	skin unit dose		
SUD	sudden unexpected death		
SUd (gen)	sister union distal	SVA	supraventricular arrhythmia
SUDH	succinate dehydrogenase		
		S-variant	smooth variant (of bacteria)
SUDI	sudden unexpected death in infancy (= SIDS)		
		SVAS	supravalvular aortic stenosis
SUMC	Stanford University Medical College		
		SVBG	saphenous vein bypass graft
SUN	serum urea nitrogen		

SVC	superior vena cava
SVCS	superior vena cava syndrome
SVD *(card)*	single vessel disease
SVE, SVES	supraventricular extrasystole
SVI	stroke volume index
SVI	slow virus infection
SVPC	supraventricular premature complex (=SVE)
SVR	systemic vascular resistance
SVRI	systemic vascular resistance index
s.v.r.	spiritus vini rectificatus (L); pure alcohol
SVRT	supraventricular re-entry tachycardia
SVT	supraventricular tachycardia
SVWM	segmental ventricular wall motion
SW	Social Worker
SW	stroke work
Sw^a factor	Swann factor, antigen Sw^a
S-wave	systolic wave (of venous pulse)
SWC	sinus wall cell
S/W complex	spike/wave complex (in the EEG)
SWD	short wave diathermy
SWG	silkworm gut
SWI	stroke work index
SWR	serum Wassermann reaction
SWR	sleep-wake rhythm
SWS	slow wave sleep
Sx	symptoms or signs
SXR	sex reversed factor (in mice)
Syn.	synonym
synth.	synthetic
Syr.	syrup
syst.	systemic
syst.	systolic
Sz	seizure

T

T *(phys)*	absolute temperature
T *(ophth)*	ocular tension
T *(gen)*	telocentric chromosome
T *(phys)*	tension
T *(phys)*	tesla (unit of magnetic induction)
T *(chem)*	testosterone
T *(pharm)*	tetracycline
T *(anat)*	thoracic (also: Th)
T *(biochem)*	thymine
T	thyroid
T	topical
T	Torr (Torricelli, measure of pressure)
T	toxicity
T *(gen)*	translocation
T *(imm)*	transplantation
T	transverse
T	tropine
T	tumor
T	type
t *(anat)*	temporal
t *(phys)*	time
t *(phys)*	ton
t *(biochem)*	transfer (e.g. tRNA)
t-	tissue (e.g. t-PA)
T.	Taenia
T. *(anat)*	tuberculum
$T\frac{1}{2}$, $t\frac{1}{2}$	half-life
T_3	triiodothyronin (=TIT)
T_4	tetraiodothyronin, thyroxine (=Thx)
T4, T8	T-cell receptors (=CD4, CD8), used for classification of thymus lymphocytes (T_h, T_s and T_c cells)
TA	Teaching Assistant
TA	temperature axillary
TA	tension artérielle (F); arterial tension (or pressure)
TA	tetracycline antibiotics
TA	thermoanalysis
TA	thermostable antigen

TA	titration acidity	TAF	tumor angiogenesis factor
TA	tolfenamic acid	TAF	tumor antigen factor
TA	tosyl arginine	TAG	Tennessee antigen
TA	toxin-antitoxin	T-agglutinin	Thomsen's agglutinin
TA	transactional analysis	TAH	total abdominal hysterectomy
TA	transaldolase		
TA *(gen)*	transforming agent (=TP)	TAI	thrombocyte aggregation inhibitor
TA	treatment allowance	TAL	triamcinolone
TA *(card)*	tricuspidal area	tal.	talis, tales (L); such ... (Rx)
TA	trophoblastic antigen		
TA	tuberculin A ("alkaline")	TALL	T-cell type acute lymphatic leukemia
T₃A	triiodothyronine acetic acid	TAM	talc adsorption method
T+A	tonsillectomy and adenotomy	TAM	thermo-acidurans agar modified
		TAM	toxoid-antitoxin mixture
TAA	thioacetamide	TAMCHA	trans-AMCHA, p-amino-methyl-cyclohexanecar-boxylic acid, tranexamic acid (=AMCHA)
TAA	tumor-associated antigen		
TAB	therapeutic abortion		
TAB	transabdominal chorion biopsy		
TAB	typhoid-paratyphoid A and B vaccine	TAME	p-tosyl-L-arginine methyl-ester
TABC	typhoid-paratyphoid A, B, and C vaccine	TAMI	transmural anterior myocardial infarction
TABDT	combination vaccine against typhoid fever, paratyphoid fever A and B, diphtheria and tetanus	TAMIS	Telemetric Automated Microbial Idenfication System
		TAN	total ammonia nitrogen
tabs.	tablets	TANS	Territorial Army Nursing Service
TABT	combination vaccine against typhoid fever, paratyphoid fever A and B and tetanus	T-antigen *(imm)*	transplantation antigen
		T-antigen	tumor antigen
TAC	triallylcyanurate	TAO	thrombangitis obliterans
TAC *(anat)*	truncus arteriosus communis	TAO	triacetyl-oleandomycin
		TAP	thiamphenicol
TACE *(pharm)*	tri-p-anisyl-chlorethylene	TAP	transluminal angioplasty
		TAP	triaminopyrimidine
TAF	target aim function	TAPA	tosyl-L-arginine-p-nitrani-lide
TAF	thrombocyte agglutinating factor		
TAF	toxoid-antitoxin floccules (vaccine)	TAPE	temporary atrial pacemaker electrode
TAF	Tuberkulin albumosefrei (G); albumose-free tuberculin	TAPE	tetra-acetate of pentaerythritol
		TAPHA	4-thiaheptane-1,7-diosyl-bis-isopropyl hydrazine

TAPVC	total anomalous pulmonary venous connection
TAPVD	total anomalous pulmonary venous drainage
TAR	tension artérielle rétinienne (F); retinal artery pressure
T-area *(imm)*	thymus-dependent area
TARI	total atrial refractory interval
TART	total apex cardiographic relaxation time
T arthrodesis *(orth)*	arthrodesis of the talocalcaneal joint
T'ase	incorrect for: T'sase
TAST	test-antigen sorbent test
TAT	tetanus antitoxin
TAT *(psych)*	thematic apperception test
TAT	thrombin-antithrombin complex
TAT	toxin-antitoxin
TAT	2-thio-6-azathymine
TAT	tyrosine aminotransferase
tat *(gen)*	transactivation of transcription (i.e. posttranscription), transactivator
TATA	tumor-associated transplantation antigen
TATD	thiamine-(3-ethylmercapto-7-methoxycarbonylheptyl)-disulfide, octothiamine
TA test	thyroid autoprecipitin test
TAVB	total atrioventricular block
TB	tetraphenylborate
TB	thymol blue
TB	toluidine blue
TB	total base
TB	tracheobronchial, tracheobronchitis
TB	tubercle bacillus (=TBa, TbB)
Tb	tuberculosis (=Tbc)
Tb 1	thiosemicarbazone
TBA	tertiary butylacetate
TBA	testosterone-binding affinity
TBA	thiobarbituric acid
TBA	thyroxine-binding albumin
TBA	tracheobronchial aspirate
TBA	transluminal balloon angioplasty
TBa	tubercle bacillus (=TB, TbB)
TBAH	tetrabutyl ammonium hydroxide
TBB	transbronchial biopsy
TbB	tubercle bacillus (=TB, TBa)
TBC	testosterone-binding capacity
TBC	thyroxine-binding capacity
Tbc	tuberculosis
TBE	tick borne encephalitis
TBE	tuberculin bacilli emulsion
TBEV	tick borne encephalitis virus (ARBO virus group B)
TBG	testosterone-binding globulin
TBG	thyroxine-binding globulin
TBGF	ethyl-3,5,6-tri-O-benzyl-D-glucofuramoside
TBGP	total blood granulocyte pool
TBI	p-aminobenzaldehyde thiosemicarbazone
TBI	triiodothyronine-binding index
TBI *(dent)*	tooth brushing instruction
TBI	total body irradiation
TBLC *(obst)*	term birth, living child
TBM	tuberculous meningitis
TBNAA	total body neutron activation analysis
TBNP	total blood neutrophil pool
TBP	testosterone-binding protein
TBP	thio-bis(4,6-dichlorophenol)
TBP	thyroxine-binding protein
TBP	tributylphosphate
TBPA	thyroxine-binding prealbumin

TBS *(pharm)*	tetraphenyl benzene sulfonate	TCC	thromboplastic cell component
TBS	tetrapropylene benzene sulfonate	TCC	total cardiac cost
TBS	tribromosalicylanilide	TCC	transitional cell carcinoma
TBS *(pharm)*	tuberculostatic (agent)	TCC	trichlorocarbanilide
tbsp	tablespoon	TCCA virus	transitional cell cancer-associated virus
TBSV	tomato bushy stunt virus	TCD	tissue culture dose (e.g. TCD_{50})
TBT *(lab)*	template bleeding time		
TBT	tolbutamide	TCD	transcranial Doppler (sonography)
TBTO	tributyl tin-oxide		
TBV	total blood volume	TCDD	2,3,7,8-tetrachlorodibenzo-p-dioxin
TBW	total body water		
TBW	total body weight	TCDNB	tetrachlorodinitrobenzene
TC	temps de coagulation (F); coagulation time	TCE	tetrachlorodiphenylethane ($=$DDD)
TC	tetracycline ($=$T)	TCE	trichloroethanol
TC	thermal conductivity	T cells	thymus-derived cells
TC	thiocarbanilide	TCESOM	trichlorethylene-extracted soybean oil meal
TC	thoracic cage		
TC	thyrocalcitonin	TCFM	trichlorofluoromethane
TC	tissue culture	TCG	time compensated gain
TC	total capacity	TCGF	T-cell growth factor ($=$interleukin-2)
TC	total cholesterol		
TC *(ophth)*	trachomatous cicatrization	TCHA	tetracyclohexyl ammonium
TC	travail cardiaque (F); cardiac work	TCID	tissue culture infective dose
TC	tuberculin C ("contagious")	TCL	triamcinolone
		TCLL	T-cell chronic lymphatic leukemia
TC	Tuberculosis Committee		
TC	tubular epithelial cell	TCM	tetracycline mustard
TC	tumor cerebri	TCM	tissue culture medium
T_c	cytotoxic T-cell	TCM	toyocamycin
$T+C$	type and crossmatch	TCM	trichloromethane
TCA	Time Correlation Analyzer	TCM	tumor-conditioned medium
TCA	transluminal coronary angioplasty	TCN	ticrynafen ($=$TS)
TCA	tricalcium aluminate	TCNB	tetrachloronitrobenzene
TCA	tricarboxylic acid (cycle)	TCNP	tetracyanopropane
TCA	trichloro-acetic acid	TCP	trichlorophenol
TCA	tricyclic antidepressants	TCP	tricresyl phosphate
TCA	tumor cell antigen	TCR *(rad)*	true count rate
TCAP	trimethyl-cetyl-ammonium pentachlorphenate (fungicide)	T_{cs}	T-contrasuppressor cell
		TCT	thrombin clotting time
		TCT	thyrocalcitonin
TCBS	thiosulfate citrate bile salts (agar)	TCT	transmission computerized tomography

Tct.	tincture	TE	transurethral excision
TCTNB	tetrachlorotrinitrobenzene	TE	trial and error
TCu	copper-T (intrauterine con-traceptive device)	Te	tetanus
		TEA	tetraethyl ammonium
TCV	thoracic cage volume	TEA	thrombendarterectomy
TD	tabes dorsalis	TEA	triethanolamine
TD	tetanus and diphtheria toxoid	TEAB	tetraethyl ammonium bro-mide
TD	therapy discontinued	TEAC	tetraethyl ammonium chlo-ride
TD *(anat)*	thoracic duct	
TD	thymus-dependent (cells), T-lymphocytes	TEAE	triethylaminoethyl
		TEB	tissue equivalent bone
TD	timed disintegration	TEC	Trauma and Emergency Center
TD	torsion dystonia	
TD	total disability	TECT	transverse emission com-puterized tomography
TD	transverse diameter	
TD	typhoid dysentery	TED	theophylline ethylene dia-mine, aminophylline
T_d	delayed-type hypersensitiv-ity T-cell	
		TED *(rad)*	threshold erythema dose
t.d.	ter die (L); three times a day (=t.i.d.)	TED	thrombo-embolic disease
		TEDD *(card)*	total end-diastolic diameter
TDD	thermo-dye dilution	
TDD	thoracic duct drainage	TEDP	tetraethyl-dithio-pyrophos-phate
T.D.D.	Tuberculous Diseases Diploma	
		TEE	L-tyrosine ethyl ester
TDE	tetrachloro-diphenylethane (=DDD, TCE)	TEE	tryptophan ethyl ester
		TEF	tracheo-esophageal fistula
TDF	testes determining factor	TEF	triethylene phosphoramide (=TEPA)
TDG	temporal dynamography	
TDI	toluene diisocyanate	$T1/2_{eff}$	effective half-life
TDN	total digestible nutrients	TEG	thrombelastogram
TDNTG	transdermal nitroglycerin (administration)	TEG	triethylene glycol
		TEL	tetra-ethyl lead
TDP	thymidine-5'-diphosphate	telex	teleprinter exchange
TDS	thiamine disulfide	TEM	transmission electron mi-croscope
t.d.s.	ter die sumendum (L); to be taken three times a day (=t.i.d.)	
		TEM	triethylene melamine
		TEMA	Trace Metabolism in Man and Animals
TDT	terminal deoxynucleotidyl transferase	
		Temp.	temperature
TDZ	thymus-dependent zone (of the lymph node)	temp.dext.	tempori dextro (L); to the right temple
TE	tonsillectomy	
TE	total estrogens	temp.sin.	tempori sinistro (L); to the left temple
TE	total extirpation (of an organ)	
		TEN	total excretion of nitrogen
TE	tracheo-esophageal	TEN	toxic epidermal necroly-sis

TENS	transcutaneous electrical nerve stimulation	TFP, TFPZ	trifluoperazine
TEP	tetraethyl pyrophosphate (=TEPF, TEPP)	TFR	total fertility rate
		T_{fr}	feedback regulator T-cell
TEP	thrombo-embolism prophylaxis	TFS	testicular feminization syndrome
TEP	total endoprosthesis	TFT	tetracycline fluorescence test
TEPA	triethylene phosphoramide (=TEF)	TG	tetraglycine
TEPF, TEPP	tetraethylpyrophosphate (=TEP)	TG	thermal gravimetry
		TG	thyroglobulin
TER	thermal enhancement ratio	TG *(obst)*	tocogram
ter.	terendo (L); by rubbing (Rx)	TG	triglycerides
		6-TG	6-thioguanine
tert.	tertiary	TGA	thermogravimetrical analysis
TES	toxic epidemic syndrome	TGA	total gonadotrop(h)ic activity
TES	transcutaneous electrostimulation	TGA	transposition of the great arteries
TESD	total end-systolic diameter		
TEST	Timolol-Encainide-Sotalol Trial	TGC *(card)*	time gain compensation
		TGE	transmissible gastroenteritis (virus)
TET	Teacher of Electrotherapy		
TET	triethylene melamine (=TEM)	TGE	tryptone glucose extract (medium)
TETD	tetraethylthiuram disulfide	TGF	transforming growth factor
TETRAC	tetraiodothyroacetate	TGFA	triglyceride fatty acid
TEV	talipes equinovarus	TGL	triglyceride lipase
TEV	total ejected volume	TGMH	teneur globulaire moyenne en hémoglobine (F); mean cell hemoglobin (=MCH)
TEV	total epithelial volume		
TEWL	transepidermal water loss		
TF	tactile fremitus	TGO	transaminase glutamique-oxalacetique (F); GOT, SGOT
TF	Thomsen-Friedenreich antigens		
TF	thymus factor	TGP	transaminase glutamique-pyruvique (F); GPT, SGPT
TF	tonofilament		
TF *(ophth)*	trachomatous inflammation (follicular)	TGRL	triglyceride-rich lipoproteins
TF	transfer factor	TGT	thromboplastin generation test
TF	tuberculin filtrate		
TF	tubular fluid	TGTN	transdermal glycerol trinitrate
TF	tuning fork		
Tf	transferrin serum groups	TGV	thoracic gas volume
TFA	total fatty acids	TGY	tryptone glucose yeast (agar)
TFG	thermofractogram		
TFN	total fecal nitrogen	TH	ethionamide
TFNS	Territorial Force Nursing Service	TH	Technische Hochschule (G); Technical University

TH	tetrahydrocortisone
TH	thyroid hormone, thyroxine
TH	tyrosine hydroxylase
Th	thoracic segment (=D)
T_h	T-helper cell
Th.	therapy (=Ther.)
THA	tetrahydroacridine (cholinesterase inhibitor)
THA	tetrahydroaldosterone
THA	tetrahydroaminoacridine
THAM	tris-(hydroxymethyl)-aminomethane, tromethamine, tris buffer
THb	total hemoglobin
THBP	trihydroxybutyrophenone
THC	tetrahydrocannabinol
THD	total harmonic distortion
Thd	thymidine
THE	tetrahydro E, tetrahydrocortisone
ThE	thromboembolism
ThEm	thorium emanation, thoron (=Tn)
Ther.	therapy (=Th.)
ther.ex.	therapeutic exercise
THF *(gen)*	assorted antigen-specific helper factors
THF	tetrahydrofolate, coenzyme F
THF	tetrahydro F, tetrahydrocortisone
THF	tetrahydrofuran
THF	thymic humoral factor
ThF	thrombocyte factor
THFA	tetrahydrofolic acid (=THF)
THFA	tetrahydrofurfuryl alcohol
THFF	tetrahydrofolate formylase
THG	thioguanine
THHP	tetrahydrohomofolic acid, tetrahydrohomopteric acid
THI	2-acetyl-4-tetrahydroxybutyl imidazole
THI	trihydroxyindole
Thi	thiamine

Thio-Tepa	triethylene thiophosphoramide
THM	thienamycin
THM	total heme mass
THM waves	Traube-Hering-Meyer waves
thor.	thorax, thoracic
THP	tetrahydropapaveroline
THP	thrombohemorrhagic phenomenon
THPA	tetrahydropteric acid
THPP	2,4,6-trihydroxy-1-propiophenone
ThPP	thiamine pyrophosphate (=TPP)
Thr	threonine
THRF	thyrotrop(h)in releasing factor
THS	tetrahydro-11-deoxycorticosterone
THT	Teacher of Hydrotherapy
THTH	thyrotrop(h)ic hormone (=TSH)
THX	thymus extract
Thx	thyroxine
Thy	thymine (=T)
TI	inspiration time
TI *(rad)*	inversion time
TI	test impulse
TI	therapeutic index
TI	thymus independent (cells)
TI *(ophth)*	trachomatous inflammation (intense)
TI	transformation index
TI	tricuspid (valve) insufficiency
TI *(card)*	triple index
TI	trypsin inhibitor
TIA	transient ischemic attack
TIB *(ophth)*	Turville infinity balance
TIBC	total iron binding capacity
TIC	trypsin inhibitory capacity
TICAS	taxonomic intracellular analytic system
TICC *(gyn)*	time interval from the cessation of contraception to conception

TICT	true isovolumic contraction time	TL	total lipids
TID	time-interval difference	TL	total load
TID	titration of initial dose	TL	transmission loss
t.i.d.	ter in die (L); three times a day (=t.d., t.d.s.)	TL *(gyn)*	tubal ligation
TIF	tumor-inducing factor	TLA	therapeutic local anesthesia
TIG	tetanus immunoglobulin	TLA	transluminal angioplasty (cp. PTA, PTCA)
TIH	time-interval histogram		
TIM	triosephosphate isomerase (=TPI)	TLA	transluminal aortography
		TL antigens	thymic leukemia antigens
TIMI	Thrombolysis in Myocardial Infarction (Study)	TLC	"tender loving care"
		TLC	thin-layer chromatography
TIMI	transmural inferior myocardial infarction	TLC	total lung capacity (=TC)
		TLCK	tosyl lysine chloromethyl ketone
t.i.n.	ter in nocte (L); three times a night	TLCL	T-cell lymphosarcoma cell leukemia
Tinct.	tincture	TLD	thermal luminescence dosimeter
TIP	terminal interphalangeal (joint)		
		TLD	thoracic lymph duct
TIP *(gen)*	translation inhibitory protein	TLE	thin-layer electrophoresis
		$T1/2_{live}$	biological half-life
TIP	tumor inhibitory principle	TLPF	transcortin-like plasma fraction
TIPP	tetraisopropylpyrophosphate		
		TLR	tonic labyrinthine reflex
TIQ	tetrahydro-isoquinoline	TLS *(psych)*	testing the limits for sex
TIRR	Texas Institute of Rehabilitation and Research	TLV	threshold limit value
		TLV	total lung volume
TIS	tumor in situ (=carcinoma in situ)	TLX	trophoblast-lymphocyte cross-reacting (antigen)
TISS	Therapeutic Intervention Scoring System	T lymphocytes	thymus-dependent lymphocytes (=T cells)
TIT	treponema pallidum immobilization test (Nelson)	TM	time motion
		TM	trade-mark
		TM	transport mechanism
TIT, TITH	triiodothyronine (=T_3)	TM	transport messenger
TIVC	true isovolumic contraction time	TM *(psych)*	transcendental meditation
		TM	Tropical Medicine
TJ	triceps jerk	TM	tympanic membrane
Tj^a	Jay factor, antigen Tj^a	Tm	maximum tubular excretory capacity
TK	thiokinase		
TK	thymidine kinase	Tm	transport maximum
TK	transketolase	Tm	tumor
TKT	tyrosine ketoglutarate transaminase	T-M	Thayer-Martin (medium)
		TMA	tetramethylammonium
TL	thermal luminiscence	TMA	thermomechanical analysis
TL	thymic leukemia		

254

TMA	trimethoxyphenyl amino-propane (hallucinogen)	TMPDS	thiamine monophosphate disulfide
TMA	trimethylamine	TMP/SMZ	trimethoprim/sulfameth-oxazole (sulfonamide com-bination)
TMAH	tetramethylammonium hydroxide		
TMAI	tetramethylammonium iodide	TMR	topic magnetic resonance
		TMS	trimethylsilane
TMAO	trimethylamine oxide	TM-scan	time-motion scan
T marker *(gen)*	temperature marker	TMT	thrombocyte migration test
TMAS *(psych)*	Taylor Manifest Anxiety Scale	TMTD	tetramethylthiuram disul-fide
T_{max}	maximal tension	TMV	tobacco mosaic virus
TMB	tetramethyl benzidine	T mycoplasma	"tiny" mycoplasma colon-ies
TMB	trimethylbenzene		
TMCS	trimethylchlorosilane	TN	tolnaftate
TMDT	trace metal detection test	TN	trigeminal neuralgia
		Tn *(ophth)*	normal intraocular ten-sion
TME	Teacher of Medical Electri-city	Tn	thoron ($=$ThEm)
TMED	tetramethylethylene dia-mine	TNA	tetrahydronaphthylamine
		TNA	trinitroaniline
TMG	tetramethylene glutarate	TNB	trinitrobenzene
Tm_G	maximum tubular reab-sorption rate for glucose	TNBS	trinitrobenzene sulfonic acid
TMHC	trimethyl hesperidine chal-cone	TNBT	tetranitro blue tetrazolium
		TNF	tumor necrosis factor
TMI	threatened myocardial infarction	TNG	trinitroglycerol
		TNHL	T-cell non-Hodgkin's lym-phoma
TMJ *(dent)*	temporomandibular joint		
		TNI	total nodal irradiation
TML	test de migration des leu-cocytes (F); leukocyte migration test ($=$LMT)	TNM	tetranitromethane
		TNM system	pathologic system of tumor classification: T$=$tumor; N$=$regional nodes; M$=$metastases
TML	tetramethyl lead		
TMMG	Teacher of Massage and Medical Gymnastics	TNP	2,4,6-trinitrophenol, picric acid
TMP	thymidine-5'-monophos-phate	TNR	tonic neck reflex
		TNS	toluidinylnaphthalene sul-fonate
TMP	transmembrane potential		
TMP *(card)*	transmural pressure	TNS	transcutaneous nerve stim-ulation
TMP	trimethoprim		
TMP	trimethylphosphate	TNT	trinitrotoluene
Tm_{PAH}	maximal tubular excretory capacity for PAH	TNTC	trinitrophenyl tetrazolium chloride
TMPD	tetramethyl-p-phenylene diamine	TNV	tobacco necrosis virus

TO	original or old tuberculin (=OT)	TP	threshold potential
TO	target organ	TP	thrombopoietin
TO	telephone order	TP	thymic polypeptide
TO	temperature taken orally	TP	tissue pressure
TO	tinctura opii (L); tincture of opium	TP	total protein
		TP *(gen)*	transforming principle
TO	tracheo-oesophageal (=TE, TOE)	TP	Treponema pallidum
		TP	triose phosphate
TO	tryptophan oxygenase	TP	triphosphate
TO	turnover	TP *(card)*	triple product (=TI)
TOCP	triorthocresylphosphate (=TCP, TOP)	TP	true positive
		TP	tuberculin precipitation
TOD	total oxygen demand	TP	tumor progression
TOE	tracheo-oesophageal (=TE, TO)	TP-5	thymopoietin pentapeptide
		TPA	tannic acid, polyphos-phomolybdic acid, amido acid (staining method)
ToE	tonsillectomy (usually: TE)		
TOF	tetralogy of Fallot	TPA	12-o-tetradecanoylphorbol-13-acetate
TOF *(rad)*	time of flight (method)		
TOF	trioctylphosphate	TPA	tissue polypeptide antigen
TOIT *(psych)*	Tien Organic Integrity Test (=OIT)	t-PA	tissue-type plasminogen activator
TOMHS	Treatment of Mild Hyper-tension Study	TPA test	tissue polypeptide antigen test
TOP	triorthocresylphosphate (=TCP, TOCP)	TPA test	treponema pallidum agglu-tination test
TOPS	"Take Off Pounds Sensi-bly" (US organization)	TPB	tetrapropylene benzene
		TPB	tryptone phosphate broth
TOPV	trivalent oral polio vaccine	TPBS	tetrapropylene benzene sulfonate (=TBS)
TORCH	toxoplasmosis, other agents, rubella, cytome-galy, herpes (group of micro-organisms asso-ciated with fetal malforma-tion)	TPC	thromboplastic plasma component
		TPCF	treponema pallidum com-plement fixation
		TPCK	tosyl-phenylethyl-chloro-methyl ketone
TORP	total ossicular replacement prosthesis	TPD	thiamine propyl disulfide
		TPD	transpapillary drainage
Torr	Torricelli (unit of pressure) (=T)	TPDH	triosephosphate dehy-drogenase
TOS	tape operating system	TPE	typhoid-paratyphoid-enter-itis (salmonelloses)
TOS	thoracic outlet syndrome		
tosyl-	p-toluenesulfonyl-	TPE	trypsin protein esterase
tox.	toxic	TPEY	tellurite polymyxin egg yolk (medium)
TP	temperature and pressure		
TP	terminal phalanx	TPF	thymus permeability factor
TP	testosterone propionate	TPF	triphenylformazane
TP	test plate		

256

TPG	tryptophan peptone glucose (agar)	TPVR	total peripheral vascular resistance
5-TPH	5-tryptophan hydroxylase	TPZ	thioproperazine
T phage	tailed coli phage	TR	Teaching and Research
TPHA	treponema pallidum hemagglutination (test)	TR	temperature, taken rectally
		TR	therapeutic radiology
TPI	triosephosphate isomerase	TR	trypan red
TPIA	treponema pallidum immune adherence (test)	TR	tuberculin R ("residue")
		TR	tubular reabsorption
TPI test	treponema pallidum immobilizing test (= TIT)	TR	turbidity reaction
		TR	turbidity reducing (cp. TRU)
TPL	total phospholipids		
TP line	line between tuberculum sellae and protuberantia occipitalis interna (in a lateral skull x-ray)	Tr.	tincture (= Tct.)
		Tr. *(anat)*	tract
		Tr.	tremor
		Tr. *(pharm)*	trituration (= Trit.)
TPM	triphenylmethane		
tpm	tours par minute (F); revolutions per minute	Tr	transferrin
		tr.	trace
TPMB	treponema pallidum methylene blue (staining)	TRA	triethanolamine, trolamine (buffer)
TPN	total parenteral nutrition	TRBF	total renal blood flow
TPN	triphosphopyridine nucleotide (= NADP)	TRC	tanned red cells
		TRCHI	tanned red cells hemagglutination inhibition
TPND	TPN diaphorase		
TPNH	reduced form of TPN	TRD	thermal regulation diagnosis
TPO	tryptophan peroxidase		
TPP	testosterone phenylpropionate	T reflex	tendon reflex
		T receptor	Thomsen receptor
TPP	thiamine pyrophosphate (= ThPP)	TRF	T-cell replacing factor
		TRF	thyrotrop(h)in releasing factor (= TRH)
TPR *(clin)*	temperature, pulse, respiration		
		TRF	tubular rejection fraction
TPR *(neur)*	tibialis posterior reflex	TRH	thyrotrop(h)in releasing hormone (= TRF)
TPR	total peripheral resistance		
TPR	total pulmonary resistance	TRH	tyrosine hydroxylase
TPR	triphenylphosphate	TRI *(psych)*	total response index
TPR	tryptophan perchloric acid reaction	Tri	trichloroethylene
		T_3-RIA	radioimmunoassay of triiodothyronine
TPRI	total peripheral resistance index		
		T_4-RIA	radioimmunoassay of thyroxine
tps *(rad)*	transmutation per second (= Bq)		
		TRIAC	triiodothyroacetate
TPT	tetraphenyl tetrazolium	TRIB	triclobisonii chloridum
TPT	thromboplastin time	TRIC	trachoma and inclusion conjunctivitis (agents)
TPT	total protein tuberculin		
TPTZ	2,4,6-tripyridil-s-triazine	tric *(gen)*	tricentric chromosome

TRIGLYME	triethyleneglycol dimethyl-ether	TS	total solids
TRINS	totally reversible ischemic neurologic symptoms	TS	toxic substance
		TS	transsexual
Tripas	trichromic PAS (staining)	TS	tricuspid stenosis
		TS	triple strength
Tripiform	trichloroacetic acid, picric acid, formol (fixation medium)	TS	tubular sound, tracheal sound
		T_s	T-suppressor cell
Tris	tris buffer, THAM	T/S	thyroid/serum (iodine ratio)
TRIT	triiodothyronine, T_3		
Trit. *(pharm)*	trituration (= Tr.)	TSA	thymus-specific antigen
TRML	Tropical Research Medical Laboratory (USA)	TSA	toluene sulfonic acid
		TSA	tumor-specific antigen
		T'sase	tryptophan synthetase
TRN *(anat)*	tegmental reticular nuclei	TSC	thiosemicarbazone
tRNA	transfer ribonucleic acid	TSCA	tumor-specific cellular (cytoplasmic) antigen
Troch. *(anat)*	trochanter	TSD *(rad)*	target skin distance
troch. *(pharm)*	trochisci (L); lozenges	TSD	Tay-Sachs disease
		TSE	testicular self-examination
TRP	total refractory period		
TRP	tubular reabsorption of phosphate	T sect.	transverse or cross section
		T-set	tracheotomy set
Trp	tryptophan (= Try)	TSF *(gen)*	assorted antigen-specific suppressor factors
TRPA	tryptophan-rich prealbumin		
		TSF	thrombosis stimulating factor
TrPl	treatment plan		
trs *(gen)*	transactivation of splicing	TSG	thyroid-stimulating globulin
TRSV	tobacco ringspot virus	TSH	thyroid-stimulating hormone, thyrotrop(h)in
TRT	thrombocyte retention test		
		TSH-RF, TSH-RH	TSH-releasing factor, ... hormone
TRU	turbidity reducing unit (measuring the enzyme activity of hyaluronidase)		
		TSH-RIA	thyrotrop(h)in radioimmunoassay
TRVV	total right ventricular volume	TSI	thyroid-stimulating immune globulin
Try	tryptophan (= Trp.)	TSI	triple sugar (glucose, sucrose, lactose) iron (Kligler's agar)
TS	Takayasu's syndrome, pulseless disease		
TS	temperature sensitive	TSIM	trimethylsilylimidazole
TS	tension space	TSN	tryptone sulfide neomycin (agar)
TS	test sample		
TS	test solution	TSP	total serum protein
TS	tetrazolium salt	TSP	tropical spastic paraparesis
TS	thoracic surgery	tsp	teaspoon
TS	thymidylate synthetase	TSR	thyroid secretion rate

TSS *(psych)*	Temperament Structure Scale	TTP	tritolylphosphate
TSS	toxic shock syndrome	TTPA	triethylene thiophosphora-mide, thio-Tepa
TSSA	tumor-specific surface anti-gen	TTPase	thiamine triphosphatase
TSSU	Theatre Sterile Supply Unit	TTR	tetrathionate reductase
		TTR	thymol turbidity reaction
TSTA	tumor-specific transplanta-tion antigen	TTR	triceps tendon reflex
		T-transfor-mation	Thomsen's phenomenon (T-test)
TSTAR	tumor-specific transplanta-tion antigen receptor	TTS	tarsal tunnel syndrome
T-strains	tiny mycoplasma colonies	TTS *(otol)*	temporary threshold shift
TSU	triple sugar urea (agar)	TTS	transdermal therapeutic system
TSVR	total systemic vascular resistance	TTSA	tissue-type specific antigen
TT	tetanus toxoid	TTT	thymol turbidity test
TT *(bact)*	tetrathionate (broth)	TTX	tetrodotoxin
TT	thrombin time	TTY	teletypewriter
TT	thymine dimer	T-type	"tetanoid" constitutional type
TT	thymol turbidity	TU	Technical University
TT	tolbutamide test	TU	toxic unit, toxoid unit
TT	tolerance test	TU	transmission unit
TT *(ophth)*	trachomatous trichiasis	TU	tuberculin unit
TT	transit time	TU	turbidity unit
TT	tuberculin tested (milk)	Tu	tumor
TTA	transtracheal aspiration	T_3U	triiodothyronine uptake
TTC	tetracycline ($=$TC)	TUD	total urethral discharge
TTC	2,3,5-triphenyl-tetrazolium chloride	TUR, TURP	transurethral resection of the prostate
TTD	tetraethylthiuram disulfid, disulfiram ($=$TETD)	TV	tachycardie ventriculaire (F); ventricular tachycardia
TTD	thoracic transverse diame-ter	TV	television
		TV	tetrazolium violet
TTD	transient tic disorder	TV	tidal volume
ttd, t.t.d.	three times a day ($=$t.i.d.)	TV	total vagotomy
T-test	Thomsen's phenomenon	TV	total volume
TTFA	tenoyltrifluoroacetone	TV	transvestite
TTFB	tetrachlorotrifluoromethyl-benzylimidazole	TV	Trichomonas vaginalis
		TV	truncular vagotomy
TTFD	thiamine tetrahydrofurfu-ryl disulfide	TV	tuberculin volutin
		TVC	triple voiding cystogram
TTH	thyrotrop(h)ic hormone, thyrotrop(h)in ($=$TSH)	TVCV	transvenous cardioversion
		TVD	transmissible viral demen-tia
TTI *(card)*	tension time index	TVE	tricuspid valve excursion
TTP	thrombotic thrombocyto-penic purpura	TVF	tactile vocal fremitus
TTP	thymidine-5'-triphosphate	TVF	thorium vulnerable factor

TVH	total vaginal hysterectomy	UAB	University of Alabama in Birmingham (USA)
TVL *(rad)*	tenth value layer		
TVP	textured vegetable protein	UABS	Union of American Biological Societies
TVP	truncular vagotomy with pyloroplasty		
		UAE	unilateral absence of excretion
TVR	tonic vibration reflex		
TVR	total vascular resistance	UAE	urinary albumin excretion (rate)
TVR	tricuspid valve replacement		
		u.a.f.	ut aliquid fiat (L); so that anything is done
TVU	total volume urine (in 24 h)		
TW	total body water (= TBW)	UAN	uric acid nitrogen
TW	travelling wave	UAP	unstable angina pectoris
TWA *(stat)*	time weighted average	UAP	urinary alkaline phosphatase
TWAR	Taiwan acute respiratory (strains of chlamydia)		
		UAPA	unilateral absence of the pulmonary artery
TWE	tap water enema		
TX	thromboxane (e.g. TXA, TXB)	UAT	uranylacetate test
		UAV	urinary albumin value
Tx	treatment	UBA	undenaturated bacterial antigen
Ty	type		
tymp.	tympanic	UBB	ultimobranchial body (embryology)
TYMV	turnip yellow mosaic virus		
		UBE	ultrasonic basic examination
typ.	typical		
TYR	tyrothricin	UBF	uterine blood flow
Tyr	tyrosine	Ubg	urobilinogen
Tz	tuberculin zymoplastiche	UBI	ultraviolet blood irradiation
		UBIP	ubiquitous immunopoietic polypeptide
		Ubn	urobilin
		UC	urinary catheter

U

		u.c.	uso cognito (L); for known use (= u.n.)
U	electrical voltage	UCB	unconjugated bilirubin
U	unit	UCB	Union Chimique Belgique
U	uracil	UCD	usual childhood diseases (= UCHD)
U	urea		
U	uridine	U cells	cells with unspecific abnormalities
u	unified mass		
U/3	upper third	UCG	ultrasound cardiography (= USCG)
UA *(phys)*	ultra-audible		
UA	uric acid	UCG	urethrocystogram
UA	urinalysis	UCG	urinary chorionic gonadotrophin
UA	uterine aspiration		
u.a.	usque ad (L); up to, as far as	UCHD	usual childhood diseases (= UCD)

UCI	urinary catheter in	UEG	ultrasound echoencepha-lography
UCL	urea clearance		
UCLA	University of California, Los Angeles	UEM	unité électromagnétique (F); electromagnetic unit
UCLAF	Usines Chimiques des Laboratoires Françaises	UEMO	Union Européenne de Médecins Omnipraticiens (F); European Union of General Practitioners
UCR	unconditioned response		
UCS	unconditioned stimulus		
Ucs	unconscious	UEMS	Union Européenne de Médecine Sociale (F); European Union of Social Medicine
UCSD	University of California, San Diego		
UCSF	University of California, San Francisco	UEMS	Union Européenne des Médecins Spécialistes (F); European Union of Medical Specialists
UCT	ultrasound computer tomography		
UCV	uncontrolled variable	UEP	Union of European Phoni-atrists
UD	ulnar deviation		
UD	urethral discharge	UEP	Union of European Pedo-psychiatrists
UD	uridine diphosphate (=UDP)		
UDC	underdeveloped countries (developing countries)	UES	upper esophageal sphinc-ter
UDC	Universal Decimal Classi-fication	UET	urinary excretion test
		U-excr.	urea excretion
UDC	usual diseases of child-hood (=UCD, UCHD)	UF	urinary formaldehyde
		UF	ultrafiltration rate
UDCA	ursodeoxycholic acid	UFA	unesterified fatty acids
UDP	uridine-5'-diphosphate	UFC	urinary free cortisol
UDPAG	uridine-5'-diphospho-N-acetylglucosamine	UF collimator	ultra-fine collimator
UDPG	uridine-diphosphate glu-cose	UFH	unfractioned heparin
		UFI	Union des Foires Interna-tionales (F); Union of International Fairs
UDPGA	uridine-diphosphate glucu-ronic acid		
UDPGDH	uridine-5'-diphosphoglu-cose dehydrogenase	UFR	urine filtration rate
		UG	urogenital (=GU)
UDPGT	uridine-diphosphate glucu-ronyl transferase	UGDP	University Group Diabetes Program
UDPXy	uridine-diphosphate xylose	UGF	unidentified growth fac-tor
UDRP	uridine diribose phosphate		
UDS	ultrasound Doppler sonog-raphy	U'gen	urobilinogen
		UGI	upper gastrointestinal
UE	upper extremity	UGT	uridylglucuronate transfer-ase
UEA	United Epilepsy Associa-tion (USA)		
		UGT	urogenital tract
UED	ultrared emission diagno-sis	UGT	urogenital tuberculosis (=GUT)

UH	upper half	UIP, UIPPA	Union Internationale de Physique Pure et Appliquée (F); Internationale Union of Pure and Applied Physics (= IUPAP)
UHF	ultra-high frequency		
UHL	universal hypertrichosis lanuginosa		
UHMW	ultra-high molecular weight		
UHT	ultra-high temperature (procedure)	UIPF	usual interstitial pulmonary fibrosis
UHV	ultra-high vacuum	UIPM	Union Internationale de la Presse Médicale (F); International Union of the Medical Press
UI	unité internationale (F); international unit (= IU)		
UIA	Union of International Associations	UISB	Union Internationale des Sciences Biologiques (F); International Union of Biological Sciences
UIBC	unsaturated iron-binding capacity		
UICC	Unio Internationalis Contra Cancrum (L); International Union Against Cancer	UISN	Union Internationale des Sciences de la Nutrition (F); International Union of Nutritional Sciences
UICPA	Union Internationale de Chimie Pure et Appliquée (F); International Union of Pure and Applied Chemistry (= IUPAC)	UIT	Union Internationale contre la Tuberculose (F); International Union against Tuberculosis (= UICT)
UICT	Union Internationale contre la Tuberculose (F); International Union against Tuberculosis (= UIT)	UIT	Union Internationale des Télécommunications (F); International Union of Telecommunication
		UIV	urographie intraveineuse (F); intravenous urography (= IVP, IVU)
UIE	International Union for Electric Heat		
UIMC	Union Internationale de Service Médicale de Chemin de Fer (F); International Union of Medical Services of Railways	UK	unknown
		UK, Uk	urokinase
		UKAEA	United Kingdom Atomic Energy Authority
		UK-TIA	United Kingdom Transient Ischaemic Attack (Study Group)
UIMTCT	Union Internationale de Médecine Thermale et de Climatothalassothérapie (F); International Union of Thermotherapy, Climatotherapy and Thalassotherapy	UL	upper lobe (of the lung)
		U/l	unit(s) per liter
		ULDH	urinary lactic acid (or lactate) dehydrogenase
		ULF	ultra-low frequency
		ULLE	upper lid left eye
UIP	usual interstitial pneumonia	ULQ	upper left quadrant
		ULRE	upper lid right eye

ULT	ultra-high temperature (pasteurization)	UNEP	United Nations Environmental Program
UM	unmarried	UNESCO	United Nations Educational, Scientific and Cultural Organization
UMC	"upper middle class"		
UMEL	Union pour la Médicine Européenne Libérale (F); Organization for Liberal Practice of Medicine in Europe	ung., Ungt.	unguentum (L); ointment
		UNICEF	United Nations International Children's Emergency Fund
UMEM	Union Mondiale des Ecrivains Médecins (F); World Union of Medical Writers	Univ.	university
		univ.	universal
		UNM	University of New Mexico (Albuquerque)
U/min	Umdrehungen pro Minute (G); rotations per minute (=rpm)	UNO	United Nations Organization
UMML	Union Médicale de la Méditerranée Latine (F); Medical Union of Latin Mediterranean Countries	UNRRA	United Nations Relief and Rehabilitation Administration
		UnS	unconditioned stimulus
UMN	upper motor neuron	UNSCEAR	United Nations Scientific Committee on the Effects of Atomic Radiation
UMNL	upper motor neuron lesion		
UMP	uridine monophosphate (U-2-MP, U-3-MP, etc.)	UO	urinary output
		UP	polyurethane
UMPK	uridine monophosphate kinase	UP	under proof
		UP	unsaturated polyester resins
UMS	Urine Monitoring System		
UN	United Nations	U/P	ratio of urine and plasma concentration of a substance
UN	urea-nitrogen (usually: BUN)		
u.n.	uso noto (L); for known use (=u.c.)	UPCV	ulcère de la petite courbure ventriculaire (F); ulcer of the lesser curvature of the stomach
UNA	urea-nitrogen appearance		
UNA	urinary noradrenaline	UPEC	uropathogenic Escherichia coli
UNC	University of North Carolina (Chapel Hill)		
		UPG	uroporphyrinogen
UNCOS	United Nations Committee on Outer Space	UPIA	Union Pharmaceutique Inter-Africaine (F); Interafrican Pharmaceutical Union
UncS	unconditioned stimulus		
UNCSTD	United Nations Committee on Science, Technology and Development		
UNDP	United Nations Development Program	UPIGO	Union Professionelle Internationale des Gynécologues et Obstétriciens (F); International Professional Union of Gynecologists and Obstetricians
UNDRO	United Nations Disaster Relief Office (Geneva)		
UNEC	urinary non-esterified cholesterol		

UPP	University of Pennsylvania, Philadelphia	USBS	United States Bureau of Standards
UPVB	unifocal premature ventricular beat	USC	University of Southern California
UQ	ubiquinones	USCG	ultrasound cardiography
UQ	upper quadrant	USCG	United States Coast Guard
UQH₂	ubihydroquinone	USD	ultrasound-Doppler (technique)
UR	ultrared, infrared (= IR)		
UR	unconditioned response (= UCR)	USD	United States Dispensatory
		USDHEW	United States Department of Health, Education and Welfare
UR	upper respiratory		
Ur	urine		
URAP	unidirectional retrograde accessory pathway	USF	unité Svedberg de flotation (F); Svedberg flotation unit
URAS	ultrared absorption spectrometry (= URS)	USGEB	Union der Schweizerischen Gesellschaften für Experimentelle Biologie (G); Union of Swiss Societies for Experimental Biology (= USSBE)
URD	unspecific respiratory disease		
Urd	uridine		
Ur-excr.	urinary excretion		
URF	unit of Reitmann-Frankel (of SGOT and SGPT)	US-HAB	United States Homeopathic Apothecary Book
URF	uterine relaxing factor	USHL	United States Hygienic Laboratory
URI	upper respiratory infection (= URTI)		
		USI	ultrasound instability
URQ	upper right quadrant	USMC	Unites States Marine Corps
URS	ultrared spectrometry (= URAS)		
URT	upper respiratory tract	USMH	United States Marine Hospital
URTI	upper respiratory tract infection		
		USN	United States Navy
US	ultrasound	USNRC	United States Nuclear Regulatory Commission
US	unconditioned stimulus (= UCS)		
		USP	United States Pharmacopeia
us	upstream		
USAF	United States Air Force	USPHS	United States Public Health Service
USAH	United States Army Hospital		
		USPS	United States Publication Service
USAMEDS	United States Army Medical Service		
		USR test	unheated serum reagin test (for syphilis)
USAN	United States Adopted Names		
USASI	United States of America Standards Institute (now: ANSI)	USSBE	Union des Sociétés Suisses de Biologie Expérimentales (F); Union of Swiss Societies for Experimental Biology (= USGEB)
USBLS	United States Bureau of Labor Statistics		
		UST	ultrasound tomography

USVB	United States Veterans Bureau	V	virus
USVH	United States Veterans Hospital	V	vision
USW	ultrasonic wave	V	vitrum (L); glass
UT *(phys)*	universal time	V	voice
UT	urinary tract	V	volt
UTBG	unbound thyroxine-binding globulin	V	volume
		V	vomitus
ut dict.	ut dictum; as directed (Rx)	V.	vena (L); vein
utend.	utendus; to be used (Rx)	V.	Vibrio
UTG	ultrasound tomography	v	ventricular
UTI	urinary tract infection	v	versus
U-time *(card)*	upstroke time	v	vide (L); see
		VA	analysis of variance (=ANOVA)
UTP	uridine triphosphate	VA	vacuum aspiration
UU	urine urobilinogen	VA	ventilation, alveolar
UUN	urinary urea-nitrogen	VA	Veterans Administration (USA)
UUTI	upper urinary tract infection	VA	visual acuity
UV	ultraviolet	VA	ventriculo-atrial
UV	Vernes unit	VA	voltampère
UV	Uppsala virus	VAB	cytotoxic combination therapy with vinblastine, actinomycin, and bleomycin
UV	urine volume		
UVDI	ultraviolet dermatitis inhibition (test)		
UVEB	unifocal ventricular ectopic beat	VAC	cytotoxic combination therapy with vincristine, adriamycin, and cyclophosphamide
UVR	ultraviolet radiation		
UVS	ultraviolet Schiff (reaction)	VAC	ventriculo-atrial conduction
UV-VIS	spectroscopy in the ultraviolet and visible range	VAC	Vernacular Name based on Adansonian Classification (of viruses)
ux	uxor (L); wife		
		vac.	vacuum
		vacc.	vaccine, vaccination
		VACTRL	vertebral, anal, cardiac, tracheo-esophageal and limb-reduction defects

V

V	value	VACURG	Veterans Administation Cooperative Research Group
V	variability (variation) coefficient		
V	velocity	VAD	cytotoxic combination therapy with vincristine, adriamycin, and dexamethasone
V	ventilation		
V	vertex		
V	virulence	VAD *(mil)*	Voluntary Aid Detachment

VAERP	ventriculo-atrial effective refractory period	VC	vernix caseosa
VAG	vertebral artery angiography	VC	vertimycin
		VC	Veterinary Corps
VAg	viral antigen	VC	vinylchloride
vag.	vaginal	VC	visual cortex
VAH	Veterans Administration Hospital	VC	vital capacity
		VCC	vasoconstrictor center
VAH	virilizing adrenal hyperplasia	VCD	vinylchloride disease
		VCE	velocity of contractile elements
Val	valine	VCF (card)	velocity of circumferential fiber shortening
val	gram equivalent		
VALG	Veterans Administration Lung Cancer Study Group	VCG	vectorcardiogram
		VCI	vena cava inferior
VAMC	Veterans Administration Medical Center	VCI	volatile corrosion inhibitor
VAMP	cytotoxic combination therapy with vincristine, amethopterin, 6-mercaptopurine, and prednisone	VCL	veine centro-lobulaire (F); sinusoidal central vein
		VCM	vancomycin
		VCM	vinylchloride monomer
V antigen	virus antigen	VCN	vancomycin hydrochloride, colistine methane sodium, nystatin (medium)
var.	variety		
VAT	pacemaker with certain actions (ventricular stimulation, atrial perception, triggered ventricular action)	VCN	vibrio cholerae neuramidase
		VCR	vincristine
		VC ratio	ventilation-circulation ratio
VAT	ventricular activation time		
VATER	syndrome of vertebral defects, anal atresia, tracheo-esophageal fistula (with esophageal atresia), renal and radial dysplasia	VCS	vasoconstrictor substance
		VCS	vena cava superior
		VCU	voiding cysto-urethrogram
		VD	vapor density
		VD	venereal disease
VB	blood volume	VD	venous drainage
VB	valence binding	VD	ventricule droit (F); right ventricle
VB	ventricular bradycardia		
VB	vinblastine	VD	virus diarrhea
VBI	vertebrobasilar insufficiency	VD	volume de distribution (F); distribution volume
VBOS	veronal-buffered oxalated saline	V_D	volume of dead air space
		vd.	vide (L); see
VBS	veronal-buffered saline (medium)	v.d.	ventrodorsal (=a.p.)
		VDA	vanillyl diethylamide
VC	acuity of color vision	VDA	visual discriminatory acuity
VC	variation coefficient		
VC	vena cava	VDC	vasodilator center
VC	venous compliance	VDC	vinylidene chloride

VDEL	Venereal Disease Experimental Laboratory	VEEV	Venezuelan equine encephalomyelitis virus
VDEM	vasodepressor material (= VDM)	V elements (psych)	vigilance elements
VDG	venereal disease – gonorrhea	VEM	vaso-excitator material
VDH	valvular disease of the heart	VEMS	volume expiratoire maximum-seconde (F); forced expiratory volume (= FEV₁)
VDH	vascular disease of the heart	ventr.	ventral
VDM	vasodepressor material (= VDEM)	VEP	visual evoked potential
		VER	visual evoked reaction
VDP	cytotoxic combination therapy with vincristine, daunomycin, and prednisone	VERP (card)	ventricular excitation repolarization phase
		VES	velocity erythrocyte sedimentation
VDRL	Venereal Disease Research Laboratory	VES	ventricular extrasystole (= VEB, VPB, VPC)
VDRT	Venereal Disease Reference Test	VES	volume d'éjection systolique (F); stroke volume (= SV)
VDS	vasodilator substance		
VDS	venereal disease – syphilis	ves.	vesica (L); bladder
VDS (orth)	ventral derotation spondylodesis	Vet.	veteran
		Vet.	veterinarian
VDS test	test using diffusing vaccine of Salvioli	vet.	veterinary
		v.et.	vide etiam (L); see also
VDU	visual display unit	VF (card)	velocity of fiber shortening
VDV	ventricular diastolic volume		
		VF	ventricular fibrillation
VE	vaginal examination	VF	visual field
VE (obst)	vacuum extraction	VF	vocal fremitus
VE	vesicular exanthema	VF	voice frequency
VE	visual efficiency	V-factor (psych)	verbal comprehension factor
VE	Voegtlin-Einheit (G); Voegtlin unit (of pituitary hormones)	VFB (lab)	viande foie bouillon (F); meat-liver broth
VE	volume ejection	VFC	ventricular function curve
VE	volume expiré (F); expired volume	VFDF	very fast death factor
		VFL	visual field length
VEB	ventricular ectopic beat (= VES)	VFM	volume flowmeter
		V form (bact)	virus form (of culture colonies)
VECP	visual evoked cortical potentials	VFP (neur)	ventricular fluid pressure
VED (card)	ventricular ectopic depolarization	VFRP	ventricular functional refractory period
VEE	Venezuelan equine encephalitis	VFT	ventricular fibrillation threshold

VG	valeur globulaire (F); mean corpuscular hemoglobin (=MCH)	VIM	video-intensified micros-copy
VG	vein graft	VIMS	volume inspiratoire maxi-mum-seconde (F); forced inspiratory volume
VG	ventricular gallop		
VG	ventricule gauche (F); left ventricle	VIN	vincamine
VG	ventriculography	VIP	vasoactive intestinal poly-peptide
VGH	very good health		
VGM	volume globulaire moyen (F); mean cell volume (=MCV)	VIP	vasoinhibitory peptide
		VIP	"very important person"
		VIP test	vaginal identification of pathogens (quick detection of Trichomonas vaginales, Candida albicans, and Corynebacterium vaginale)
VGRS	Verdun Geriatric Rating Scale		
VGT	volume gazeux thoracique (F); thoracic gas volume (=TGV)		
		visc.	visceral
VGT	volume globulaire total (F); total cell volume	ViSV	viper sarcoma virus (Rus-sell)
vGTT	venous glucose tolerance test	Vit.	vitamin
		Vit.ov.	vitellum ovi (L); egg yolk
VH	Veterans Hospital (=VAH)	Vitr.	vitrum (L); glass, bottle
		VJ agar	Vogel-Johnson selective agar
VH	viral hepatitis (e.g. VHA, VHB)	VL (ophth)	vision left
VHD	valvular heart disease (=VDH)	VLB	vincaleucoblastine, vin-blastine
VHF (phys)	very high frequency	VLBW	very low birthweight
VHFV	very high frequency venti-lation	VLDL	very low density lipopro-teins
VI	vaginal irrigation	VLF (phys)	very low frequency
VI	variable intervals	VLM	ventrolateral medulla (oblongata)
VI	ventilation index		
VI	virgo intacta	VLP	ventricular late potentials
VI	vitality index	VLP	virus-like particles
VI	volume indicator	VLR	vinleurosine
VI	volume inspiré (F); inspired volume	VM	maximal ventilation
		VM	vasomotor
VI	volume index	VM	vestibular membrane
VIA	virus inactivating agent	VM	viomycin
Vi antigen	virulence antigen	VM, Vm	voltmeter
VIBS (psych)	vocabulatory, information, block design, similarities (test)	VMA	vanillylmandelic acid
		V_{max}	maximum velocity
		VMC	vasomotor center
VIC	vasoinhibitory center	V.M.D.	Doctor of Veterinary Med-icine
vid.	vide (L); see (=vd.)		
VIG	vaccinia immune globulin	VMH	ventromedial hypothal-amic

VMM	ventilation maximale minute (F); maximum ventilation volume per minute (= MBC, MVV)	VPC	ventricular premature contraction (= VEB, VES, VPB)
VMR	vasomotor rhinitis	VPC	volume packed cells
VN	virus neutralization	VPD	ventricular premature depolarization
VN	Visiting Nurse		
VN	Vocational Nurse	VPM	ventilation pulmonaire maximum (F); maximal pulmonary ventilation
VNA	Visiting Nurse Association		
VNS	vegetatives Nervensystem (G); autonomic nervous system	VPP (vet)	viral porcine pneumonia
		VPR	Voges-Proskauer reaction
VO	varices oesophagiennes (F); esophageal varices	VP ratio	ventilation-perfusion ratio
		VPS	ventricular premature stimulation
VO	veine ombilicale (F); umbilical vein	vps	vibrations per second
VO	verbal order	VPT	Voges-Proskauer test
VOC	voltage-operated channel	VQ	ventilation quotient
VOD	venous occlusive disease; Stuart-Bras syndrome, Budd-Chiari syndrome	VQE	Visa Qualifying Examination (USA)
		VR	variable ratio
		VR	venous return
VOD	visus oculi dextri (L); vision of right eye	VR	ventilation rate
		VR	ventral root (of a spinal nerve)
Vol.	volume		
Vol.»	volume/per cent	VR (ophth)	vision right
volfr.	volume fraction	VR	vocal resonance
VOM	vinylchloride monomer	VR	volume résiduel (F); residual volume (= RV)
VON	Victorian Order of Nurses (Canada)		
		VRA	Vocational Rehabilitation Administration
VOP (card)	ventricular overdrive pacing		
		VRE	volume de reserve expiratoire (F); expiratory reserve volume (= ERV)
VOR (phys)	very high frequency omnirange		
VOS	visus oculi sinistri (L); vision left eye	VRI	valvular regurgitation index
v.o.s.	vitello ovi solutus (L); dissolved in egg yolk	VRI	virus respiratory infection
		VRI	volume de reserve inspiratoire (F); inspiratory reserve volumen (= IRV)
VP	plasma volume		
VP	variegate porphyria		
VP	vapor pressure	VRL	Virus Reference Laboratory
VP	venous pressure		
VP (neur)	ventricle puncture	VRP	"very reliable product"
VP	Voges-Proskauer (test)	VRV	ventricular residual volume
VPA	volume pulse amplitude		
VPB	ventricular premature beat (= VEB, VES, VPC)	VS	vaccination scar
		VS	venaesectio
VPC	venous pulse curve	VS (anat)	ventricular septum

269

VS	vesicular sound (on auscultation)	VTOL	vertical take-off and landing
VS	vesicular stomatitis	VTSRS	Verdun Target Symptom Rating Scale
VS	vital signs	VU	very urgent
VS	volumetric solution	VUR	vesico-ureteral reflux
Vs	voltsecond	VV	vice versa
V.S.	Veterinary Surgeon	VV	vulvovaginal
vs	vibration seconds	Vv.	venae (L); veins
vs	versus (= v)	v/v	volume of dissolved substance per volume of solvent
VSAM	Virtual Storage Access Method	VVG	vasovesiculography
VsB	venaesectio brachii (L); venesection of the arm	VVI (card)	ventricular pacing and ventricular sensing, inhibited mode
VSD	ventricular septal defect		
VSG	vitesse de sedimentation globulaire (F); erythrocyte sedimentation rate (= BSR, ESR)	VVT (card)	ventricular pacing and ventricular sensing, triggered mode
VSHD	ventricular septal heart defect (= VSD)	VW	vessel wall
VSM	vena saphena magna	v/w	volume of a substance per unit of weight of another component
VSMC	vascular smooth muscle cells		
VSP	vena saphena parva	VWD, vWD	von Willebrand disease
VSS	vital signs stable	vWJS	von Willebrand-Jürgens syndrome
VSSGBI	Vascular Surgical Society of Great Britain and Ireland	Vx	vertex
		V-Z	varicella-zoster
VSV	vesicular stomatitis virus	VZIG	varicella-zoster immune globulin
VT	tidal volume		
VT	vacuum tuberculin	VZV	varicella-zoster virus
VT	vagotomy		
VT	vasotonin		
VT	ventricular tachycardia		
V + T	volume and tension (of the pulse)		
VTA	ventricular tachyarrhythmia		

W

VTA	Veterinary Technical Assistant	W	water
VTAM	Virtual Telecommunication Access Method	W (phys)	watt (unit of electric energy)
VTE (psych)	vicarious trial and error	W (rad)	wehnelt (unit of x-ray hardness)
V-test	Voluter test	W	weight (= wt)
VTG	volume thoracic gas	W	widow(er)
VTH (gyn)	vaginal total hysterectomy	W	width
VTI	volume thickness index	w	week (= wk)

w	wife
WA *(card)*	warning arrhythmias
WAC	Women's Army Corps
WACS	West African College of Surgeons
WAIS *(psych)*	Wechsler Adult Intelligence Scale
WAK	wearable artificial kidney
WAPS	World Association of (Anatomic and Clinical) Pathology Societies
WaR	Wassermann reaction
w.a.r.	without additional reagents
WARIS	Warfarin Re-Infarction Study
WAS	Wiskott-Aldrich syndrome
WASP	World Association of Societies of Pathology and Clinical Pathology (cp. WAPS)
WB	warm blood
WB	water bottle
WB *(psych)*	Wechsler-Bellevue scale
WB	weight-bearing (e.g. bone or joint)
WB	Western Blot
WB	whole blood
Wb *(phys)*	weber (unit of magnetic flow)
WBC	white blood cells
WBC	white blood count
WBE	whole body extract
Wb factor	Webb factor; antigen Wb
WBH	whole body hyperthermia
WBPTT	whole blood partial thromboplastin time
WBR	whole body radiation
WBRS *(psych)*	Word Behavior Rating Scale
WBS	whole body scan
WC	ward clerk
WC	wheel chair
WC	white cell
WC	whooping cough
WCET	World Council of Enterostomal Therapists
WCGS	Western Collaborative Group Study
WCL	Wenckebach cycle length
WCD	Weber-Christian disease
WCPT	World Confederation for Physical Therapy
WCST	Wisconsin Card Sorting Test
WCT	Word in Context Test
WD	Waller degeneration
WD	watery diarrhea
WD	well developed
WD	wet dressing
WD	wrist disarticulation
WDHA	watery diarrhea, hypokalemia, anacidity (achlorhydria) syndrome; Verner-Morrison syndrome (cp. WDHH)
WDHH	watery diarrhea, hypokalemia, anacidity (achlorhydria), hyperglycemia syndrome; Verner-Morrison syndrome (cp. WDHA)
WDWN	well developed – well nourished
WEE	western equine encephalomyelitis
WEF	War Emergency Formula
WEP	water blue (aniline blue), eosin, phloxin (staining method)
WEUP syndrome	"wilful exposure to unwanted pregnancy"
WF	warm front
WF	white female
WFAS	World Federation of Anesthesiological Societies
WFD	World Federation of the Deaf
WFH	World Federation of Hemophilia
WFMH	World Federation for Mental Health
WFN	World Federation of Neurology

WFNS	World Federation of Neurosurgical Societies	wk	week
WFOT	World Federation of Occupational Therapists	WK disease	Wilson-Kimmelstiel disease
WFP	World Federation of Parasitologists	WKK reaction	Witebsky-Klingenstein-Kuhn reaction
WFPA	World Federation for the Protection of Animals	WKY	Wistar-Kyoto rats
		WL	waiting list
WFPHA	World Federation of Public Health Associations	WL	wave length
		WLE	wide local excision
WFR	Weil-Felix reaction	WLM	Women's Liberation Movement
WFS	Waterhouse-Friderichsen syndrome		
		WLM *(rad)*	Working Level Month
WFSA	World Federation of Societies of Anesthesiology	WLSP	World List of Scientific Periodicals
WFSW	World Federation of Scientific Workers	WL test	water load test
		WM	Ward Manager
WFUMB	World Federation of Ultrasound in Medicine and Biology	WM	white male
		WMA	World Medical Association
WG	Wegener's granulomatosis	WMD	white muscle disease
WGA	wheat germ agglutinin	WMP	World Medical Periodicals
WGA-HRP	horse radish peroxidase conjugated to wheat germ agglutinin (= HRP-WGA)	WMR	World Medical Relief
		WMS *(psych)*	Wechsler Memory Scale
		WMSC	Women's Medical Specialists Corps
WGL	wheat germ lipase		
Wh	watthour	WMSI *(card)*	wall motion score index
WHA	World Health Assembly		
WHAP	Women's Health and Abortion Project	WMX	whirlpool, massage, exercise
WHHL	Watanabe heritable hyperlipidemia	WN	well nourished
		WNL	within normal limits
WHML	Wellcome Historical Medical Library	WN virus	west Nile virus
		WO *(lab)*	wash-out
WHO	World Health Organisation	WO	written order
WHO-HYRAP	Hypertension Research Action Program of the WHO	W/O	water in oil (emulsion)
		w/o	without
		WONCA	World Organization of National Colleges, Academies, and Academic Associations of General Practitioners
WHR	waist-hip ratio		
WHRC	World Health Research Center		
WHVP	wedged hepatic venous pressure		
		WP	wet pack
WIA *(mil)*	wounded in action	WP	whirlpool
WISC *(psych)*	Wechsler Intelligence Scale for Children	WP	working point
		WPA	World Psychiatric Association
WIT *(psych)*	Wilde Intelligence Test		

WPB	whirlpool bath
WPPSI	Wechsler Primary and Preschool Scale of Intelligence
WPRS	Wittenborn Psychiatric Rating Scale
WPW	Wolff-Parkinson-White syndrome
WR	Wassermann reaction (=WaR)
WR	whole response
WR	Widal reaction
Wr *(card)*	work of right ventricle (=WRV)
WRAIR	Walter Reed Army Institute of Research (Washington, DC)
WRAT	Wide Range Achievement Test
WRC	washed red cells
WRC	water retention coefficient
Wr factor	Wright factor, antigen Wr
WRT	Waaler-Rose test
WRV *(card)*	work of right ventricle (=Wr)
WS, ws	water soluble
wt	weight
WV	wasted ventilation
w/v	weight in volume
WVA	World Veterinary Association
WW	"Weight Watchers"
w/w	weight in weight
WWCP *(mil)*	Walking Wounded Collecting Post
WxB *(dent)*	wax bite
WxP *(dent)*	wax pattern
WZa	wide zone alpha (hemolysis)

X

X	unknown quantity
X	xanthine (=Xan)
X	xanthosine (=Xao)
X	Xenopsylla
XA	xanthurenic acid
Xa	chiasma
XA mixture	xylene alcohol mixture
XAN	xanthinol nicotinate
Xan	xanthine
Xanth.	xanthomatosis
Xao	xanthosine
X-bacilli	Shigella flexneri type X
XDH	xanthine dehydrogenase
XE *(rad)*	X-Einheit (G); X-unit (Kienböck unit, Siegbahn unit) (=XU)
XES	x-ray energy spectrometer
XF	xylene formaldehyde
XL	excess lactate
XLD	xylose lysine deoxycholate agar
Xmas factor	Christmas factor
XMP	xanthosine-5-monophosphate
XO, XOD, XOX	xanthine oxidase
XP	xeroderma pigmentosum
XPS, XPES	x-ray photoelectron spectroscopy
XR	xeroradiography
XSA	cross-sectional area
XSE	xylane sulfuric acid ester
XT *(ophth)*	exotropia
XTH	xanthomatose tendineuse hypercholesterolemique (F); hypercholestolemic tendon xanthomatosis
XTP	xanthosine triphosphate
XU	excretion urogram
XU	X-unit (see XE)
Xu, Xul	xylulose
Xu-5-P	xylulose-5-phosphate
Xyl	xylose

273

Y

Y.	Yersinia
y	yellow
y	young
YADH	yeast alcohol dehydroge- nase
YAG laser	yttrium-aluminium-granate laser
Y-bacilli	Shigella flexneri type Y
YCB	yeast carbon base
yd	yard
YE	yellow enzyme
YEH	yellow enzyme, reduced
YF	yellow fever
Y-forceps	Young forceps
YPLL	Years of Potential Life Lost (statistical term per- taining to death due to murder or suicide)
yr, yrs	year, years
YS *(ophth)*	yellow spot
YSI	Yellow Springs Instruments

Z

Z *(phys)*	impedance
Z. *(anat)*	zona (L); zone
z	zero
ZAC	zinc-dimethyl-dithiocarba- mate cyclohexamine com- plex
ZAP	zero airway pressure
ZAP	zymosan-activated plasma complement
ZE	Zollinger-Ellison syn- drome (=ZES)

ZEEP	zero end-expiratory pres- sure
zero-g	zero gravity (=O-g)
ZES	Zollinger-Ellison syn- drome
ZG	zymogenic granula
ZI	zona incerta
ZIA	zonal immunoassay
ZIG	zoster immune globulin
ZIP	zoster immune plasma
ZKBS	Zentralkommision für Biologische Sicherheit (G); Central Commission of Biological Safety (part of the German Drug Author- ity BGA)
Z-line	zigzag line (ora serrata) as a border between squa- mous epithelium of the esophagus and columnar epithelium of the gastric cardia
ZMBH	Zentrum für Molekular- biologie und Humangene- tik; Center of Molecular Biology and Human Genetics (Heidelberg/Ger- many)
ZNS	Zentralnervensystem (G); central nervous system (=CNS)
ZOC	zone of concealment
ZOE	zinc oxide eugenol
ZPB	zero pressure breathing
ZPG	Zero Population Growth
ZPI	zinc protamine insulin
ZPO	zinc peroxide
ZPP	zinc protoporphyrin
ZS	Zieve's syndrome
Z-test *(psych)*	Zulliger's test
Zz	zingiber (L); ginger

Appendix

Abbreviated Titles of Medical-Scientific Journals

One keeps meeting uncertainty about the format of journal title abbreviations in the bibliographies in specialist literature. They vary from publisher to publisher according to the opinions of individual authors and editors, and the result is confusion.

There have been attempts in the past to lay down an international standard format, like the World List of Scientific Periodicals (WLSP) and the International Standards Organization (ISO). World Medical Periodicals (WMP), an outstanding reference work once produced in London, contained every journal title known at that time in the world; unfortunately, it has been out of print for years, and no further publication is envisaged. We have therefore decided to add a selection of magazine titles to this Dictionary of Medical Abbreviations.

There is a simple rule of thumb for the format recommended by the above-mentioned bodies: nouns start with a capital letter and adjectives do not, except for indications of nationality (e.g.J. Amer. med. Ass.; exception: Latin journal titles, e.g. Acta otorhin. belg.). There is a fullstop after abbreviated words (e.g. med.), but not after condensed words (e.g. Jt = Joint, Hlth = Health). The place of publication is sometimes placed after the journal title (e.g. Nature "Paris", Nature "London") to avoid confusion between the same or similar titles. People's names are not usually abbreviated (e.g. Virchow, Johns Hopkins), and neither are journal titles consisting of only one word (e.g. Lancet, Practitioner, Infection); such one-word titles are therefore not included in the following list.

Because of the sheer quantity of specialist journals, only the more important titles or those that are cited most often in the literature are shown here. The majority of them are in the English language, for this is the dominant one in science today and these journals are read and understood all over the world.

Abdom. Surg.	Abdominal Surgery
Acta allerg. *(Kbh.)*	Acta allergologica (Copenhagen)
Acta card. *(Brux.)*	Acta cardiologica (Brussels)
Acta chem. scand.	Acta chemica scandinavica
Acta chir. scand.	Acta chirurgica scandinavica
Acta cytol.	Acta cytologica
Acta endocr. *(Kbh.)*	Acta endocrinologica (Copenhagen)
Acta gastroent. belg.	Acta gastroenterologica belgica
Acta haemat. *(Basel)*	Acta haematologica (Basel)
Acta histochem.	Acta histochemica

Acta med. scand.	Acta medica scandinavica
Acta neurol. scand.	Acta neurologica scandinavica
Acta obstet. gynec. scand.	Acta obstetricia et gynaecologica scandinavica
Acta ophthal.	Acta ophthalmologica
Acta orthop. scand.	Acta orthopaedica scandinavica
Acta otolaryng. (Stockh.)	Acta otolaryngologica (Stockholm)
Acta otorhin. belg.	Acta otorhinolaryngologica belgica
Acta paediat. scand.	Acta paediatrica scandinavica
Acta paediat. (Upps.)	Acta paediatrica (Uppsala)
Acta path. microbiol. scand.	Acta pathologica et microbiologica scandinavica
Acta pharmacol. toxi-col.	Acta pharmacologica et toxicologica
Acta physiol. scand.	Acta physiologica scandinavica
Acta psychiat. scand.	Acta psychiatrica et neurologica scandinavica
Acta radiol. (Stockh.)	Acta radiologica (Stockholm)
Acta rheumat. scand.	Acta rheumatologica scandinavica
Adv. Biosci.	Advances in Biosciences
Adv. Plann. Parenth.	Advances in Planned Parenthood
Albrecht v. Graefes Arch. Ophthal.	Albrecht von Graefes Archiv für Ophthalmologie
All. Asthma	Allergy and Asthma
Amer. Fam. Phys.	American Family Physician
Amer. Fam. Pract.	American Family Practice
Amer. Heart J.	American Heart Journal
Amer. J. Anat.	American Journal of Anatomy
Amer. J. Cardiol.	American Journal of Cardiology
Amer. J. clin. Nutr.	American Journal of Clinical Nutrition
Amer. J. clin Path.	American Journal of Clinical Pathology
Amer. J. dig. Dis.	American Journal of Digestive Diseases
Amer. J. Dis. Child.	American Journal of Diseases of Children
Amer. J. Epidem.	American Journal of Epidemiology
Amer. J. Gastroent.	American Journal of Gastroenterology
Amer. J. Hosp. Pharm.	American Journal of Hospital Pharmacy
Amer. J. hum. Genet.	American Journal of Human Genetics
Amer. J. Hyg.	American Journal of Hygiene
Amer. J. Med.	American Journal of Medicine
Amer. J. med. Sci.	American Journal of Medical Sciences
Amer. J. med. Technol.	American Journal of Medical Technology
Amer. J. ment. Def.	American Journal of Mental Deficiency
Amer. J. Obstet. Gynec.	American Journal of Obstetrics and Gynecology
Amer. J. Ophthal.	American Journal of Ophthalmology
Amer. J. Path.	American Journal of Pathology
Amer. J. Physiol.	American Journal of Physiology
Amer. J. Psychiat.	American Journal of Psychiatry

Amer. J. publ. Hlth	American Journal of Public Health
Amer. J. Radiol.	American Journal of Radiology
Amer. J. Roentgenol.	American Journal of Roentgenology
Amer. J. Sociol.	American Journal of Sociology
Amer. J. Surg.	American Journal of Surgery
Amer. J. trop. Med. Hyg.	American Journal of Tropical Medicine and Hygiene
Amer. J. vet. Med.	American Journal of Veterinary Medicine
Amer. Rev. Biochem.	American Review of Biochemistry
Amer. Rev. respir. Dis.	American Review of Respiratory Diseases
Amer. Surg.	American Surgeon
Anat. Rec.	Anatomical Record
Ann. All.	Annals of Allergy
Ann. chir. gynaec. fenn.	Annales chirurgiae et gynaecologiae fennicae
Ann. clin. Lab. Sci.	Annals of Clinical and Laboratory Science
Ann. clin. Res.	Annals of Clinical Research
Ann. Derm. Vener. (Paris)	Annales de Dermatologie et Venereologie (Paris)
Ann. hum. Genet.	Annals of Human Genetics
Ann. Inst. Pasteur	Annales de l'Institut Pasteur
Ann. intern. Med.	Annals of Internal Medicine
Ann. med. intern. fenn.	Annales medicinae internae fennicae
Ann. N. Y. Acad. Sci.	Annals of the New York Academy of Sciences
Ann. Ophth. Otol. Laryng.	Annals of Ophthalmology, Otology and Laryngology
Ann. ORL	Annals of Otorhinolaryngology
Ann. Rev. Biochem.	Annual Review of Biochemistry
Ann. Rev. Genet.	Annual Review of Genetics
Ann. Rev. Med.	Annual Review of Medicine
Ann. Rev. Pharmacol. Toxicol.	Annual Review of Pharmacology and Toxicology
Ann. Rev. Physiol.	Annual Review of Physiology
Ann. rheumat. Dis.	Annals of Rheumatic Diseases
Ann. Surg.	Annals of Surgery
Antibiot. Chemother.	Antibiotics and Chemotherapy
Antimicrob. Agents Chemother.	Antimicrobial Agents and Chemotherapy
Arch. All. appl. Immunol.	Archives of Allergy and Applied Immunology
Arch. Biochem. Biophys.	Archives of Biochemistry and Biophysics
Arch. Derm. (Chicago)	Archives of Dermatology (Chicago)
Arch. Dis. Childh.	Archives of Diseases in Childhood
Arch. gen. Psychiat.	Archives of General Psychiatry
Arch. ges. Virusforsch.	Archiv für die gesamte Virusforschung
Arch. Gynäk.	Archiv für Gynäkologie
Arch. Hyg. (Berlin)	Archiv für Hygiene (Berlin)

Arch. industr. Hlth	Archives of Industrial Health
Arch. intern. Med.	Archives of Internal Medicine
Arch. intern. Pharmacodyn. Ther.	Archives of Internal Pharmacodynamics and Therapy
Arch. klin. Chir.	Archiv für Klinische Chirurgie
Arch. klin. exp. Derm.	Archiv für Klinische und Experimentelle Dermatologie
Arch. Neurol.	Archives of Neurology
Arch. Orthop. Unfall-chir.	Archiv für Orthopädie und Unfallchirurgie
Arch. Otolaryng.	Archives of Otolaryngology
Arch. Path.	Archives of Pathology
Arch. Path. Lab. Med.	Archives of Pathology and Laboratory Medicine
Arch. Pediat.	Archives of Pediatrics
Arch. Physiol.	Archives of Physiology
Arch. phys. Med. Rehab.	Archives of Physical Medicine and Rehabilitation
Arch. Psychiat. Ner-venkr.	Archiv für Psychiatrie und Nervenkrankheiten
Arch. sex. Behav.	Archives of Sexual Behaviour
Arch. Surg.	Archives of Surgery
Arthr. Rheum.	Arthritis and Rheumatism
Arzneim.-Forsch./Drug Res.	Arzneimittelforschung/Drug Research
Aust. dent. J.	Australian Dental Journal
Aust. J. Derm.	Australasian Journal of Dermatology
Aust. J. exp. Biol. med. Sci.	Australian Journal of Experimental Biology and Medical Science
Aust. N. Z. J. Med.	Australian and New Zealand Journal of Medicine
Aust. N. Z. J. Obstet. Gynaec.	Australian and New Zealand Journal of Obstetrics and Gynaecology
Aust. N. Z. J. Psychiat.	Australian and New Zealand Journal of Psychiatry
Aust. paediat. J.	Australian Paediatric Journal
Aust. Radiol.	Australasian Radiology
Bact. Rev.	Bacteriological Reviews
Beitr. path. Anat. allg. Path.	Beiträge zur Pathologischen Anatomie und Allgemeinen Pathologie
Biochem. Genet.	Biochemical Genetics
Biochem. J.	Biochemical Journal
Biochem. Z.	Biochemische Zeitschrift
Biochim. biophys. Acta	Biochimica et biophysica Acta
Brit. dent. J.	British Dental Journal
Brit. Heart J.	British Heart Journal
Brit. J. Cancer	British Journal of Cancer
Brit. J. clin. Pharm.	British Journal of Clinical Pharmacology
Brit. J. clin. Pract.	British Journal of Clinical Practice
Brit. J. exp. Path.	British Journal of Experimental Pathology
Brit. J. Haemat.	British Journal of Haematology

Brit. J. Hosp. Med.	British Journal of Hospital Medicine
Brit. J. industr. Med.	British Journal of Industrial Medicine
Brit. J. Nutr.	British Journal of Nutrition
Brit. J. Ophthal.	British Journal of Ophthalmology
Brit. J. Pharmacol.	British Journal of Pharmacology
Brit. J. Psychiat.	British Journal of Psychiatry
Brit. J. Radiol.	British Journal of Radiology
Brit. J. sex. Med.	British Journal of Sexual Medicine
Brit. J. Surg.	British Journal of Surgery
Brit. J. Urol.	British Journal of Urology
Brit. J. vener. Dis.	British Journal of Venereal Diseases
Brit. med. Bull.	British Medical Bulletin
Brit. med. J.	British Medical Journal
Bull. Hist. Med.	Bulletin of the History of Medicine
Bull. Hyg.	Bulletin of Hygiene
Bull. Johns Hopkins Hosp.	Bulletin of the Johns Hopkins Hospital
Bull. N. Y. Acad. Med.	Bulletin of the New York Academy of Medicine
Bull. Soc. méd. Paris	Bulletins et Mémoires de la Société de Médecine de Paris
Bull. Wld Hlth Org.	Bulletin of the World Health Organization
Canad. J. Biochem.	Canadian Journal of Biochemistry and Physiology
Canad. J. Physiol. Pharmacol.	Canadian Journal of Physiology and Pharmacology
Canad. J. Surg.	Canadian Journal of Surgery
Canad. med. Ass. J.	Canadian Medical Association Journal
Canad. psychiat. Ass. J.	Canadian Psychiatric Association Journal
Cancer Res.	Cancer Research
Cardiol. prat.	Cardiologia pratica
Cardiovasc. Res.	Cardiovascular Research
Cell Tiss. Kinet.	Cell and Tissue Kinetics
Chem. Abstr.	Chemical Abstracts
Chin. med. J.	Chinese Medical Journal
Circ. Res.	Circulation Research
Clin. All.	Clinical Allergy
Clin. chim. Acta	Clinica chimica acta
Clin. Endocr.	Clinical Endocrinology
Clin. exp. Immunol.	Clinical and Experimental Immunology
Clin. Gastroent.	Clinics in Gastroenterology
Clin. Genet.	Clinical Genetics
Clin. genet. Res.	Clinical Genetic Research
Clin. Haemat.	Clinics in Haematology
Clin. Immunol. Immunopathol.	Clinical Immunology and Immunopathology
Clin. Obstet. Gynec.	Clinical Obstetrics and Gynecology
Clin. Orthop.	Clinical Orthopedics
Clin. Pediat.	Clinical Pediatrics
Clin. Perinat.	Clinics in Perinatology

Clin. Pharmacokin.	Clinical Pharmacokinetics
Clin. Pharmacol. Ther.	Clinical Pharmacology and Therapy
Clin. Res.	Clinical Research
Clin. Sci.	Clinical Science
Clin. Sci. molec. Med.	Clinical Science and Molecular Medicine
Contemp. Obstet. Gynec.	Contemporary Obstetrics and Gynecology
C. R. Acad. Sci.	Comptes Rendus de l'Académie des Sciences
C. R. Soc. Biol.	Comptes Rendus de la Société de Biologie
Curr. med. Res. Opin.	Current Medical Research and Opinion
Curr. Probl. Obstet. Gynec.	Current Problems in Obstetrics and Gynecology
Dent. Practit. dent. Rec.	Dental Practitioner and Dental Record
Dermat. Mschr.	Dermatologische Monatsschrift
Develop. Biol.	Developmental Biology
Dis. Chest	Diseases of the Chest
Dtsch. Ärztebl.	Deutsches Ärzteblatt
Dtsch. Apoth. Z.	Deutsche Apotheker-Zeitung
Dtsch. Arch. klin. Med.	Deutsches Archiv für Klinische Medizin
Dtsch. Gesundheitsw.	Deutsches Gesundheitswesen
Dtsch. med. Wschr.	Deutsche Medizinische Wochenschrift
Dtsch. Z. Chir.	Deutsche Zeitschrift für Chirurgie
Dtsch. Z. Verd. Stoffwechselkr.	Deutsche Zeitschrift für Verdauungs- und Stoffwechsel-krankheiten
Erg. Chir. Orthop.	Ergebnisse der Chirurgie und Orthopädie
Erg. inn. Med. Kinderh.	Ergebnisse der Inneren Medizin und Kinderheilkunde
Eur. Heart J.	European Heart Journal
Eur. J. clin. Pharmacol.	European Journal of Clinical Pharmacology
Eur. J. Obstet. Gynaec.	European Journal of Obstetrics and Gynaecology
Eur. J. Pediat.	European Journal of Pediatrics
Eur. J. Rheum. Inflam.	European Journal of Rheumatism and Inflammation
Exp. Cell Res.	Experimental Cell Research
Exp. Eye Res.	Experimental Eye Research
Exp. Med. Surg.	Experimental Medicine and Surgery
Exp. molec. Path.	Experimental and Molecular Pathology
Fed. Proc.	Federation Proceedings
Fert. Steril.	Fertility and Sterility
Fol. all. immunol. clin.	Folia allergologica et immunologica clinica
Fol. cardiol.	Folia cardiologica
Fol. endocr. japon.	Folia endocrinologica japonica
Fortschr. Med.	Fortschritte der Medizin
Fortschr. Röntgenstr.	Fortschritte auf dem Gebiet der Röntgenstrahlen
Fortschr. Tuberk. Forsch.	Fortschritte der Tuberkulose-Forschung
Gastrointest. Endosc.	Gastrointestinal Endoscopy
Geburtsh. u. Frauen-heilk.	Geburtshilfe und Frauenheilkunde

Giorn. clin. Med.	Giornale di Clinica Medicina
Giorn. Geront.	Giornale di Gerontologia
Guy's Hosp. Rep.	Guy's Hospital Reports
Gynäk. Prax.	Gynäkologische Praxis
Gynec. Oncol.	Gynecological Oncology
Gynec. prat.	Gynécologie pratique
Heart. Bull.	Heart Bulletin
Helv. med. Acta	Helvetica medica acta
Helv. physiol. Acta	Helvetica physiologica acta
Hoppe-Seylers Z. physiol. Chem.	Hoppe-Seylers Zeitschrift für Physiologische Chemie
Hosp. Pract.	Hospital Practice
Hum. Genet.	Human Genetics
Hum. Hered.	Human Heredity
Ind. Heart J.	Indian Heart Journal
Ind. J. med. Res.	Indian Journal of Medical Research
Ind. med. Gaz.	Indian Medical Gazette
Infect. Immunol.	Infection and Immunology
Intern. Prax.	Internistische Praxis
Int. Arch. All.	International Archives of Allergy
Int. J. Cancer	International Journal of Cancer
Int. J. Cardiol.	International Journal of Cardiology
Int. J. Epidemiol.	International Journal of Epidemiology
Int. J. Urol. Nephr. *(Budap.)*	International Journal of Urology and Nephrology (Budapest)
Int. J. Vit. Nutr. Res.	International Journal of Vitamin and Nutrition Research
Int. Rev. conn. Tiss. Res.	International Review of Connective Tissue Research
Invest. Radiol.	Investigative Radiology
Invest. Urol.	Investigative Urology
Irish J. med. Sci.	Irish Journal of Medical Science
Isr. J. med. Sci.	Israel Journal of Medical Sciences
J. abnorm. soc. Psychol.	Journal of Abnormal Social Psychology
J. acoust. Soc. Amer.	Journal of the Acoustic Society of America
J. All. clin. Immunol.	Journal of Allergy and Clinical Immunology
J. Amer. Acad. Derm.	Journal of the American Academy of Dermatology
J. Amer. chem. Soc.	Journal of the American Chemical Society
J. Amer. Coll. Cardiol.	Journal of the American College of Cardiology
J. Amer. dent. Ass.	Journal of the American Dental Association
J. Amer. geriat. Soc.	Journal of the American Geriatric Society
J. Amer. med. Ass.	Journal of the American Medical Association
J. Amer. psychoanal. Soc.	Journal of the American Psychoanalytical Society
J. Anat. *(Lond.)*	Journal of Anatomy (London)
J. antimicr. Chemother.	Journal of Antimicrobial Chemotherapy
Jap. Circ. J.	Japanese Circulation Journal
Jap. Heart J.	Japanese Heart Journal

Jap. J. Med.	Japanese Journal of Medicine
Jap. J. Pharmacol.	Japanese Journal of Pharmacology
J. appl. Physiol.	Journal of Applied Physiology
J. Ass. Phys. India	Journal of the Association of Physicians of India
J. Atheroscl. Res.	Journal of Atherosclerosis Research
J. Bact.	Journal of Bacteriology
J. Biol. Chem.	Journal of Biology and Chemistry
J. biophys. biochem. Cytol.	Journal of Biophysical and Biochemical Cytology
J. biosoc. Sci.	Journal of Biosociological Sciences
J. Bone Jt Surg.	Journal of Bone and Joint Surgery
J. cardiovasc. Pharmacol.	Journal of Cardiovascular Pharmacology
J. Cell Biol.	Journal of Cell Biology
J. cell. comp. Physiol.	Journal of Cellular and Comparative Physiology
J. chem. Soc.	Journal of the Chemical Society
J. chron. Dis.	Journal of Chronic Diseases
J. clin. Endocr. Metab.	Journal of Clinical Endocrinology and Metabolism
J. clin. Invest.	Journal of Clinical Investigation
J. clin. Microbiol.	Journal of Clinical Microbiology
J. clin. Path.	Journal of Clinical Pathology
J. clin. Pharmacol.	Journal of Clinical Pharmacology
J. clin. Ultras.	Journal of Clinical Ultrasound
J. consult. clin. Psychol.	Journal of Consulting and Clinical Psychology
J. cutan. Path.	Journal of Cutaneous Pathology
J. dent. Res.	Journal of Dental Research
J. Endocr.	Journal of Endocrinology
J. exp. Med.	Journal of Experimental Medicine
J. Fam. Pract.	Journal of Family Practice
J. gen. Microbiol.	Journal of General Microbiology
J. gen. Physiol.	Journal of General Physiology
J. Geront.	Journal of Gerontology
J. Hist. Med. all. Sci.	Journal of the History of Medicine and Allied Sciences
J. Histochem. Cytochem.	Journal of Histochemistry and Cytochemistry
J. Hyg. *(Cambr.)*	Journal of Hygiene (Cambridge)
J. Immunol.	Journal of Immunology
J. Ind. med. Ass.	Journal of the Indian Medical Association
J. infect. Dis.	Journal of Infectious Diseases
J. int. Coll. Surg.	Journal of the International College of Surgeons
J. intern. Med. Res.	Journal of Internal Medicine Research
J. invest. Derm.	Journal of Investigative Dermatology
J. Irish med. Ass.	Journal of the Irish Medical Association
J. Lab. clin. Med.	Journal of Laboratory and Clinical Medicine
J. Lip. Res.	Journal of Lipid Research
J. med. Genet.	Journal of Medical Genetics

J. méd. Lyon	Journal Médical de Lyon
J. med. Sci.	Journal of Medical Sciences
J. Mt Sinai Hosp. (N. Y.)	Journal of the Mount Sinai Hospital (New York)
J. natl Cancer Inst.	Journal of the National Cancer Institute
J. nerv. ment. Dis.	Journal of Nervous and Mental Diseases
J. Neurol. Neurosurg. Psychiat.	Journal of Neurology, Neurosurgery and Psychiatry
J. Neurophysiol.	Journal of Neurophysiology
J. Neurosurg.	Journal of Neurosurgery
J. Nutr.	Journal of Nutrition
J. Obstet. Gynaec. Brit. Cmwlth	Journal of Obstetrics and Gynaecology of the British Commonwealth
J. Obstet. Gynaec. India	Journal of Obstetrics and Gynaecology of India
J. Parasit.	Journal of Parasitology
J. Pathol.	Journal of Pathology
J. Path. Bact.	Journal of Pathology and Bacteriology
J. Pediat.	Journal of Pediatrics
J. pediat. Surg.	Journal of Pediatric Surgery
J. Pharmacol. exp. Ther.	Journal of Pharmacology and Experimental Therapy
J. Pharm. Pharmacol.	Journal of Pharmacy and Pharmacology
J. Physiol. (Lond.)	Journal of Physiology (London)
J. psychosom. Res.	Journal of Psychosomatic Research
J. Reprod. Fertil.	Journal of Reproduction and Fertility
J. reprod. Med.	Journal of Reproductive Medicine
J. Rheumat.	Journal of Rheumatology
J. roy. Coll. Surg. Ed.	Journal of the Royal College of Surgeons of Edinburgh
J. roy. micr. Soc.	Journal of the Royal Microscopical Society
J. roy. Soc. Med.	Journal of the Royal Society of Medicine
J. sex. Res.	Journal of Sexual Research
J. small Anim. Pract.	Journal of Small Animal Practice
J. Steroid Biochem.	Journal of Steroid Biochemistry
J. surg. Res.	Journal of Surgical Research
J. theoret. Biol.	Journal of Theoretical Biology
J. thorac. cardiovasc. Surg.	Journal of Thoracic and Cardiovascular Surgery
J. trop. Med. Hyg.	Journal of Tropical Medicine and Hygiene
J. Urol.	Journal of Urology
Klin. Monatsbl. Augenheilk.	Klinische Monatsblätter für Augenheilkunde
Klin. Wschr.	Klinische Wochenschrift
Lab. Invest.	Laboratory Investigation
Langenbecks Arch. klin. Chir.	Langenbecks Archiv für Klinische Chirurgie
Life Sci.	Life Sciences
Mayo Clin. Proc.	Mayo Clinic Proceedings
Med. Clin. N. Amer.	Medical Clinics of North America

Med. J. Austr.	Medical Journal of Australia
Med. Klin.	Medizinische Klinik
Med. Press	Medical Press
Med. Rec. Ann.	Medical Record and Annals
Med. Welt	Medizinische Welt
Meth. biochem. Anal.	Methods of Biochemical Analysis
Meth. Cancer Res.	Methods of Cancer Research
Milit. Med.	Military Medicine
Min. cardioang.	Minerva cardioangiologica
Min. ginec.	Minerva ginecologica
Min. med. *(Torino)*	Minerva medica (Torino)
Min. nefrol.	Minerva nefrologica
Minn. Med.	Minnesota Medicine
Mod. Conc. cardiovasc. Dis.	Modern Concepts of Cardiovascular Diseases
Mod. Geriat.	Modern Geriatrics
Mod. Med.	Modern Medicine
Morb. Mort. wkly Rep.	Morbidity and Mortality Weekly Report
Mschr. Kinderheilk.	Monatsschrift für Kinderheilkunde
Münch. med. Wschr.	Münchener Medizinische Wochenschrift
Naturwiss. Rdsch.	Naturwissenschaftliche Rundschau
Naunyn-Schmiedebergs Arch. exp. Path. Pharmakol.	Naunyn-Schmiedebergs Archiv für Experimentelle Pathologie und Pharmakologie
Ned. T. Geneesk.	Nederlandsch Tijdschrift van Geneeskunde
New Engl. J. Med.	New England Journal of Medicine
Nouv. Presse méd.	Nouvelle Presse Médicale
Nouv. Rev. Franç. Hémat.	Nouvelle Revue Française d'Hématologie
Nutr. Abstr. Rev.	Nutrition Abstracts and Reviews
Obstet. Gynec.	Obstetrics and Gynecology
Obstet. gynec. Surv.	Obstetrical and Gynecological Survey
Otolaryng. Head Neck Surg.	Otolaryngology, Head and Neck Surgery
Pädiat. Pädol.	Pädiatrie und Pädologie
Pädiat. Prax.	Pädiatrische Praxis
Pediat. Ann.	Pediatric Annals
Ped. Clin. N. Amer.	Pediatric Clinics of North America
Pediat. Res.	Pediatric Research
Penn. med. J.	Pennsylvania Medical Journal
Pflügers Arch. ges. Physiol.	Pflügers Archiv für die Gesamte Physiologie
Pharmacol. Rev.	Pharmacological Reviews
Pharm. J.	Pharmaceutical Journal
Physiol. Rev.	Physiological Reviews
Postgrad. Med.	Postgraduate Medicine
Postgrad. med. J.	Postgraduate Medical Journal

Pract. Gastroent.	Practical Gastroenterology
Prensa med. Arg.	Prensa Medica Argentina
Prensa med. Mex.	Prensa Medica Mexicana
Presse méd. *(Paris)*	Presse Médicale (Paris)
Proc. Staff. Meet. Mayo Clin.	Proceedings of the Staff Meetings of the Mayo Clinic
Proc. ntl Acad. Sci. *(USA)*	Proceeding of the National Academy of Sciences (USA)
Proc. roy. Soc. Med.	Proceedings of the Royal Society of Medicine
Proc. Soc. exp. Biol. Med. *(N. Y.)*	Proceedings of the Society for Experimental Biology and Medicine (New York)
Prog. All.	Progress in Allergy
Prog. Biochem. Pharmacol.	Progress in Biochemistry and Pharmacology
Prog. cardiovasc. Dis.	Progress in Cardiovascular Diseases
Prog. Hemost. Thromb.	Progress in Hemostasis and Thrombosis
Prog. med. Genet.	Progress in Medical Genetics
Prog. med. Virol.	Progress in Medical Virology
Psychol. Bull.	Psychological Bulletin
Psychol. Rev.	Psychological Reviews
Psychosom. Med.	Psychosomatic Medicine
Psychother. med. Psychol.	Psychotherapy and Medical Psychology
Publ. Hlth Rep. *(Wash.)*	Public Health Reports (Washington)
Quart. J. exp. Physiol.	Quarterly Journal of Experimental Physiology
Quart. J. Med.	Quarterly Journal of Medicine
Rec. Progr. Horm. Res.	Recent Progress in Hormone Research
Rev. Arg. cardiol.	Revista Argentina Cardiologica
Rev. méd. Franç.	Revue Médicale Française
S. Afr. J. Surg.	South African Journal of Surgery
S. Afr. med. J.	South African Medical Journal
Scand. J. Gastroent.	Scandinavian Journal of Gastroenterology
Scand. J. infect. Dis.	Scandinavian Journal of Infectious Diseases
Scand. J. Urol. Nephrol.	Scandinavian Journal of Urology and Nephrology
Schweiz. med. Wschr.	Schweizerische Medizinische Wochenschrift
Schweiz. Rdsch. Med. (Praxis)	Schweizerische Rundschau für Medizin (Praxis)
Schweiz. Z. Gynäk. Geburtsh.	Schweizerische Zeitschrift für Gynäkologie und Geburtshilfe
Schweiz. Z. Tuberk.	Schweizerische Zeitschrift für Tuberkulose
Sci. Amer.	Scientific American
Sci. Basis Med.	Scientific Basis of Medicine
Scot. med. J.	Scottish Medical Journal
Sem. Hôp. Paris	Semaine des Hôpitaux de Paris
Ser. haematol.	Series haematologica
South. med. J.	Southern Medical Journal
Stanford med. Bull.	Stanford Medical Bulletin

Surg. Clin. N. Amer.	Surgical Clinics of North America
Surg. Gynec. Obstet.	Surgery, Gynecology and Obstetrics
Tex. Rep. Biol. Med.	Texas Report of Biology and Medicine
Ther. d. Gegenw.	Therapie der Gegenwart
Ther. Umsch.	Therapeutische Umschau
Thromb. diath. haemorrh.	Thrombosis et diathesis haemorrhagica
Trans. Amer. Coll. Cardiol.	Transactions of the American College of Cardiology
Transpl. Bull.	Transplantation Bulletin
Trans. Soc. Path. Jap.	Transactions of the Society of Pathology of Japan
Trop. Dis. Bull.	Tropical Diseases Bulletin
Ugeskr. Laeg.	Ugeskrift for Laeger
Urol. Clin. N. Amer.	Urological Clinics of North America
Urol. Surv.	Urological Survey
Verh. Dtsch. Ges. inn. Med.	Verhandlungen der Deutschen Gesellschaft für Innere Medizin
Verh. Dtsch. Ges. Path.	Verhandlungen der Deutschen Gesellschaft für Pathologie
Vet. Med.	Veterinary Medicine
Vet. Rec.	Veterinary Record
Virchows Arch. path. Anat.	Virchows Archiv für Pathologische Anatomie
West. J. Surg. Obstet. Gynec.	Western Journal of Surgery, Obstetrics and Gynecology
Wien. klin. Wschr.	Wiener Klinische Wochenschrift
Wien. med. Wschr.	Wiener Medizinische Wochenschrift
Wien. Z. inn. Med.	Wiener Zeitschrift für Innere Medizin
Wld Med.	World Medicine
Yale J. Biol. Med.	Yale Journal of Biology and Medicine
Zbl. Bakt.	Zentralblatt für Bakteriologie
Zbl. Chir.	Zentralblatt für Chirurgie
Zbl. Gynäk.	Zentralblatt für Gynäkologie
Zbl. inn. Med.	Zentralblatt für Innere Medizin
Zbl. Neurochir.	Zentralblatt für Neurochirurgie
Zbl. Vet. Med.	Zentralblatt für Veterinärmedizin
Z. Chem.	Zeitschrift für Chemie
Z. Gastroent.	Zeitschrift für Gastroenterologie
Z. Geburtsh. Gynäk.	Zeitschrift für Geburtshilfe und Gynäkologie
Z. Geburtsh. Perinat.	Zeitschrift für Geburtshilfe und Perinatologie
Z. ges. exp. Med.	Zeitschrift für die gesamte experimentelle Medizin
Z. Hautkrankh.	Zeitschrift für Hautkrankheiten
Z. Hyg. Infekt.-Kr.	Zeitschrift für Hygiene und Infektionskrankheiten
Z. Immun.-All.-Forsch.	Zeitschrift für Immunitäts- und Allergieforschung
Z. inn. Med.	Zeitschrift für Innere Medizin
Z. Kardiol.	Zeitschrift für Kardiologie
Z. klin. Chemie	Zeitschrift für Klinische Chemie und Biochemie
Z. klin. Med.	Zeitschrift für Klinische Medizin

Z. Krebsforsch.	Zeitschrift für Krebsforschung
Z. Kreislaufforsch.	Zeitschrift für Kreislaufforschung
Z. Naturforsch.	Zeitschrift für Naturforschung
Z. Orthop.	Zeitschrift für Orthopädie
Z. Rheumaforsch.	Zeitschrift für Rheumaforschung
Z. Urol.	Zeitschrift für Urologie